American Casino Guide

1997 Edition

Written By
Steve Bourie

Contributing Writers
Anthony Curtis
Dewey Bryan
Henry Tamburin
Stanford Wong
Jeffrey Compton
Max Rubin

This book is dedicated to the memory of my mother,
Terry Bourie, who always enjoyed taking a chance.

American Casino Guide - 1997 edition

Copyright ©1997, Casino Vacations

Published By:
Casino Vacations
P.O. Box 703
Dania, Florida 33004
(954) 989-2766
Fax (954) 966-7048

E-mail: casinos@aol.com

ISBN: 1-883768-06-3
ISSN: 1086-9018

Table of Contents

About Your Guide

This guide was written to help you plan your visit to casino gambling areas and also to help you save money once you are there. The first edition of this guide began six years ago as an eight-page newsletter and it has continued to grow each year as casino gambling has spread throughout the country. We have listed information on all of the states that offer any type of traditional casino table games or slot machines (including video lottery terminals). We have also included some stories to help you understand how casinos operate; how video poker and slot machines work; how to make the best plays in blackjack and roulette; and how to take advantage of casino promotional programs. Additionally, we have included a casino coupon section that will save you many times the cost of this book.

Besides listing general information about each casino, this guide also notes those casinos that offer free fun books as well as those that have casino marketing departments. Knowing this information can be very helpful. As an example: almost every large casino has a "comp" program whereby you can get free rooms, food, shows, gifts or cash based upon your level of play at their table games or slot machines. Just call the casino marketing department for details on their current programs. Another program many casinos offer is a free fun book. These are coupon books that contain free and discounted offers on various items such as: bets, food, drinks, shows, rooms, souvenirs and more. Your guide lists all of the casinos that offer fun books, plus details on how to get them. For more information on fun books and how best to use them, be sure to read the "Couponomy" story on the following two pages.

A good suggestion to save you money when visiting a casino is to join their slot club. It doesn't cost anything and you would be surprised at how quickly those points can add up to earn you gifts, cash, food or other complimentaries. Also, as a slot club member you will usually receive periodic mailings from the casino with money-saving offers that are generally not available to the public.

When using your guide please remember that all of the listed casino/resort room rates reflect the lowest and highest prices charged during the year. During holidays and peak periods, however, higher rates may apply. Also, since the gambling games offered at casinos vary from state to state, a listing of available games is found at the start of each state heading. We hope you enjoy your guide and we wish you good luck on your casino vacation!

Couponomy

By Anthony Curtis

One of the best sources of value during a vacation to a casino gambling area is the casino fun book. Many visitors ignore fun books and coupons, passing them off as "playthings of the unsophisticated." The true bargain hunter, however, understands that these casino giveaways are a source of meal discounts, free meals, show discounts, souvenirs, free drinks and a mathematical advantage at the gambling tables.

I call the systematic and efficient use of casino coupons "Couponomy" (the suffix "o-m-y" usually indicates removal, so this art/science represents the extraction of wealth via coupon). For years, Couponomy has been the province of a small group of informed consumers (Couponomists), but the simple concept of analyzing and using valuable coupons can be applied by anyone.

There are two categories of coupon in a standard fun book: gambling and non-gambling. A typical fun book contains a combination of both. Non-gambling coupons include discounts for drinks, meals or shows; souvenir offers; and discounts for other casino amenities. Gambling coupons called "lucky bucks" allow players to collect bonuses on winning wagers at table games, and sometimes slot machines.

Analyzing coupons for food, drinks, shows and souvenirs is easy. If the coupon says FREE or two for one, you have a money-saver. If the offer applies to something you want, use it. Most fun books contain offers for free cocktails in the lounge or two-for-one buffets. A husband and wife can save up to $20 per day by eating on the coupon circuit. The souvenirs are usually cheap trinkets or a deck of cards, but you'll find that virtually anything bearing a casino logo makes for a treasured gift back home. Discounts for beauty shops, health clubs, car rentals, etc. are usually insignificant and can be ignored.

The real value in most fun books comes from the gambling coupons. Few realize that there is significant profit potential associated with their use. Gambling is a prudent investment when wagers are accompanied by a coupon because the player has an advantage on every bet.

Lucky bucks for blackjack, craps, roulette, baccarat and big 6 pay a bonus, usually $1, on winning wagers. For example: 2-1's pay $2 for a winning $1 wager. There are also 3-2's, 7-5's and a few other variations.

It may surprise you, but the ratio of wins to losses in most casino games is relatively close. In craps for example, after 100 bets (on the pass line), you expect to win about 49 times and lose the other 51. The casino edge generated by this 49/51 ratio, multiplied by thousands of decisions, is enough to guarantee the casino handsome long-term profits.

Adding the bonus payoff from a 2-1 coupon turns the situation around. The win/loss ratio remains the same; however, the 49 winning bets are now paid two dollars instead of one. The result after 100 decisions is $98 in winnings (49 x $2), and $51 in losses. The difference is a net profit of $47 for the player. The advantage of the bonus is too great for the casino to overcome.

Perhaps most important, coupons provide insurance against disappointment. Although your wins won't be huge - you can only make so much with $1 and $2 bets - they will be consistent. It's hard to lose while playing coupons. I once played fun books in 19 casinos for an article in my newsletter. After a total of 80 bets, my record was 35 wins and 45 losses. Still, because of the bonuses paid on the winners, I made a $50 profit. With Couponomy, even bad is good.

One of my favorite recommendations for Las Vegas visitors is that they construct a coupon run. This entails traveling to five or six casinos to play lucky bucks, collect souvenirs, and partake of a free cocktail or two. A husband and wife team can expect to clear $25 or more doing this. Those profits can later be applied to dinner, a show, or even some coupon-less gambling - also known as "gambling on the square."

You get the point. Keep an eye open for opportunities to use coupons at all times. Utilize meal and show discounts. Play your lucky bucks on the table games. Avoid coupons for discounts on race bets, sports bets or keno unless they are free, or are discounted at least 50 percent ($2 ticket for $1). Before leaving on your trip, ask your travel agent to supply you with coupons. Also, be sure to use the information supplied in this guide to get your fun books at the casinos that offer them. Coupons will make your vacation better!

One more point. Remember that the practice of Couponomy is not limited to playing coupons. You might call it a state of mind. It means staying alert for opportunities to take advantage of your casino visit in all areas — dining, entertainment and anywhere else that competition has created value for consumers.

Anthony Curtis is the publisher of Las Vegas Advisor, a 12-page monthly newsletter that offers up-to-the-minute details on the best deals for lodging, dining, entertainment and gambling in Las Vegas. Ordering information for Las Vegas Advisor is on page 157.

Your Best Casino Bets - Part I

by Henry Tamburin

The majority of casino players leave too much to chance when playing in a casino. To put it bluntly, they do not have a clue as to how to play. They are literally throwing their money away with little chance of winning. Luck most certainly has a lot to do with your success in a casino but what really separates the winners from the losers is the skill of the players. Granted, there is no guarantee that you will win, but on the other hand, there is no guarantee that you must lose. My objective in this article is to educate you on the casino games so that at the very least, you'll be able to enjoy yourself in the casino with a minimum risk to your bankroll.

Let's begin our understanding of casino gambling by learning how casinos win as much as they do. They don't charge admission, and they certainly don't depend on the luck of their dealers to generate the income they need to pay their overhead. In fact, they guarantee themselves a steady income by having a built in advantage, or house edge, on every bet. Think of it as a very efficient hidden tax that generates them a guaranteed daily profit.

Here's an example of how this works. Suppose we take a coin and play heads or tails. Every time you lose a flip of the coin you pay me $1. Every time you win a flip, I pay you 90¢. Would you play? I hope you said no. Here's why. In this simple game I would have an advantage over you and I created that advantage by not paying you at the true odds of one-to-one (or $1).

Casinos do this very same thing to create their advantage. They simply pay off winning bets at less than the true odds. For example, the true odds of winning a bet on number 7 on roulette are 37-to-1 (the latter means you have 37 chances to lose vs. one chance to win). If you get lucky and the roulette ball lands in the number seven slot, you'd expect the casino to pay you 37 chips as winnings for the one chip you bet on number 7 (37-to-1 payoff). If they did that, the casino's advantage would be zero. However, as I mentioned above, the casinos create their advantage by paying off winning bets at less than true odds. In the case of our bet on number 7, the winning payoff is 35 chips (instead of 37 chips). The two chips the casino quietly kept is what pays their bills. Mathematically, the casino advantage is 5.26% on this bet which simply means day in and day out, the casino expects to win (or keep) 5.26 % of all money wagered in roulette.

The casino games with the lowest casino advantage (less than 1.25%) and your best bets are blackjack, craps, baccarat, and video poker. Now don't sell the ranch and run over to your nearest casino just yet. These games, plus table poker, are your best bets but you must learn how to play these games properly to enhance your chances of winning. Here are some tips to get you started:

BLACKJACK - This is your best casino game, but you must learn how to play your hands (when to hit, stand, double-down, split, etc.). This is known as the basic strategy. Learn it and you can reduce the casino's advantage to virtually zero. And if you learn how to keep track of the cards as they are played (i.e. card counting) you can actually turn the tables on the casino and have the edge over them! Do not try to play blackjack if you haven't learned the correct basic strategy. If you do, your chances of winning are slim.

CRAPS - The game of craps intimidates most casino players because of the complicated playing layout and the multitude of bets. In fact craps is an easy game to play. And it also has some of the best bets in the casino (and also some of the worst). Your best bet is the pass line with odds and come with odds. Next best is a place bet on six or eight. Stay away from all other bets on the layout because the casino's advantage is too high.

ROULETTE - Every bet on the American roulette layout (with 0 and 00 on the wheel) has a high casino advantage. That goes for bets straight up on numbers that pay 35 to 1, as well as even money wagers on red or black. Atlantic City players get a break. If you bet on an even money payoff bet and 0 or 00 hits, you lose only half your wager. This cuts the casino's advantage in half. Also, some casinos offer a European layout with only one zero. This is a better bet than wheels with 0 and 00.

BACCARAT - Many casinos offer a low stakes version called mini-baccarat. Not a bad game to play. If you bet on the bank hand, the casino's edge is only 1.17%. And when you play baccarat, there are no playing decisions to make which makes the game very easy to play.

BIG SIX WHEEL - Stay away from spending a lot of time (and money) at this game. The casino's advantage is astronomical (11% to 26%). Its drawing card for the novice player is the low minimum bet ($1). Save your money for the better games.

CARIBBEAN STUD POKER - This popular cruise ship game has found its way to land and dockside casinos. Unlike regular table poker where players compete against each other, in this game the players play against the house. But the rules favor the casino and their advantage is about 5%. The part of this game that appeals to players is the progressive jackpot side bet. You should not make this side bet, however, unless the jackpot exceeds $280,000 for the $1 ante and the $1 jackpot bet.

PAI GOW POKER - Strange name for a casino game. The game is a cross between Pai Gow, a Chinese game of dominoes, and the American game of seven-card poker. Players are dealt seven cards and they must arrange (or set) their cards into a five-card poker hand and a two-card poker hand. Skill is involved in setting the two hands which can help reduce the casino's advantage.

SLOT MACHINES - Casinos earn more money from slot machines than all the table games combined. The casino's advantage varies from one machine to another. Typically the higher denomination machines ($1 and up) pay back more than the nickel, quarter and fifty cent machines. Slots are not your best bet in the casino, but here are a few tips: Always play the maximum number of coins the machine will accept or you won't be eligible for the jackpot. Don't waste hours looking for a machine that's "ready to hit." Join the slot clubs. They are free and you'll be rewarded with discounts and other freebies. Machines that have lower jackpots pay smaller amounts more frequently which means you normally get more playing time for your money. If you are lucky to hit a jackpot, discipline yourself to quit a winner.

VIDEO POKER - Your best bet if you enjoy playing slot machines. Skill is involved as well as learning to spot the better payoff machines. Check the full house, flush payoff schedule. On machines that pay on jacks or better the better paying machines pay nine coins for a full house and six coins for the flush for each coin played. These machines are known as 9/6 machines. They are readily available; seek them out.

KENO - This casino game has a very high casino advantage (usually 20% and up). Stay away if you are serious about winning.

RED DOG - This is the casino version of the old acey-deucey. The stakes are low, but the casino edge is a wee-bit steep (3.5%). If you play, only make the raise wager when the spread between the two cards is seven or more.

SIC BO - This is an oriental game in which players bet on the outcome of the roll of three dice. There are lots of bets on the layout, some that pay odds of 150 to 1. However, most have a very high casino advantage. Your best bet is a bet on the big or small wager.

LET IT RIDE - This relatively new casino table game is based on the all-American game of poker. Like Caribbean Stud Poker, players compete against the house rather than against each other. What makes this game so unique is that the players can remove up to two of their initial mandatory three bets if they don't think they can win. The objective is to end up with a five-card poker hand of at least 10's or higher. The higher the rank, the greater the payoff; up to 1,000 to 1 for the royal flush. The casino edge is about 3% and about 70% of the hands will be losing hands. Let It Ride gaming tournaments offer top prizes of up to $3 million. If you are lucky enough to catch a high payoff hand, be smart, push your chair back, and take the money and run!

Henry Tamburin has more than 25 years experience as a casino player, author, columnist and instructor. He has written more than 500 articles on casino gambling for numerous national gaming publications. He is also the author of numerous books and instructional videos. Ordering information for his books and videos can be found on page 66.

Your Best Casino Bets - Part II

by Steve Bourie

In the previous story Henry gave you his choices for your best casino bets based on which ones offer you the best mathematical odds. Now, Henry is a great mathematician who is truly an expert at crunching numbers to figure out what the theoretical odds are, but what about real life? By this I mean - at the end of the week, or the month, or the year, how much does a casino really make from blackjack, or craps, or roulette? Sure, you can do the math to calculate the casino advantage on a bank hand in mini-baccarat as 1.17%, but at the end of the day what percent of those bets on mini-baccarat actually wind up in the hands of the casino? Is it precisely 1.17%? or is it less? or is it more? And, if you knew how much the casino truly averaged on all of the games it offered, which one would turn out to be your best bet based on that information?

To find the answer to this question I began my search by looking at the annual gaming revenue report issued by Nevada's State Gaming Control Board. It lists the win percentages (based on the drop - more on this later) for all of the games offered by the casinos and you might be surprised at which game had the lowest win percentage. Go ahead and take a guess...nice try, but you're wrong! The answer is bingo, where casinos won only 1.74% of the total money they handled. The first column below lists the actual win percentages (based on the drop) for Nevada's various games for the fiscal year ending June 30, 1996:

GAME	WIN %	ADJUSTED WIN %
Wheel of Fortune	44.06	8.81
Red Dog	29.65	5.93
Keno	27.31	27.31
Caribbean Stud Poker	24.71	4.94
Let It Ride	23.61	4.72
Roulette	22.70	4.54
Pai Gow	21.60	4.32
Pai Gow Poker	20.03	4.01
Race Book	15.03	15.03
Baccarat	14.28	2.86
Craps	14.23	2.85
Twenty-One	13.69	2.74
Mini-Baccarat	11.18	2.24
Sports Pool	4.28	4.28
Bingo	1.74	1.74

Usually bingo would rank as one of the games with the worst odds, but not in Nevada where it's used as a "loss leader." Just like your local Kmart runs especially low prices on a couple of items to bring you into the store where they believe you'll buy some other items, Nevada casinos use bingo to bring people into their casinos, believing that while they're there they'll play other games and also develop a loyalty to that casino. So, if you're a bingo player Nevada casinos are the best places you'll ever find to play your game!

Before we go on to the other games you'll need a brief explanation of how the win percentages are calculated and we'll start off with a basic lesson in how casinos do their accounting.

Casinos measure their take in table games by the *drop* and the *win*. The *drop* is the count of all of the receipts (cash and credit markers) that go into the drop box located at the table. Later, an accounting is made to see how much more (or less) they have than they started with. This amount is known as the *win*.

What the first column in the table shows you is how much the casinos won as a percentage of the drop. For example, on the roulette table for every $100 that went into the drop box the casino won $22.70 or 22.70%. What it doesn't tell you, however, is how much the casinos won as a percentage of all the bets that were made. In other words, the drop tells you how many chips were bought at that table, but it doesn't tell you how many bets were made with those chips. For example, if you buy $100 worth of chips at a blackjack table and play $10 a hand you don't bet for exactly 10 hands then leave the table, do you? Of course not. You win some hands and you lose some hands and if you counted all of the times you made a $10 bet before you left the table you would see that your original $100 in chips generated many times that amount in bets. In other words, there is a multiplier effect for the money that goes into the drop box. We know that for every dollar that goes into the drop box there is a corresponding number of bets made. To find out exactly what that number is I asked Henry for some help. He replied that there is no exact answer, but during a 1982 study of the roulette tables in Atlantic City it was discovered that the total amount bet was approximately five times the amount of the buy-in. This means that for every $100 worth of chips bought at the table it resulted in $500 worth of bets being made.

The multiplier effect for the money that goes into the drop box is also dependent on the skill of the player. A blackjack player that loses his money quickly because he doesn't know good playing strategy will have a much lower multiplier than a player who uses a correct playing strategy. For purposes of this story, however, we'll assume that they balance each other out and we'll also assume that all games have the same multiplier of five. We can now return to our win percentage tables and divide by five the percentages for those games that have a multiplier effect. These new adjusted numbers lets us know approximately how much the casinos actually won as a percentage of the amount bet on each of those games. Keep in mind, however, that besides bingo there are three other game categories that do not need to be adjusted: keno, race book and sports pool. They need no adjustment because there is no drop involved. On these particular games the casinos know the exact total of the bets they take in and the exact total of the bets they pay out.

After calculating our adjusted win numbers we can now go back and take another look at which games are your best casino bets. The worst game, by far, is keno with its 27.31% edge. Next comes the race book with 15.03%. Then we have four relatively high casino advantage games: wheel of fortune (big six wheel) at 8.81%; red dog (acey-deucey) at 5.93%; Caribbean Stud Poker at 4.94%; and Let It Ride at 4.72%. They're followed by roulette at 4.54%; Pai Gow at 4.32%; and pai gow poker at 4.01%. Also in this group is sports betting at 4.28%, but that number deserves a closer look. There are actually five different types of bets that make up that 4.28% figure: football - 4.80%; basketball - 2.80%; baseball - 1.71%; sports parlay cards - 32.75%; and other sports - 3.58%. As you can see, all sports bets carry a relatively low house edge, except for sports parlay cards which you may want to avoid. Finally, we come to the four best casino bets that all have roughly the same house edge of less than three percent: baccarat at 2.86%; craps at 2.85%; blackjack at 2.74%; and mini-baccarat at 2.24%.

So there you have it. After discounting bingo, mini-baccarat is your best casino bet! Henry said it was a good game to play and he was right. But didn't he also say that blackjack was your *best* casino bet? Was he wrong about that? Not really, because he prefaced it by saying "you must learn how to play your hands." You have to remember that of all the table games offered in a casino (other than poker) only blackjack is a game of skill. This means that the better you are at playing your cards, the better you will be able to beat the house average. The 2.74% figure shown is just an average and if you learn your basic strategy you can cut it down even more which would then make it your best bet. Good luck!

Casino Comps - Part I

by Steve Bourie

In the world of casino gambling a "comp" is short for complimentary and it refers to anything that the casino will give you for free in return for your play in their casino.

Naturally, the more you bet, the more the casino will be willing to give you back. For the truly "high roller" (those willing to bet thousands, tens of thousands or even hundreds of thousands on the turn of a card) there is no expense spared to cater to their every whim, including: private jet transportation, chauffeur-driven limousines, gourmet chef-prepared foods, the finest wines and champagnes, plus pampered butler and maid service in a $10 million penthouse suite. But what about the lower-limit bettor?

Well, it turns out that pretty much any gambler can qualify for comps no matter what their level of play and if you know you're going to be gambling anyway, you might as well ask to get rated to see what you can get on a comp basis.

When you sit down to play be sure to tell the dealer that you want to be rated and they'll call over the appropriate floorperson who will take down your name and put it on a card along with information on how long you play and how much you bet. The floorperson won't stand there and constantly watch you, instead they'll just glance over every once in awhile to see how much you're betting and note it on the card. If you change tables be sure to tell the floorperson so that they can continue to track your play at the new table.

Usually a casino will want you to play for at least three hours and virtually all casinos use the same formula to calculate your comp value. They simply take the size of your average bet and multiply it by: the casino's advantage on the game you're playing; the decisions per hour in your game; and the length of your play in hours. The end result is what the casino expects to win from you during your play and most casinos will return about 40% of that amount to you in the form of comps.

So, let's say you're a roulette player that averages $20 a spin and you play for four hours. What's that worth in comps? Well, just multiply your average bet ($20), by the casino's advantage in roulette (5.3%) to get $1.06, which is the average amount the casino expects to make on you on each spin of the wheel. You then multiply that by the number of decisions (or spins) per hour (40) to get $42.40, which is the average amount the casino expects to make on you after one hour. Then, multiply that by the total hours of play (4) to get $169.60, which is the average amount the casino expects to make on you during your

4 hours of play. Since the average casino will return about 40% of that amount in comps you should qualify for $67.84 in casino comps.

One thing to keep in mind about comps is that you don't have to lose in order to qualify. The casino only asks that you put in the time to play. So, in our example if, after 4 hours of gambling, our roulette player ended up winning $100, they would still be eligible for the same amount of $67.84 in comps.

The last thing to mention about comps is that some casino games require skill (blackjack and pai gow poker), or offer various bets that have different casino advantages (craps) so those factors are sometimes adjusted in the equation when determining the casino advantage in those games. Just take a look at the chart below to see how the average casino will adjust for skill in blackjack and pai gow poker as well as for the types of bets that are made in craps.

Game	Game Advantage	Decisions Per Hour
Blackjack	.0025 (Card Counter) .01 (Good Basic Strategy) .015 (Soft Player)	70
Roulette	.053	40
Craps	.005 (Pass Line/Full Odds) .01 (Knowledgeable) .04 (Soft)	144
Baccarat	.012	70
Mini-Baccarat	.012	110
Pai Gow Poker	.01 (Knowledgeable) .02 (Average)	25

Casino Comps - Part II

by Max Rubin

Dom Perignon delivered to jacuzzi suites. "King's-row" booths at the hottest shows in town. Hundred-dollar entrees washed down with rare vintage wines. Fully stocked stretch limos at your beck and call. First-class airline tickets. Unlimited golf on ultra-exclusive courses. Seats next to the ring girls at world-championship boxing matches. These are the images that rush to mind at the mere mention of the subject of casino comps. Getting treated like royalty just for doing what you enjoy (gambling) is an exciting prospect, even if it's only a fantasy for most of us.

But just because you don't have a spare $10,000 to risk at the tables doesn't mean that you can't get a slice of the half a billion dollars in comps the casinos lavish on their deserving customers each year. Fact is, the comp system is designed to reward gamblers at every level. Even if you play the nickel slots or blackjack at $2 a hand, your action makes you eligible for something in the grand comp plan. Free beer and soft drinks, snack-bar meal chits, free parking, line passes, and perks for paycheck cashing are all casino comps. The trick to getting your share is to understand what you're entitled to.

What Gets What - The first step is to size up your gambling bankroll. The casinos are after your money, so how much you wager is the dominant factor in determining what type of comps you get. Careful here! The strategy is not to increase the amount that you gamble just to get the comps you'd like. On the contrary, it's to stay at your normal level and let the comps you qualify for enhance your result (by either cutting losses or augmenting wins). While casino policies vary, the following provides a good overview of the compensation you can expect.

At the lowest levels, you'll have to be content with the little comps, such as complimentary parking and funbook freebies. Of course, even the lowly nickel slot-machine or minimum-bet table-game players can get get free drinks while gambling; it's as simple as flagging down a cocktail waitress.

By playing $1 slots or making $5 and $10 wagers at table games, you graduate to low-level comps. These include meals at snack bars, breakfasts in coffee shops, and a round of drinks at the bar. Betting $10-$25 per hand lands the best buffets, dinner in the coffee shops, line passes to shows, and a little-known but valuable comp called the "casino rate" on a room (a discount that averages 50% off the retail rate). The secret to getting the low-stakes comps is simple. Ask for them. Bosses in the table-game pits have what's called "the power of the pen," which means they can give away inexpensive meals without having to answer to superiors. Ask, ask, ask-even if you're winning. A popular belief is that you have to be losing to get comped. Not true. And here's a little tip: women have an easier time getting comps than men, especially when they hit up a male pit boss.

Bigger bettors get better comps. If you regularly bet $25-$100 per hand, you can look forward to gourmet meals and showroom seats. At these levels, though, the strategy changes. Now it's best to get "rated" by the casino, which means having a boss watch your action to evaluate you for the better perks.

At the $100-$250 level, you're in line for the main event-"RFB," meaning room, food, and beverage. Now the whole vacation (except airfare) is on the house. The RFB gambler gets most of the high-end amenities mentioned at the top of this article (limos, gourmet meals, full-scale room service). He has a private liaison called a "host," who tends to practical needs like securing dinner and show reservations. Of course, the $100-per-hand bettor is also responsible for whatever financial consequences result from his high-risk gambling recreation.

Beyond the $250-per-hand level, the sky's the limit: private suites with butler service, $500 rounds of golf, trips to the Super Bowl, Christmas gifts (the most imaginative I've heard of is an entire side of beef), almost anything is possible. Many of the high rollers who get this treatment have casino lines of credit in excess of $1 million. At these levels, a strange symbiotic bond is forged between the casino and the gambler. The casino is happy because its winnings far exceed the expense of hosting the gambler. The gambler is happy because he considers the attention and status he receives a fair trade for his losses.

You may have noticed that a prominent category did not appear in the overview: quarter slot and video poker players. That's because a whole separate department attends to the needs of these players-namely, the slot club. Slot clubs are an extension of the casino comp system. If you don't relish dealing with the bosses face to face, the slot-club route is an excellent, less complicated alternative for tapping into casino comps. Sign up, insert your card when you play, and redeem your accrued points for cash and casino amenities.

Go Where They Want You - Some friends of mine once played blackjack at The Mirage. One friend bet $50 to $200 per hand, the other played black chips exclusively, about $100 to $300 per hand. After nearly three hours at the table, they decided to cash out, called a boss over, and asked what their three hours of black-chip play would get them. He grudgingly offered dinner. "Dinner where?" one asked. "Coffee shop." "That's all?" "Best I can do," the boss shrugged.

They took their action to the Rio. After playing (at the same stakes) for less than 20 minutes, a boss approached and offered each of them full RFB. They'd gone from peons to princes just by switching casinos. Depending on their size, facilities, and philosophies, casinos cater to players with different gambling profiles. One joint's dream player is another's yawner. It's up to you to determine where your action is coveted.

The best way to find out where your player profile will be most appreciated is, once again, to ask. You don't even have to do it in person. "Scouting" via telephone from the comfort of your home or office will get the job done. Call several casinos you'd like to stay at, ask for a host, and fire away. "What kind of play do you need to comp me a room?" "How about RFB?" "Airfare reimbursement? Golf?" You get the idea. Scouting is important. After comparing five or six casinos, you'll know where you're wanted.

The Equation - The comp determination process isn't really as mysterious as you might think. Gambling games are designed to give the casino a small advantage. Over time, that advantage wins the casino an amount that's directly related to how much you bet and how long you play. To ease the blow to the losing players, the casino is willing to give back a portion of what it wins (usually around 40%) in the form of comps. It's a unique marketing technique-not a giveaway, but a giveback. Or more precisely, a rebate on losses.

Though the particulars vary from casino to casino, the equation is always some variation of the following: (Average Bet x Hands Per Hour x Hours Played x Casino Advantage) x 40% = Comp Equivalency (the amount the casino will give back in complimentaries).

Just plug in the proper values. Assuming a blackjack player bets $25 per hand at 60 hands per hour for four hours with an estimated casino edge of 2%, the equation would read: ($25 x 60 x 4 x .02) x .4 = $48. In this example, the player would be entitled to $48 in casino comps.

Comp Wizardry - Now that you know what the prizes are, you might be wondering how well you can learn to play the game. Due to the complexity of the comp system, there are lots of loopholes waiting to be exploited by savvy practitioners of the art. For the ultimate insider's view, my book, *CompCity-A Guide to Free Las Vegas Vacations* ($42.95 pp, 1-800-741-1596), details the techniques used by "comp wizards" to beat the casinos at their own game by getting a dollar's worth of comps for every dime they lose. Short of a crash course in comp strategy, though, just asking for meals, drink tickets, and line passes every time you play for moderate stakes is 90% of what you need to know, especially at the lower levels. Don't miss out on your share.

Max Rubin is a former casino idustry executive and author of the book <u>Comp City - A Guide to Free Las Vegas Vacations</u>. He is also a contributing writer for Casino Player Magazine and a featured speaker at gambling seminars. Ordering information for his book can be found on page 63.

Slot Clubs

by Jeffrey Compton

Raise your right hand and repeat after me: I will join every slot club at every casino I visit. I will not deposit my hard-earned money into any slot or video poker machine unless I belong to that slot club. I will always use my slot club card, even if I deposit a single quarter.

Why should you join every slot club? Because you have nothing to lose and literally everything to gain. Slot clubs are free, the rewards are unlimited, and incredibly, even if you never drop a coin into a slot or video poker machine you stand to profit: Many clubs give free gifts or discount coupons to anyone who fills out the enrollment form. Casino shops and restaurants frequently extend 10%-15% discounts to card-carrying members. Just having your name in the computer can result in mailbox surprises, like a discounted room offer or a two-for-one buffet coupon. And if you do play, the sky's the limit.

Slot clubs were born in Atlantic City. What, not Las Vegas? No, Atlantic City. With a clientele of cost-conscious day-trippers playing quarter slot machines, the A. C. casino execs quickly realized that unless their bread-and-butter customers were recognized and rewarded, they would walk next door. In 1982, the Galaxy Slot Club debuted at the Sands. Selected slot customers were invited to special parties and given gold lapel pins that identified them as casino VIPs. After its first year, the club had 600 members and was considered a rousing success. The following year, Harrah's Atlantic City expanded on the concept. Borrowing directly from the airline's frequent-flyer programs, Harrah's devised a system whereby players received one ticket (a sort of bonus buck) for every hundred dollars or so they put through a slot machine. Players could redeem their tickets in the hotel restaurants and gift shops, or apply them to their hotel bills.

The rest is history. Slot clubs can now be found in every casino in Atlantic City, throughout Nevada, on Mississippi riverboats, and at Indian casinos across America.

Why the great success? Because slot clubs are a win-win for both the casino and the player. The advantage for the casino is obvious. Based on the information provided by the player (including the player's name, address, interests, type of play, amount of play, and favorite benefits), the casino can design giveaways, promotions, direct-mail campaigns, and even entire gaming areas to get a better shot at the gambler's bankroll.

The main advantage for the player can be summed up in two words: ties win! In an article for *Casino Player*, Anthony Curtis wrote that the creators of video poker did something that no other gambling-game developer has ever been able to do: they made a push (tie) seem like a win. In video poker, a pair of jacks, queens, kings, or aces returns your original wager, and even though it's a push, it still feels like a profit. It's even better when you belong to a slot club- a push is a profit. That's because every coin you send through a machine counts toward something of value later on. Take a look.

Two people are playing quarter slots. After eight hours of action, both are even; neither has won nor lost any money. Player A, the slot club member, walks away with two free meals, a $50 discount on her room, and a $40 cash rebate. Player B gets nothing. They both tied, but who won?

Slot club benefits can be divided into two categories: tangible and intangible. Tangible benefits include cash, comps, and merchandise, and are awarded in direct proportion to your point total. The specifics are usually spelled out in the club's written material and any slot club employee should be able to issue you a tangible benefit.

I define "intangible" as any benefit you receive from the slot club that does not affect (i.e., reduce) your point total. This can be an additional free meal, a free tournament, a shopping discount, or some other VIP perk. Though intangible benefits are determined by the amount and level of play, you receive them along with (not instead of) your tangible benefits. Sort of like having your cake and your cash, too.

Unlike tangible benefits, intangible benefits are not publicized. To get the most from intangibles, you should carefully read all of a club's printed materials (especially the newsletter), talk as much as you can with other club members and, most importantly, develop a good relationship with a slot host. Unlike slot-booth personnel, slot hosts can write a comp without having to clear it with anyone else. They are hired to keep people happy.

How do you find a slot host? After giving the casino about $2,000 in slot or video poker play, ask a change person to send one over. Do not leave your chair! Introduce yourself and inquire politely about a meal comp. One of three things will happen. The host will say yes on the spot. The host will say no on the spot. The host will check the computer, then tell you yes or no. If the answer is no, ask him how much more play you need to get what you want. At worst, you'll have made a valuable contact and determined exactly what you need to get the comp. At best, you'll get a free meal. Whatever happens, you've lost nothing.

The full range of slot club benefits has to be discovered, and to the best combination of detective, diplomat and behavioral researcher goes the spoils.

Imagine the team of Holmes, Kissinger, and Pavlov playing at a slot machine and you'll get the idea. Believe me, it's worth the effort. Soon, your slot club benefits list will include the following:

• Cash - Depending on the casino, slot club members receive rebates ranging from 6¢ to $1 for every $100 they play. Occasionally, that rebate results in a mathematical edge playing the game. For example, perfect play on a full-pay jacks or better video poker machine at Las Vegas' Golden Nugget yields $100.17 for every $100 wagered when the slot club cash rebate is added in.

• Meal comps - In theory, a slot club member should average one meal comp per every two hours of quarter play. In reality, due to slot club research, I put on 15 pounds last year.

• Casino rate - When members need rooms, they typically pay half of what the average player pays at any hotel. Often, rooms can be obtained for free.

• Entertainment comps - Caesars Palace, for one, occasionally sends members free tickets to its headliner shows, including David Copperfield and Jerry Seinfeld. Even more common are two-for-one coupons to week day performances of casino production shows.

• Gifts - Hate your birthday? Join a slot club. My 40th birthday brought forth a plentiful bounty: a Circus Circus sweatshirt, $100 free play at the The Mirage on a Megabucks machine, several meals, coupons worth $50 in cash, and a free weekend stay complete with meals at the Ramada Express in Laughlin. I can't wait for 41.

• Priority treatment - As a casino VIP, active slot club members are given special handling for meal, room, and show reservations. I've used my card as a buffet line pass, to secure room reservations on busy weekends for out-of-town guests, even to get my car parked when the valet lot is "full."

The list goes on and on ... After you've joined several clubs, I suggest you create a personal "ABC" system, which you can use to categorize the various clubs. "C" clubs are those that you simply join. Since you will join every club, no club can be less than a C. "B" clubs are those that you'll use, at least a little, because you have one or two good reasons for playing at that casino. For example, you might play just enough at a casino with a good buffet, such as the Rio in Las Vegas, to earn a comp, or at least the right to use the VIP line. "A" clubs are your gems; you'll work these hard. These are the slot clubs at the casinos you enjoy playing, eating, and sleeping in the most. Your goal is to know everything there is to know about the rewards system, become friends with one or two slot hosts, and learn every angle imaginable.

Several factors should be considered when picking your A, B, and C clubs. Does the casino have the machines you like to play? Serious video poker players avoid casinos that do not offer certain games (such as 9/6 jacks or better). If you play quarters or certain types of slots, such as Quartermania or Megabucks, you'll want a casino that includes your favorite slot machines in its mix. If you like certain table games, you'll want a casino that offers favorable rules and good comps for your action.

Are you comfortable with the overall ambience of the casino? How about the restaurants? Meal comps are the most popular non-cash benefit a slot club offers, especially to locals. The video poker might be great and the slot club generous, but if the buffet is losing customers to the city mission, then why spend time or money qualifying for it?

Other selection factors might include location, child care, bowling, the color of the carpet, the cleavage of the cocktail waitresses, the attitude of the staff, or even the hotel's history of labor relations.

Which is the best slot club? That depends on what you want (and what you play). Different people use different slot clubs for different purposes, whether for a cheap holiday, a luxurious vacation, a free meal, or even a principal source of income. But first you have to join. I hope to see you at your favorite slot club booth someday, or better yet, in the VIP line at the buffet.

Treasure Island Slot Club

by Steve Bourie

On a trip to Las Vegas in February 1996 my friend and I investigated the slot club at Treasure Island to see what it offered. I was planning a return visit to Las Vegas with my wife and two children in October and I knew we wanted to stay at Treasure Island so I was curious to see what kind of savings, if any, I could get by becoming a member of the slot club.

My friend and I filled out our registration forms at the slot club desk and we were each issued a temporary card. Before playing any slot or video poker machine you have to insert the plastic card into a special reader on the machine and it then tracks how much money you put into play. The card only works on $1 machines (or higher) and for every $15 you put into a machine you earn one point. To get a permanent card you have to accumulate 150 points which means you have to put in a total of $2,250 ($15 x 150 = $2,250).

When your permanent card is issued you also get a $15 cash rebate and two free buffets. At that point you are also eligible for line passes for the buffets and a special club member room rate on a future visit of up to four nights. At the time of my visit in February the club room rate was $45 (Sun-Thu), $59 (Fri/Sat) or $75 (holidays).

We both began our play on 9/7 double bonus video poker machines. These machines have an expected return of 99% with perfect play. They offer a bonus payout on four-of-a-kind but only return even money on two pairs. Within 20 minutes my friend got four 7's and was up more than $250. My luck wasn't quite as good. After accumulating 44 points by putting $660 in the machine ($15 x 44 = $660) I had lost $200. If I continued to lose at that rate it would have cost me about $800 to qualify for the slot club - a lot more than I wanted to risk.

The solution was to form a partnership with my friend. By combining our bankrolls we spread the risk and we were fairly confident that we couldn't get hurt too badly. The other thing that we did was to switch to an 8/5 progressive machine that had a jackpot of about $5,000. The expected return on this machine (with perfect play) was around 98% but it returned two-to-one for two pairs which occurs much more frequently than four-of-a-kind.

We took turns inserting our cards in the machine, alternating cards every time five points had accumulated on a card. Eventually, we both got our 150 points, but the cost was $160 each. Since my friend had won more than that previously, he joined the club at a profit. Since I had lost $200 previously, that meant it cost me $360 to join. After getting my $15 cash rebate that brought my cost down to $345.

In August I called the slot club to make reservations for a three-night, mid-week, stay in October for me, my wife and our two kids. The club rates had been raised slightly to $49 (Sun-Thu) and $79 (Fri/Sat/holidays). I made reservations for three nights at $49 per night for the four of us and I then called the regular reservation number to see what they were charging. I was quoted $149, plus $25 for each child, for a total of $199 per night. For the next few weeks I called to see if the quoted price would change and it did: $119, $99 and even $79 (plus $50 for the two kids on all rates). It seemed that the closer I called to the arrival date, the lower the price, but certainly nowhere near the $49 rate I was going to pay. So, I was definitely going to save some money, the question was how much? I guess there was no way to put an exact number on it but it had to be a minimum of $80 per night because that was the difference between the lowest price I was quoted ($129) and what I was going to pay ($49) for each night. That meant I saved at least $240. If you used the first rate I was quoted ($199) then I would have saved $450 but I doubt anyone pays $199 a night for a standard room at Treasure Island.

So, going with the $240 savings that brought my cost down to $105. Deduct the two free buffets valued at $22.50 (2 x $11.25) and the cost went down to $82.50. Not a huge amount, but certainly not as good a deal as my friend who won money going through the process!

As this book goes to press we are preparing for our trip so I can't say if there are any other extra benefits once you arrive. I did, however, call one month ahead and ask a Slot Host about getting tickets to Mystere. He made reservations for us and said we could pick the tickets up at the box office after 2pm on the day of the show. That was nice. He also said that they might pick up all or part of the cost of the tickets, depending upon my play.

Once you're a permanent member of the club you continue to get a cash rebate of 10% of the points you earn. So, if you earn 50 points you would get $5 back. In real numbers this works out to a cash rebate of .67%, or 67 cents for every $100 you put through a machine. One other thing, if you want to continue to get the club rate on a room you have to re-qualify on each visit with an average of 100 points for each day you stay. For me this means that I'll have to get 300 points on my three-day stay in order to get the club rate on my next visit of up to four nights. 300 points is equivalent to $4,500, or twice the amount I originally had to gamble in order to qualify, so I'm not sure I'll do it.

Keep in mind that not all clubs are as costly as Treasure Island's and if you'd like to learn more about slot clubs be sure to read *The Las Vegas Advisor Guide To Slot Clubs*, by Jeffrey Compton (see page 22). It gives detailed information on every slot club in Las Vegas and gives you tips on how to choose the club that's right for your particular kind of play.

Slot Machines

by Steve Bourie

Virtually anyone who visits a casino, even for the first time, is familiar with a slot machine and how it operates: just put in your money, pull the handle and wait a few seconds to see if you win. It isn't intimidating like table games where you really need some knowledge of the rules before you play and it's this basic simplicity that accounts for much of the success of slot machines in the modern American casino.

As a matter of fact, the biggest money-maker for casinos is the slot machine with approximately 60 to 65 percent of the average casino's profits being generated by slot machine play. As an example, in Nevada's fiscal year ending June 30, 1996 the total win by all of the state's casinos was a little more than $7.5 billion. Of that amount, slightly more than $4.6 billion, or about 62 percent, was from slot machine winnings.

With this in mind, you must ask yourself, "can I really win money by playing slot machines?" The answer is a resounding yes...and no. First the "no" part: in simplest terms a slot machine makes money for the casino by paying out less money than it takes in. In some states, such as Nevada and New Jersey, the minimum amount to be returned is regulated. In Nevada the minimum is 75 percent and in New Jersey it's 83 percent. However, if you look at the slot payback percentages for those particular states in this book you will see that the actual average payback percentages are much higher. In New Jersey it's about 91 percent and in Nevada it's about 95 percent. Even though the actual paybacks are higher than the law requires, you can still see that on average for every $1 you play in an Atlantic City slot machine you will lose 9¢ and in a Las Vegas slot machine you will lose 5¢. Therefore, it doesn't take a rocket scientist to see that if you stand in front of a slot machine and continue to pump in your money, eventually, you will lose it all. On average, it will take you longer to lose it in Las Vegas rather than Atlantic City, but the result is still the same: you will go broke.

Gee, sounds kind of depressing, doesn't it? Well, cheer up because now we go on to the "yes" part. But, before we talk about that, let's first try to understand how slot machines work. All modern slot machines contain a random number generator (RNG) which is used to control the payback percentage for each machine. When a casino orders a slot machine it tells the manufacturer what percentage it wants that machine to pay back and that amount is programmed into the RNG. A casino can always change the payback percentage, but in order to do that it must go back to the manufacturer to have them reprogram the RNG. For this reason, most casinos rarely change their payback percentages unless there is a major revision in their marketing philosophy. And what exactly is a random number generator? Well, it's a little computer chip that is constantly working to (as its name implies) generate number combinations on a random basis. It does this extremely fast and is capable of producing hundreds of combinations each second. When you put in a coin, or push the bet button, the RNG stops and the combination it stops at is used to determine where the reels will stop in the pay window. Unlike video poker machines, you have no way of knowing what a slot machine is programmed to pay back just by looking at it. The only way to tell is by knowing what is programmed into the RNG.

Okay, now let's get back to the "yes" part. Yes, you can win money on slot machines by using a little knowledge, practicing some money management and, mostly, having lots of luck. First, the knowledge part. You need to know what kind of player you are and how much risk you are willing to take. Do you want to go for the giant progressive jackpot that could make you a millionaire in an instant or would you be content walking away just a few dollars ahead?

An example of a slot machine with a large progressive jackpot is Nevada's Megabucks where the jackpot starts at $5 million. These $1 machines are located at more than 125 Nevada casinos at various locations around the state and are linked together by a computer. It's fine if that's the kind of machine you want to play, but keep in mind that the odds are fairly astronomical of you hitting that big jackpot. Also, the overall payback percentage is lower on these machines than the average $1 machine. During Nevada's 1995 fiscal year Megabucks averaged a little less than 90 percent payback while the typical $1 machine in Nevada averaged a little more than 95 percent. So, be aware that if you play the machines with the linked progressive jackpots you'll win fewer small payouts and it will be very difficult to leave as a winner. Unless, of course, you hit that big one! If you really like to play the linked progressive machines your best bet is probably to set aside a small percentage of your bankroll (maybe 10 to 15 percent) for chasing that big jackpot and saving the rest for the regular machines.

One other thing you should know about playing these linked progressives is that on most of them, including Megabucks, you will receive your jackpot in equal payments over a period of 20 years. You can avoid this, however, by playing at one of the casinos that will pay you in one lump sum. The Circus Bucks slots at the Circus Circus properties in Nevada offer this as well as the Big Bucks slots at Bally's Park Place in Atlantic City.

Knowledge also comes into play when deciding how many coins to bet. You should always look at the payback schedule posted on the machine to see if a bonus is payed for playing the maximum number of coins that the machine will accept. For example, if it's a two-coin machine and the jackpot payout is 500 coins when you bet one coin, but it pays you 1,200 coins when you bet two coins, then that machine is paying you a 200 coin bonus for playing the maximum number of coins and you should always bet the maximum two coins to take advantage of that bonus. However, if it's a two-coin machine that will pay you 500 coins for a one-coin bet and 1,000 coins for a two-coin bet, then there is no advantage to making the maximum bet on that machine and you should only bet the minimum amount.

Knowledge of which casinos offer the best payback percentages is also helpful. When available, we print that information in this book to help you decide where to go for the best return on your slot machine dollar. You may want to go to the Las Vegas Strip to see the free pirate show at Treasure Island, but take a look at the slot machine payback percentages for the Strip area casinos in the Las Vegas section and you'll see that you can get better returns for your slot machine dollar by playing at the off-Strip area casinos.

The final bit of knowledge you need concerns slot clubs. Every major casino has a slot club and you should make it a point to join the slot club before you insert your first coin. It doesn't cost anything to join and as a member you will be able to earn complimentaries from the casinos in the form of cash, food, shows, drinks, rooms or other "freebies." When you join the club you'll be issued a card (similar to a credit card) that you insert in the machine before you start to play and it will track how much you bet, as well as how long you play. Naturally, the more money you gamble, the more "freebies" you'll earn. Just make sure you don't get carried away and bet more than you're comfortable with just to earn some extra "comps." Ideally, you want to get "comps" for gambling that you were going to do anyway and not be pressured into betting more than you had planned.

Now let's talk about money management. The first thing you have to remember when playing slot machines is that there is no skill involved. Unlike blackjack or video poker, there are no decisions you can make that will affect whether you win or lose. It is strictly luck, or the lack of it, that will determine whether or not you win. However, when you are lucky enough to get ahead (even if it's just a little) that's where the money management factor comes in. As stated earlier, the longer you stand in front of a machine and put in your money, the more likely you are to go broke. Therefore, there is only one way you can walk away a winner and that's to make sure that when you do win, you don't put it all back in. You really need to set a "win goal" for yourself and to stop when you reach it. A realistic example would be a "win goal" of roughly 25 percent of your bankroll. If you started with $400, then you should stop if you win about $100. The "win goal" you decide on is up to you, but keep in mind that the higher your goal, the harder it will be to reach it, so be practical. And what if you should happen to reach your goal? Take a break! Go have a meal, see a show, visit the lounge for a drink or even just take a walk around the casino. You may have the urge to keep playing, but if you can just take a break from the machines, even it's just for a short time, you'll have the satisfaction of leaving as a winner. If, later on, you get really bored and find that you just *have* to go back to the machines you can avoid a total loss by not risking more than half of your winnings and by playing on smaller denomination machines. If you made your winnings on $1 machines, move down to quarters. If you won on quarters, move down to nickels. The idea now is basically to kill some time and have a little fun knowing that no matter what happens you'll still leave as a winner.

And now, let's move on to luck. As stated previously, the ultimate decider in whether or not you win is how lucky you are when you play. But, is there anything you can do to help you choose a "lucky" or "winning" machine? Not really, because there is no such thing as a "winning" machine. Remember, in the long run, no machine will pay out more than it takes in. There are, however, some things you could try to help you find the more generous machines and avoid the stingy ones. Keep in mind that all of the slot machine payback percentages shown in this book are averages. Some machines are programmed to pay back more than average and some machines are programmed to pay less. Also, like everything else in life, machines have good cycles where they pay out more than average and bad cycles where they pay out less than average. Ultimately, what you want to find is a high-paying machine in a good cycle. Of course if I knew how to find that machine I wouldn't be writing this story, instead I'd be standing in front of it with a $100 bill in my hand and looking for the change attendant. So, I guess you'll have to settle for my two recommendations as to how you *might* be able to find the better paying machines.

First, is the "accounting" method. With this method you always start with a pre-determined number of coins and after playing them in the machine you take an accounting of your results. If you have more than you started with you stay at that machine and start another cycle. Just keep doing this until the machine returns less than you started with. As an example, let's say you start with 20 coins. After playing those 20 coins you count how many you got back. If it's more than 20 you start over again with another 20 coins and then do another accounting. If, after any accounting, you get back less than the 20 you started with, stop playing and move on to a different machine. This is an especially good method because you have to slow down your play to take periodic accountings and you will always have an accurate idea of how well you are doing.

The other method is even simpler and requires no math. It's called the "baseball" method and is based on the principle of three strikes and you're out. Just play a machine until it loses three times in a row, then move on to a different machine. Both of these methods will prevent you from losing a lot of money in a machine that is either set for a low payback or is going through a bad cycle; yet both will still allow you to take advantage of a high payback machine or one that is going through a good cycle. Give one of them a try on your next trip. Good luck!

Video Poker

by Steve Bourie

Okay, who knows the main difference between video poker and slot machines? C'mon now, raise your hands if you think you know it. If you said "a slot machine is a game of luck and video poker is a game of skill" then you are correct! When you play a slot machine there is no decision you can make which will affect the outcome of the game. You put in your money; pull the handle; and hope for the best. In video poker, however, it is your skill in playing the cards which definitely affects the outcome of the game.

Okay, who knows the other major difference between video poker and slot machines? Well, you're right again if you said "you never know what percentage a slot machine is set to pay back, but you can tell a video poker machine's payback percentage just by looking at it." Of course if you knew that answer then you also knew that video poker machines almost always offer you better returns than slot machines (provided you make the right playing decisions).

Now for those of you who didn't know the answers to those two questions, please read on. You others can skip the rest of this story as I am sure you're eager to get back to your favorite video poker machine.

First, let's cover the basics. Video poker has virtually the same rules as a game of five card draw poker. The only difference is that you have no opponent to beat and you can't lose more than your initial bet. First, you deposit from one to five coins in the machine to make your bet. You are then shown five cards on the video screen and your goal is to try to make the best poker hand possible from those cards. Since it is a draw game, you are given one opportunity to improve your hand. This is done by allowing you to discard from one, up to all five cards from your original hand. Of course, you don't have to discard any if you don't want to. After choosing which cards you want to discard (by pushing the button below each card) the machine will then replace each of those cards with a new card. Based on the resulting final hand the machine will then pay you according to the pay schedule posted on the machine. Naturally, the better your hand, the higher the amount the machine will pay you back.

That's pretty much how a video poker machine works from the outside, but what about the inside? Well, I had three specific questions about that so I contacted International Game Technology, which is the world's largest manufacturer of video poker machines (as well as slot machines), to see if they could provide some answers. Here's what they said:

#1: Are the cards dealt to you on a random basis?

IGT: Gaming regulations require that gaming devices must have random outcomes of game play results. In order to satisfy this requirement, games of all types use a random number generator (RNG) software algorithm to determine game outcome. While the game is in the idle state, i.e. waiting for someone to deposit a coin or push a play credit button, the RNG algorithm is called hundreds of times every second. The RNG has approximately 16,000,000,000,000,000,000 possible outcomes and, depending on the game type, there will be many billions of outcomes that map into any set of cards, or keno balls, or slot machine symbols. This ensures that all IGT games are completely random, just as if the cards were dealt from a perfectly shuffled deck.

#2: When does the shuffling actually stop?

IGT: On all game types, when the start, deal or bet button is pushed, the randomly selected outcome is determined. This result is determined solely by the RNG and is not dependent on any factors of game play, such as how many coins are bet, or on what happened in the last game played or on how many seconds you wait before deciding what cards to draw.

#3: Is there a draw card assigned to each dealt card?

IGT: No, IGT games operate as follows: the first five cards dealt are displayed and additional cards are taken from the top of the deck as needed. So, if you discard one card it doesn't matter which card you discard, the draw card will be the same.

According to IGT's first answer we know that all of the hands are generated randomly. Some people believe that the machine knows what cards it initially deals you and then it gives you bad draw cards so you won't have a winning hand. This isn't true. The deck is shuffled randomly and then all cards are dealt and drawn in order. By the way, the number with all the zeros is 16 quintillion. Don't feel ignorant if you didn't know it because neither did I. Of course, when our national debt gets that high, we'll all be familiar with it!

One other point must be made here regarding random outcomes in video poker machines. Please notice that the above answer stated *gaming regulations* require that the machines must have random outcomes. You should be aware that there are casinos operating in places that *do not* have gaming regulations. Examples are cruise ships which operate in international waters and some Indian reservations that are not subject to state regulations. You should also be aware that the technology exists for machines to be set so they do not act randomly. These machines are actually programmed to avoid giving the players better hands and they wind up giving the house a much bigger advantage. These machines are illegal in Nevada, New Jersey, Colorado and all other states that pattern their gaming regulations after those states. You may, however, come across them in unregulated casinos.

With the second answer we know that the RNG stops when you deposit the first coin, or when you push the bet or deal button. This means that the results will be the same whether we deposit one coin or the maximum coins. Some people think that the outcome will be different depending on how many coins are deposited. This is not true. If you put in one coin and get a royal flush, you would have gotten that same royal flush if you had put in five coins.

The last answer clears up some confusion about how the draw cards are dealt. Some people believe that the machine initially deals 10 cards: five up cards that you see, plus one other card under each of those cards as a draw card. This is not true. The draw card you receive is in the same order as if it were being dealt off the top of the deck. Example: You are dealt (10♣,J♣,Q♣,6♦,6♥). You discard (6♦,6♥) and draw (6♣,6♠). Had you kept (6♦,6♥) and discarded (10♣,J♣,Q♣) you would have had four sixes.

One final point you should keep in mind - IGT is not the only manufacturer of video poker machines. There are quite a few others and they may engineer their machines to work in a different manner. Their RNG may not stop in the same way and their draw cards may be dealt differently. IGT, however, is by far the largest and it is the type of machine you will most often encounter in a casino.

Now that you understand how a video poker machine works let's learn how to pick out the best paying ones. In the beginning of this story it was mentioned that "you can tell a video poker machine's payback percentage just by looking at it." That's true, but it takes a little bit of knowledge to know the difference among all the different types of machines. An example of some of the different machines available are: Tens or Better; Jacks or Better; Two Pairs or Better; Joker Poker; and Deuces Wild. To make it even more confusing, not only are there different machines, but each of those machines can have a different pay schedule for the same hand. Fortunately, every video poker machine's payback percentage can be mathematically calculated. Not only does this let you know which machines offer you the best return, but it also tells you the best playing decisions to make on that particular machine based on the odds of that combination occurring. The bad news, however, is that it's fairly impossible to do on your own so you'll have to either buy a book that lists all of the percentages and strategies or buy a computer program that does the work for you. *Winning Strategies for Video Poker* by Lenny Frome is a 113-page book that lists payback percentages, plus the best strategies to use on more than 50 of the most popular video poker variations. For those of you with a computer, *VP Exact* by Stanford Wong can determine the exact payback percentage for any video poker machine. It retails for $29.95. The only drawback to that particular software, though is that it only analyzes the odds and you can't play a game with it. *Stanford Wong Video Poker* software is much better for the average user because it will allow you to play a game as well as practice your skills on various types of machines. That's the program I use most often. You can set the game to automatically show you the best decision each time or you can set it to just warn you if you make a wrong decision on your own. It's so simple that my seven-year-old son plays it and I'm confident he can play better than the average Las Vegas visitor. "I'm going for the flush, daddy!" I also have another program called *Video Poker* by Masque Publishing which offers five different versions of video poker, plus the ability to run computer simulations of up to five million hands for statistical analysis.

If you have no desire to get quite that serious about learning video poker then I'll try to provide some general tips to help you out. First, you'll need to find the machines that offer you the highest returns. One of the best is the 9/6 Jacks or Better machine. Of course, you're probably wondering "what exactly is a 9/6 Jacks or Better machine?" Well, the Jacks or Better part refers to the fact that you won't win anything from the machine unless you have at least a pair of Jacks. The 9/6 part refers to the payback schedule on this kind of machine. As stated earlier, each machine can have a different payback schedule and there are at least 20 different kinds of payback schedules available on Jacks or Better machines. In Las Vegas the two most common Jacks or Better machines you will find are 8/5 and 9/6. Here's a comparison of their pay schedules (per coin, for five-coin play):

Hand	9/6	8/5
Royal Flush	800	800
Straight Flush	50	50
4-of-a-Kind	25	25
Full House	9	8
Flush	6	5
Straight	4	4
3-of-a-Kind	3	3
Two Pairs	2	2
One Pair J's	1	1

As you can see, the schedules are identical except for the better payoffs on the 9/6 machines for Flushes and Full Houses. The payback on a 9/6 machine is 99.5 percent with perfect play, while the 8/5 machines return 97.3 percent with perfect play. Of course, it doesn't make any sense to play an 8/5 machine if a 9/6 machine is available. Yet, in Las Vegas you'll see lots of people playing an 8/5 when a 9/6 can easily be found in the same casino. The reason they do that is because they don't know any better; you do. Always look for the 9/6 machines. They can be found in every downtown Las Vegas casino and most, but not all, strip casinos. In other states, including New Jersey, they won't be found as easily. On a trip to Mississippi I found a few, but it took some searching and not every casino had them. If you can't find one be sure to double check with the Slot Host to see if they're offered.

One other common machine you will come across is an 8/5 Jacks or Better progressive. These feature the same 8/5 pay table as above except for the royal flush which pays a jackpot amount that is displayed on a meter above the machine. The jackpot will continue to build until someone hits a royal flush;

then it will reset and start to build again. If the jackpot on a 25¢ machine is above $2,240 (for five coins) then you should play it. If it's below $2,240 then stick to the regular 9/6 machines.

Another good tip is to restrict your play to the same kind of machine all the time. Each video poker machine has its own particular strategy and what works best on a Jacks or Better machine is definitely much different from what works best on a Deuces Wild machine. I only play 9/6 Jacks or Better machines because that is what I practice on and I automatically know the best decision to make all the time. Keep in mind that when you calculate the payback percentage for a video poker machine the number you arrive at is based on perfect play. As an example, a 9/6 Jacks or Better video poker machine has a 99.5 percent payback with perfect play. This means that, theoretically, it will return $99.50 for every $100 played in the machine, but only if the player makes the correct decision every time. If you make mistakes, and most players do, the return to the casino will be higher. If you play several different kinds of machines it becomes increasingly harder to remember the correct play to make and you will make mistakes. Therefore, it only makes sense to memorize the correct decisions for one kind of machine and to always play on that same kind of machine (of course, in order to learn those proper strategies, you may want to buy that book or software).

Now that you've decided which machines to play, you'll need some help with your playing strategy. Reproduced on the next two pages are charts that show you the expert strategy for both 9/6 and 8/5 video poker machines. T h e s e charts were derived from computer simulations of millions of hands of video poker and they show you the proper way to play any initial hand that you may be dealt. The only difference between the two tables are the poker hands that have been *italicized* in the 8/5 strategy tables.

To use the chart just look up your hand and play it in the manner that is closest to the top of the chart. For example: you are dealt (6♣,6♦,7♥,8♠,9♣). You keep (6♣,6♦) rather than (6♦,7♥,8♠,9♣) because a low pair (#16) is higher on the chart than a four-card straight with no high cards (#21). Remember to always look for the highest possible choice on the chart when there are multiple ways to play your hand. As another example: you are dealt (8♣,8♦, J♥,Q♥,K♥). You keep (J♥,Q♥,K♥) rather than (8♣,8♦) because a three-card royal flush (#13) is higher on the chart than a low pair (#16). As a final, but radical, example of how to play your hand by the chart what would you do if you're dealt (6♥,10♥,J♥,Q♥,K♥)? Yes, you have to break up your flush by discarding the 6♥ and go for the royal flush because the four-card royal flush (#4) is higher on the chart than the pat flush (#6).

When looking at the chart there are a few things that should seem rather obvious:

1) A low pair is pretty good. Of the 36 possible hands, a low pair is #16 which means there are 20 hands worse than a low pair. If you look at the 15 hands that are better than a low pair eight of them are pat hands that require no draw.

Expert Strategy Table For 9/6 Jacks or Better

1. Royal Flush
2. Straight Flush
3. 4 of a kind
4. 4 card Royal Flush
5. Full House
6. Flush
7. 3 of a kind
8. Straight
9. 4 card Straight Flush
10. Two Pairs
11. 4 card inside Straight Flush
12. Pair of Jacks or higher
13. 3 card Royal Flush
14. 4 card Flush
15. 4 card straight with 3 high cards
16. Low Pair
17. 4 card Straight with 2 high cards
18. 4 card Straight with 1 high card
19. 3 card Inside Straight Flush with 2 high cards
20. 3 card Straight Flush with 1 high card
21. 4 card Straight with no high cards
22. 3 card Double Inside Straight Flush with 2 high cards
23. 3 card Inside Straight Flush with 1 high card
24. 3 card Straight Flush with no high cards
25. 2 card Royal Flush with no Ace or 10
26. 4 card Inside Straight with Ace
27. 2 card Royal Flush with Ace and no 10
28. 3 card Double Inside Straight Flush with 1 high card
29. 4 card Inside Straight with 3 high cards
30. 3 card Inside Straight Flush with no high card
31. 3 high cards with no Ace
32. 2 high cards
33. 2 card Royal Flush with 10 and no Ace
34. 1 high card
35. 3 card Double Inside Straight Flush with no high card
36. All New Cards

Expert Strategy Table For 8/5 Jacks or Better

1. Royal Flush
2. Straight Flush
3. 4 of a kind
4. 4 card Royal Flush
5. Full House
6. Flush
7. 3 of a kind
8. Straight
9. 4 card Straight Flush
10. Two Pairs
11. 4 card inside Straight Flush
12. Pair of Jacks or higher
13. 3 card Royal Flush
14. 4 card Flush
15. 4 card straight with 3 high cards
16. Low Pair
17. 4 card Straight with 2 high cards
18. 4 card Straight with 1 high card
19. 3 card Inside Straight Flush with 2 high cards
20. 3 card Straight Flush with 1 high card
21. 4 card Straight with no high cards
22. 3 card Double Inside Straight Flush with 2 high cards
23. 3 card Inside Straight Flush with 1 high card
24. 3 card Straight Flush with no high cards
25. *4 card Inside Straight with Ace*
26. *2 card Royal Flush with no Ace or 10*
27. 2 card Royal Flush with Ace and no 10
28. *3 high cards with no Ace*
29. 4 card Inside Straight with 3 high cards
30. *3 card Double Inside Straight Flush with 1 high card*
31. *2 high cards*
32. *3 card Inside Straight Flush with no high card*
33. 2 card Royal Flush with 10 and no Ace
34. 1 high card
35. 3 card Double Inside Straight Flush with no high card
36. All New Cards

Of the other seven hands, six of them are four card hands and the remaining hand is a three-card royal flush.

2) Don't hold three cards trying to get a straight or flush. Nowhere on the chart do you see that you should hold three cards to try for a straight or flush. In some instances you should hold three cards to try for a straight flush, but *never* a straight or flush.

3) Rarely draw to an inside straight. Inside straights (6,7,_,9,10) appear only twice on the chart and in rather bad positions: #29 (with three high cards) and #26 (with an ace high). It is much easier to draw to an outside straight (_7,8,9,10_) where you can complete your straight by getting the card you need on either end. Open end straights appear four times on the chart and in much higher positions than inside straights: #21 (with 0 high cards), #18 (with one high card), #17 (with two high cards) and #15 (with three high cards).

4) Don't hold a kicker. A kicker is an unpaired card held with a pair. For example (8,8,K) or (K,K,9) are examples of hands where an extra card (the kicker) is held. *Never* hold a kicker because they add no value to your hand!

Keep in mind that the strategy tables shown here are only for Jacks or Better and are not valid for games played with wild cards such as Joker Poker, Deuces Wild, Double Joker, etc. Those games employ a completely different strategy and it would be wrong to use these strategies for those kinds of machines.

For your information there are exactly 2,598,960 unique poker hands possible on a video poker machine (when played without a joker). On a 9/6 Jacks or Better machine a royal flush will occur about once every 40,000 hands; a straight flush about every 9,000 hands; four-of-a-kind about every 425 hands; a full house about every 87 hands; a flush about every 91 hands; a straight about every 89 hands; three-of-a-kind about every 14 hands; two pairs about every 8 hands; and a pair of Jacks or better about every 5 hands. The interesting thing to note here is that both a flush and a straight are harder to get than a full house, yet a full house always has a higher payback than either of them.The majority of the time, about 55% to be exact, you will wind up with a losing hand on a 9/6 machine.

The next bit of advice concerns how many coins you should bet. Always bet the maximum amount because it will allow you to earn bonus coins if you happen to hit the royal flush. Example: For a royal flush on a 9/6 machine with one coin played you receive 250 coins; for two coins you get 500; for three coins you get 750; for four coins you get 1,000 and for five (maximum) coins you get 4,000 coins. This translates into a bonus of 2,750 coins! A royal flush can be expected once every 40,400 hands on a 9/6 machine; once every 40,200 hands on an 8/5 machine; and once every 32,700 hands on an 8/5 progressive. The odds are high, but the added bonus makes it worthwhile. If you can't afford to play the maximum coins then move down to a lower denomination machine. And, if you absolutely insist on playing less than the maximum, be sure to play only one coin at a time. It doesn't make any sense to play two, three or four coins, because you still won't be eligible for the bonus.

Another tip concerns slot clubs. Every major casino has a slot club and you should make it a point to join the slot club before you insert your first coin. It doesn't cost anything to join and as a member you will have the opportunity to earn complimentaries from the casinos in the form of cash, food, shows, drinks, rooms or other "freebies." When you join the club you'll be issued a card (similar to a credit card) that you insert in the machine before you start to play and it will track how much you bet, as well as how long you play. Naturally, the more money you gamble, the more freebies you'll earn. Just make sure you don't get carried away and bet more than you're comfortable with just to earn some extra comps. Ideally, you want to get comps for gambling that you were going to do anyway and not be pressured into betting more than you had planned.

The story you are reading was originally written in 1994 and is still valid today. The only difference is that it is getting a little harder to find 9/6 machines in Las Vegas. Many of them have been replaced by new machines called *Bonus Poker*, *Double Bonus Poker* or *Double Double Bonus Poker*. Casinos are always introducing new machines and these particular ones are now very popular. The perfect strategy for these machines is much more complicated and the two strategy tables in this book don't apply to them. If you have a computer you can use the *Stanford Wong Video Poker* program to practice the strategy for the new machines. Otherwise, keep an eye out for the 9/6 machinses. They're harder to find but they're still out there - especially in downtown.

Blackjack

by Steve Bourie

Blackjack is the most popular casino game in America and one of the biggest reasons for that is its relatively simple rules that are familiar to most casino visitors. Blackjack also has a reputation as being "beatable" and although that is true in some cases, the vast majority of players will always be playing the game with the house having a slight edge over them.

At most blackjack tables there are 7 boxes, or betting areas, on the table. This means that up to 7 people can play at that table and each player has their own box in front of them in which they'll place their bet. Now, before you take a seat at any blackjack table the first thing you should do is to take a look at the sign that's sitting on each table because it will tell you the minimum amount that you must bet on each hand. If you're a $5 player you certainly wouldn't want to sit at a table that has a $25 minimum so, once again, be sure to look before you sit down.

Once you're at the table you'll need chips to play with and you get them by giving your cash to the dealer who will exchange it for an equal amount of chips. Be careful, however, that you don't put your cash down into one of the betting boxes because the dealer might think you're playing it all on the next hand!

After everyone has placed their bets in their respective boxes the dealer will deal out 2 cards to each player. He will also deal 2 cards to himself; one of those cards will be face up and the other face down. Now, if you've ever read any brochures in a casino they'll tell you that the object of the game of blackjack is to get a total of cards as close to 21 as possible, without going over 21. However, that really isn't the object of the game. The true object is to beat the dealer and you do that by getting a total closer to 21 than the dealer, or by having the dealer bust by drawing cards that total more than 21.

The one thing that's strange about blackjack is that the rules can be slightly different at each casino and this is the only game where this happens. If you play baccarat, roulette or craps you'll find that the rules are virtually the same at every casino in the U.S. but that isn't the case with blackjack. For example, in Atlantic City all of the casinos use 6 or 8 decks of cards that are always dealt from a little rectangular box called a shoe and the cards are always dealt face up. In Las Vegas, some casinos will offer that same kind of game while others will offer games that use only 1 or 2 decks that are dealt directly from the dealer's hand and all of the cards will be dealt face down. To make it even stranger, some casinos in Las Vegas will offer both kinds of games in their

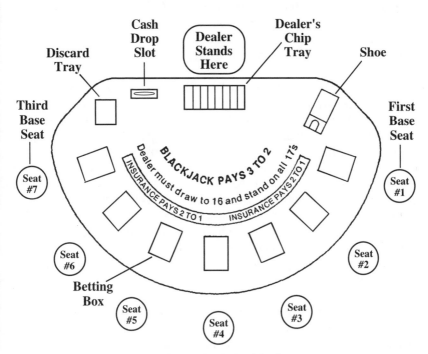

Typical Blackjack Table Layout

casinos and the rules will probably change when you move from one table to another. There can also be other rules variations concerning doubling down and splitting of pairs but we'll talk about those later. For now, just be aware that different casinos can have different blackjack rules and some of those rules will be good for you while others will be bad for you. Hopefully, after reading this story you'll know the good rules from the bad ones and which tables are the best ones to play at.

For our purposes, we'll assume we're playing in a casino that uses 6 decks of cards that are dealt out of a shoe and all of the player's cards are dealt face up. By the way, whenever you play blackjack in a casino where the cards are dealt face up don't touch the cards. In that kind of game the dealer is the only who is allowed to touch the cards and if you do happen to touch them they'll give you a warning not to do it again - so, don't touch the cards!

After the cards are dealt the players must determine the total of their hand by adding the value of their two cards together. All of the cards are counted at their face value except for the picture cards - jack, queen and king which all have a value of 10 - and the aces which can be counted as either 1 or 11. If you have an ace and any 10-value card you have a blackjack which is also called a natural and your hand is an automatic winner, unless the dealer also has a blackjack in which case the hands are tied. A tie is also called a *push* and when that happens it's a standoff and you neither win nor lose. All winning blackjacks are paid at 3-to-2, or one-and-a-half times your bet, so if you bet $5 and got a blackjack you would be paid $7.50

If the dealer has an ace as his up card the first thing he'll do is ask if anyone wants to buy **insurance**. When you buy insurance you're betting that the dealer has a blackjack by having a 10 as his face down card. To make an insurance bet you would place your bet in the area just above your betting box that says "insurance pays 2-to-1" and you're only allowed to make an insurance bet of up to one-half the amount of your original bet. So, if you originally bet $10 you could only bet a maximum of $5 as your insurance bet. After all the insurance bets are made the dealer will check his face down card and if it's a 10 he'll turn it over and all of the insurance bets will be paid off at 2-to-1. If he doesn't have a 10 underneath, the dealer will then take away all of the losing insurance bets and the game will continue. By the way, according to basic strategy, insurance is a bad bet and you should never make an insurance bet.

If the dealer has a 10 as his up card the first thing he'll do is check to see if he has an ace underneath which would give him a blackjack. If he does have an ace he'll turn it face up and start collecting the losing bets that are out on the table. If he doesn't have an ace underneath the game will continue. In some casinos, however, the dealer won't check his hole card until after all of the hands are played out.

If the dealer doesn't have an ace or a 10 as his up card the game continues and the dealer will start with the player to his immediate left to see if they want another card. If a player wants another card they indicate that with a hand signal by tapping or scratching the table with their finger to show they want another card. Taking a card is also known as *hitting* or taking a hit. If a player doesn't want another card they would just wave their hand palm down over their cards. Not taking another card is known as *standing*. The reason hand signals are used is because it eliminates any confusion on the part of the dealer as to exactly what the player wants and it also allows the security people to follow the game on the closed-circuit cameras that are hung from the ceiling throughout the casino.

Keep in mind that the hand signals will be slightly different if you're playing in a casino where the cards are dealt face down and you're allowed to pick them up. In that situation a player would signal that they wanted another card by scratching the table with the edges of the two cards they're holding. If they didn't want another card, they would simply place their two cards under the bet in their box.

In either case, if a player draws another card the value of that card is added to the total of the other cards and the player can continue to draw cards unless he gets a total of more than 21 in which case he busts and loses his bet.

When a player doesn't want any more cards, or stands, the dealer then moves on to the next player and after all of the players are finished then it's the dealer's turn to play. While each player can decide whether or not they want another card the dealer doesn't have that option and he must play by a fixed set of rules that require him to draw a card whenever his total is 16 or less and to stop when his total is 17 or more. If the dealer goes over 21 then he has busted and all of the players remaining in the game will be paid 1-to-1, or even money, on their bet.

If the dealer doesn't bust then each player's hand is compared to the dealer's. If the player's total is higher than the dealer's then they win and are paid even money. If the player's hand has a total that is lower than the dealer's hand then the player loses his bet. If the player and the dealer have the same total then it's a tie, or a push and neither hand wins. After all of the bets have been paid off, or taken by the dealer, a new round begins and new hands are dealt to all of the players.

When deciding how to play your hand there are also three other options available to you besides standing or hitting. The first is called *doubling down* and most casinos will allow a player to double their bet on their first two cards and draw only one more card. To do this you would place an amount equal to your original bet right next to it and then the dealer would give you one more card, sideways, to indicate that your bet was a double down. To double down in a game where the cards are dealt face down you would turn up your original two cards and tell the dealer you wanted to double down. Then, after you double your bet, the dealer would give you one more card face down. Some casinos may have restrictions on this bet and may only allow you to double down if the total of your 2 cards is 10 or 11, but it's always to your advantage if they allow you to double down on any two cards.

Another thing you can do is *split* your cards if you have a pair and then play each card as a separate hand. For example, if you had a pair of 8's you would place a bet equal to your original bet right next to it and tell the dealer you wanted to split your pair. The dealer would then separate your two 8's and give you one card on your first 8. Unlike doubling down, however, you are not limited to only getting one card and you can play your hand out normally. When you were finished with your first hand the dealer would then give you a card on your other 8 and you would play that hand out. Although I said that you weren't limited to just one card on your splits there is one instance where that will happen and that's when you split aces. Virtually all casinos will only give you one card on each ace when you split them. Also, if you get a 10-value card with your ace it will only count as 21 and not as a blackjack so you'll only get even money on that bet if you win. Besides splitting pairs you can also split all 10-value cards such as jack-king or 10-queen but it would be a very bad idea to do that because you would be breaking up a 20 which is a very strong hand and you should never split 10's. By the way, if you wanted to split a pair in a casino where the cards are dealt face down you would simply turn your original 2 cards face-up and then tell the dealer that you wanted to split them.

The last option you have is not available in most casinos but you may come across it in a few Las Vegas Strip casinos and it's called *surrender*. With the surrender option you're allowed to lose half of your bet if you decide you don't want to play out your hand after looking at your first 2 cards. Let's say you're dealt a 10-6 for a total of 16 and the dealer has a 10 as his face-up card. A 16 is not a very strong hand, especially against a dealer's 10, so in this case it would be a good idea to surrender your hand and when the dealer came to your cards you would say "surrender." The dealer would then take half of your bet and remove your cards. Surrender is good for the player because in the long run you will lose less on the bad hands you're dealt and you should always try to play in a casino that offers the surrender option.

All right, we've covered the basics of how to play the game of blackjack and all of the possible options a player has, so the next question is how do you win? Well, the best way to win is to become a card counter, but for the average person that isn't always possible so let's start off by taking a look at basic blackjack strategy.

Computer studies have been done on the game of blackjack and millions of hands have been analyzed to come up with a basic formula for how to play your hand in any given situation. The main principle that these decisions are based on is the dealer's up card because, remember that the dealer has no say in whether or not he takes a card - he must play by the rules that require him to draw a card until he has a total of 17 or more. Now, according to these computer calculations the dealer will bust more often when his up card is a 2,3,4,5 or 6 and he will complete more hands when his up card is a 7,8,9,10-value card or an ace. Take a look at the following chart that shows how each up-card affects the dealer's chance of busting:

Chance The Dealer's Up Card Will Bust

2	35%
3	38%
4	40%
5	43%
6	42%
7	26%
8	24%
9	23%
10	21%
Ace	11%

As you can see, the dealer will bust most often when he has a 5 or 6 as his upcard and he will bust the least amount, approximately 11% of the time, when his upcard is an ace. This means it's to your advantage to stand more often when the dealer's upcard is a 2 through 6 and hope that the dealer will draw cards that make him bust. It also means that when the dealer's upcard is a 7 through ace he will complete more of his hands and in that situation you should draw cards until you have a total of 17 or more.

Now let's show you how to play your hands by using the basic strategy and we'll start off with the ***hard hand*** strategy and by hard hand I mean a 2-card total without an ace. A hand with an ace is known as a soft hand because the ace can be counted as either a 1 or an 11. So, if you had an ace-6 you would have a soft 17 hand and if you had a 10-6 you would have a hard 16 hand. Later on we'll take a look at how to play soft hands, but for now we'll concentrate on the hard hand totals. Oh yes, one more thing, the basic strategy I'm going to give you applies to casinos where they deal more than one deck at a time and the dealer stands on soft 17 which is the situation you'll find in the majority of casinos today. So, keep in mind that the strategy would be slightly different if you were playing against a single deck and it would also be slightly different if the dealer hit a soft 17.

Whenever your first 2 cards total 17 through 21, you should stand, no matter what the dealer's up card is.

If your cards total 16, you should stand if the dealer has a 2 through 6 as his upcard otherwise, draw a card. By the way, 16 is the worst hand you can have because you will bust more often with 16 than with any other hand. So, if that's the case then why would you want to ever hit a 16? Well, once again, those computer studies have shown that you should hit a 16 when the dealer has 7 through ace as his upcard because in the long run you will lose less often. This means that yes, 16 is a terrible hand, but you should hit it because if you don't you will lose even more often than when you do take a card.

If your cards total 15, you should also stand if the dealer has a 2 through 6 as his upcard otherwise, draw cards until your total is 17 or more.

The same rules from 15 and 16 also apply if your cards total 14. Stand if the dealer has a 2 through 6, otherwise draw cards until your total is 17 or more. The same rules also apply if your cards total 13. Stand if the dealer has a 2 through 6, otherwise draw cards until your total is 17 or more.

When your cards total 12 you should only stand when the dealer has a 4,5 or 6 as his upcard, remember - those are his 3 weakest cards and he will bust more often with those cards, so you don't want to take a chance on busting yourself. If the dealer's upcard is a 2 or a 3, then you should take just one card and stop on your total of 13 or more. Finally, if the dealer has a 7 through ace as his upcard then you should draw cards until your total is 17 or more.

When your cards total 11 you would always want to hit it because you can't bust, but before you ask for a card you should consider making a double down bet. If the casino allows you to double down then you should do that if the dealer has anything but an ace as his upcard. After you double down the dealer would give you just one additional card on that hand. If the dealer's upcard is an ace then you shouldn't double down. Instead, you should hit the hand and continue to draw until your total is 17 or more. If the casino doesn't allow you to double down then you should just hit your hand and then, depending on your total, play it by the rules I gave you for the hands that totaled 12 through 21. So, if you had an 11 and the dealer had a 5 as his upcard, you should take a card. Then let's say you draw an ace which gives you a total of 12. Well, as I said before, if you have a 12 against a dealer's 5 you should stand and that's how you should play that hand.

If your total is 10 you would, once again, want to double down unless the dealer showed an ace or a 10. If the dealer had an ace or a 10 as his upcard you should hit your hand and then use the standard rules for a hand valued at 12 through 21. So, if you had a 10 and the dealer had an 8 as his up card you would want to double down and take one more card. If you weren't allowed to double, then you would take a hit and let's say you got a 4 for a total of 14. You should then continue to hit your hand until your total is 17 or more.

If your total is 9 you would want to double down whenever the dealer was showing a 3,4,5 or 6 as his upcard. If the dealer had a 2 as his upcard, or if he had a 7 through ace as his upcard, you should hit your hand and then use the standard playing rules as discussed before. So, let's say you had a 9 and the dealer had a 4 as his upcard you would want to double down and take one more card. If you weren't allowed to double then you should take a hit and let's say you got a 2 for a total of 11, you would then take another hit and let's say you got an ace. That would give you a total of 12 and, as I showed you previously, you should stand on 12 against a dealer's 4.

Finally, if your total is 8 or less you should always take a card and then use the standard playing rules that we already discussed.

Now, let's take a look at splitting pairs, but keep in mind that the rules for splitting will change slightly depending on whether or not the casino will allow you to double down after you split your cards. Most multiple deck games allow you to double down after splitting so that's the situation we'll cover first and then I'll tell you about the changes if you're not allowed to double down after splitting.

Basic Strategy - Single Deck

Dealer stands on soft 17 • Double on any 2 cards • Double allowed after split

Your Hand	Dealer's Upcard									
	2	**3**	**4**	**5**	**6**	**7**	**8**	**9**	**10**	**A**
17	ALWAYS STAND ON HARD 17 (OR MORE)									
16	-	-	-	-	-	H	H	H	H*	H
15	-	-	-	-	-	H	H	H	H*	H
14	-	-	-	-	-	H	H	H	H	H
13	-	-	-	-	-	H	H	H	H	H
12	H	H	-	-	-	H	H	H	H	H
11	ALWAYS DOUBLE									
10	D	D	D	D	D	D	D	D	H	H
9	D	D	D	D	D	H	H	H	H	H
8	-	-	-	D	D	-	-	-	-	-
A,8	-	-	-	-	D	-	-	-	-	-
A,7	-	D	D	D	D	-	-	H	H	-
A,6	D	D	D	D	D	H	H	H	H	H
A,5	H	H	D	D	D	H	H	H	H	H
A,4	H	H	D	D	D	H	H	H	H	H
A,3	H	H	D	D	D	H	H	H	H	H
A,2	H	H	D	D	D	H	H	H	H	H
A,A	ALWAYS SPLIT									
10,10	ALWAYS STAND (NEVER SPLIT)									
9,9	Sp	Sp	Sp	Sp	Sp	-	Sp	Sp	-	-
8,8	ALWAYS SPLIT									
7,7	Sp	Sp	Sp	Sp	Sp	Sp	**Sp**	H	-*	H
6,6	Sp	Sp	Sp	Sp	Sp	**Sp**	H	H	H	H
5,5	NEVER SPLIT (PLAY AS 10 HAND)									
4,4	H	H	**Sp**	**Sp**	**Sp**	H	H	H	H	H
3,3	**Sp**	**Sp**	Sp	Sp	Sp	Sp	Sp	H	H	H
2,2	**Sp**	H	Sp	Sp	Sp	Sp	H	H	H	H

- =Stand   H=Hit   D=Double   Sp=Split   *= Surrender if allowed
shaded boxes show strategy changes from chart on next page

Basic Strategy - Single Deck

Dealer stands on soft 17 • Double on any 2 cards • Double NOT allowed after split

Your Hand	Dealer's Upcard									
	2	3	4	5	6	7	8	9	10	A
17	ALWAYS STAND ON HARD 17 (OR MORE)									
16	-	-	-	-	-	H	H	H	H*	H*
15	-	-	-	-	-	H	H	H	H*	H
14	-	-	-	-	-	H	H	H	H	H
13	-	-	-	-	-	H	H	H	H	H
12	H	H	-	-	-	H	H	H	H	H
11	ALWAYS DOUBLE									
10	D	D	D	D	D	D	D	D	H	H
9	D	D	D	D	D	H	H	H	H	H
8	H	H	H	D	D	H	H	H	H	H
A,8	-	-	-	-	D	-	-	-	-	-
A,7	-	D	D	D	D	-	-	H	H	-
A,6	D	D	D	D	D	H	H	H	H	H
A,5	H	H	D	D	D	H	H	H	H	H
A,4	H	H	D	D	D	H	H	H	H	H
A,3	H	H	D	D	D	H	H	H	H	H
A,2	H	H	D	D	D	H	H	H	H	H
A,A	ALWAYS SPLIT									
10,10	NEVER SPLIT (ALWAYS STAND)									
9,9	Sp	Sp	Sp	Sp	Sp	-	Sp	Sp	-	-
8,8	ALWAYS SPLIT									
7,7	Sp	Sp	Sp	Sp	Sp	Sp	H	H	-*	H
6,6	Sp	Sp	Sp	Sp	Sp	H	H	H	H	H
5,5	NEVER SPLIT (PLAY AS 10 HAND)									
4,4	NEVER SPLIT (PLAY AS 8 HAND)									
3,3	H	H	Sp	Sp	Sp	Sp	H	H	H	H
2,2	H	Sp	Sp	Sp	Sp	Sp	H	H	H	H

- =Stand　　H=Hit　　D=Double　　Sp=Split　　*= Surrender if allowed

Basic Strategy - Multiple Decks

Dealer stands on soft 17 • Double on any 2 cards • Double allowed after split

Your Hand	Dealer's Upcard									
	2	3	4	5	6	7	8	9	10	A
17	ALWAYS STAND ON 17 (OR MORE)									
16	-	-	-	-	-	H	H	H*	H*	H*
15	-	-	-	-	-	H	H	H	H*	H
14	-	-	-	-	-	H	H	H	H	H
13	-	-	-	-	-	H	H	H	H	H
12	H	H	-	-	-	H	H	H	H	H
11	D	D	D	D	D	D	D	D	D	H
10	D	D	D	D	D	D	D	D	H	H
9	H	D	D	D	D	H	H	H	H	H
8	ALWAYS HIT 8 (OR LESS)									
A,8	ALWAYS STAND ON SOFT 19 (OR MORE)									
A,7	-	D	D	D	D	-	-	H	H	H
A,6	H	D	D	D	D	H	H	H	H	H
A,5	H	H	D	D	D	H	H	H	H	H
A,4	H	H	D	D	D	H	H	H	H	H
A,3	H	H	H	D	D	H	H	H	H	H
A,2	H	H	H	D	D	H	H	H	H	H
A,A	ALWAYS SPLIT									
10,10	ALWAYS STAND (NEVER SPLIT)									
9,9	Sp	Sp	Sp	Sp	Sp	-	Sp	Sp	-	-
8,8	ALWAYS SPLIT									
7,7	Sp	Sp	Sp	Sp	Sp	Sp	H	H	H	H
6,6	Sp	Sp	Sp	Sp	Sp	H	H	H	H	H
5,5	D	D	D	D	D	D	D	D	H	H
4,4	H	H	H	Sp	Sp	H	H	H	H	H
3,3	Sp	Sp	Sp	Sp	Sp	Sp	H	H	H	H
2,2	Sp	Sp	Sp	Sp	Sp	Sp	H	H	H	H

- =Stand   H=Hit   D=Double   Sp=Split   *= Surrender if allowed

Basic Strategy - Multiple Decks

Dealer stands on soft 17 • Double on any 2 cards • Double <u>NOT</u> allowed after split

Your Hand	Dealer's Upcard									
	2	3	4	5	6	7	8	9	10	A
17	ALWAYS STAND ON HARD 17 (OR MORE)									
16	-	-	-	-	-	H	H	H*	H*	H*
15	-	-	-	-	-	H	H	H	H*	H
14	-	-	-	-	-	H	H	H	H	H
13	-	-	-	-	-	H	H	H	H	H
12	H	H	-	-	-	H	H	H	H	H
11	D	D	D	D	D	D	D	D	D	H
10	D	D	D	D	D	D	D	D	H	H
9	H	D	D	D	D	H	H	H	H	H
8	ALWAYS HIT 8 (OR LESS)									
A,8	ALWAYS STAND ON SOFT 19 (OR MORE)									
A,7	-	D	D	D	D	-	-	H	H	H
A,6	H	D	D	D	D	H	H	H	H	H
A,5	H	H	D	D	D	H	H	H	H	H
A,4	H	H	D	D	D	H	H	H	H	H
A,3	H	H	H	D	D	H	H	H	H	H
A,2	H	H	H	D	D	H	H	H	H	H
A,A	ALWAYS SPLIT									
10,10	ALWAYS STAND (NEVER SPLIT)									
9,9	Sp	Sp	Sp	Sp	Sp	-	Sp	Sp	-	-
8,8	ALWAYS SPLIT									
7,7	Sp	Sp	Sp	Sp	Sp	Sp	H	H	H	H
6,6	H	Sp	Sp	Sp	Sp	H	H	H	H	H
5,5	NEVER SPLIT (PLAY AS 10 HAND)									
4,4	H	H	H	H	H	H	H	H	H	H
3,3	H	H	Sp	Sp	Sp	Sp	H	H	H	H
2,2	H	H	Sp	Sp	Sp	Sp	H	H	H	H

- =Stand   H=Hit   D=Double   Sp=Split   *= Surrender if allowed

shaded boxes show strategy changes from chart on previous page

As I said earlier, when your first two cards are the same most casinos will allow you to split them and play them as two separate hands so let's go over the basic strategy rules on when you should do this.

The first thing you should remember is that you always split aces and 8's. The reason you split aces is obvious because if you get a 10 on either hand you'll have a perfect 21, but remember that you won't get paid for a blackjack at 3-to-2, instead it'll be counted as a regular 21 and you'll be paid at even money. If you have a pair of 8's you have 16 which is a terrible hand and you can always improve it by splitting your 8's and playing them as separate hands.

The next thing to remember about splitting pairs is that you never split 5's or 10's. Once again, the reasons should be rather obvious, you don't want to split 10's because 20 is a great hand and you don't want to split 5's because 10 is a great hand to draw to. Instead, you would want to double down on that 10, unless the dealer was showing a 10 or an ace as his upcard.

2's, 3's and 7's should only be split when the dealer is showing a 2 through 7 as his upcard. Split 4's only when the dealer has a 5 or 6 as his upcard (remember 5 and 6 are his weakest cards!), 6's should be split whenever the dealer is showing a 2 through 6 and finally, you should always split 9's unless the dealer is showing a 7, 10 or ace. The reason you don't want to split 9's against a 10 or an ace should be rather obvious, but the reason you don't want to split them against a 7 is in case the dealer has a 10 as his hole card because in that case your 18 would beat out his 17.

If the casino will not allow you to double down after splitting then you should make the following three changes: For 2's and 3's only split them against a 4,5,6 or 7; never split 4's; and for a pair of 6's only split them against a 3,4,5 or 6. Everything else should be played the same.

Now, let's take a look at how to play *soft hands* and remember a soft hand is any hand that contains an ace that can be counted as 1 or 11. For a soft hand of 19 or more you should always stand.

For soft 18 against a 2,7 or 8 you should always stand. If the dealer shows a 9, 10 or an ace you should always take a hit and for a soft 18 against a 3,4,5 or 6 you should double down, but if the casino won't allow you to double then you should just stand.

For soft 17 you should always take a hit, but if the casino allows you to double down, then you should double against a dealer's 3,4,5 or 6.

For soft 16 or a soft 15 you should always take a hit, but if the casino allows you to double down then you should double against a dealer's 4,5 or 6.

For soft 14 you should always take a hit, but if the casino allows you to double down then you should double against a dealer's 5 or 6.

Finally, for a soft 13 you should always take a hit, but if the casino allows you to double down then you should double against a dealer's 5 or 6.

The last thing we need to cover is surrender which, as I said before, isn't offered in many casinos but it is an option that does work in your favor and if available, you should play in a casino that offers it. The surrender rules are very simple to remember and only apply to hard totals of 15 or 16. If you have a hard 16 you should surrender it whenever the dealer has a 9, 10 or ace as his upcard and if you have a hard 15 you should surrender it whenever the dealer has a 10 as his upcard. That's all there is to surrender.

Now that you know how to play the game and you have an understanding of the basic strategy let's take a quick look at how the rules variations can affect the game of blackjack. As I said before, various computer studies have been made on blackjack and these studies have shown that each rule change can either hurt or help the player by a certain amount. For example, a single-deck game where you can double on any first 2 cards (but not after splitting pairs), the dealer stands on soft 17 and no surrender is allowed has no advantage for the casino when using the basic strategy. That's right, in a game with those rules in effect the game is dead even and neither the casino nor the player has an edge!

Take a look at the following chart and you'll see how some rules changes can hurt you or help you as a player. Minus signs in front mean that the casino gains the edge by that particular amount while plus signs mean that you gain the edge by that amount.

RULES THAT HURT YOU		RULES THAT HELP YOU	
Two decks	-0.35%	Double after split	+0.13%
Four decks	-0.48%	Late surrender	+0.06%
Six decks	-0.54%	Resplit Aces	+0.14%
Eight decks	-0.58%	Double anytime	+0.20%
Dealer hits soft 17	-0.20%		
No soft doubling	-0.14%		

As you can see, it's always to your advantage to play against as few decks as possible. The house edge goes up substantially as you go from 1 deck to 2, but the change is less dramatic when you go from 2 to 4, or from 4 to 6, and it's barely noticeable when you go from 6 to 8. You can also see that you would prefer not to play in a casino where the dealer hits a soft 17 because that gives the dealer a slight edge. You would also want to play in a casino where you're allowed to double down on your soft hands or else you would be giving another added edge to the casino.

You can also see from these charts that you would want to play in a casino where you were allowed to double down after splitting cards and you would also want to play in a casino that offered surrender. The other two rules variations that help the player are somewhat rare but they were put in to show you how these rules changes can affect your odds in the game. Some casinos will allow you to resplit aces again if you draw an ace to one of your original aces and this works to your advantage. Also, some casinos will allow you to double down on any number of cards rather than just the first two. In other words, if you got a 2- 4-3-2 as your first four cards you would then be allowed to double down on your total of 11 before receiving your 5th card. If they allow you to do this then, once again, you have a rule that works in your favor.

The point of showing you these charts is to help you understand that when you have a choice of places to play you should always choose the casino that offers the best rules. So, if you find a single-deck game with good rules you could be playing an even game by using the basic strategy, or at worst be giving the casino an edge of less than one-half of 1%.

Now, there is one way that you can actually have the edge working in your favor when you play blackjack and that's by becoming a card counter. As I said before, card counting is not for the average person but I do think it's important that you understand the concept of card counting and if you think you'd like to learn more about counting cards then it's something you can follow up on later.

Many people think that to be a card counter you have to have a photographic memory and remember every single card that's been played. Fortunately, it's not quite that difficult. Actually, the main concept behind card counting is the assumption that the dealer will bust more often when there are a lot of 10's in the deck and that he will complete more hands when there are a lot of smaller cards in the deck. Now, if you stop to think about it, it makes sense doesn't it? After all, the dealer has to play by set rules that make him take a card until he has a total of 17 or more. If there are a lot of 2's, 3's and 4's in the deck the dealer won't bust very often when he draws cards, but if there are a lot of 10's in the deck then chances are he will bust more often when he is forced to draw cards.

The card counter tries to take advantage of this fact by keeping a running total of the cards that have been played to give him an idea of what kind of cards remain in the deck. If there are a lot of 10 cards remaining in the deck then the counter will bet more money because the odds are slightly in his favor. Of course, if there are a lot of small cards remaining then the counter would only make a small bet because the odds would be slightly in favor of the dealer. Another thing that the card counter can do is to change his basic strategy to take advantage of the differences in the deck.

There are at least a dozen different card counting systems but let's take a quick look at a relatively simple one (it's also the most popular) and it's called the high-low count. With this system you assign a value of +1 to all 2's, 3's, 4's, 5's and 6's, while all 10's, Jacks, Queens, Kings and Aces are assigned a value of -1. The remaining cards: 7, 8 and 9 have no value and are not counted.

$$+1 = 2, 3, 4, 5, 6$$
$$-1 = 10, J, Q, K, A$$

When you look at these numbers you'll see that there are an equal number of cards in each group: there are five cards valued at +1 and five cards valued at -1. This means that they balance each other out and if you go through the deck and add them all together the end result will always be a total of exactly zero.

What a card counter does is to keep a running total of all the cards as they're played out and whenever the total has a plus value he knows that a lot of small cards have appeared and the remaining deck is rich in 10's which is good for the player. But, if the total is a minus value then the counter knows that a lot of 10-value cards have appeared and the remaining deck must be rich in low cards which is bad for the player. To give you an example of how to count let's say the following cards have been dealt on the first hand from a single deck:

$$2, 3, 3, 4, 5, 5, 5, 6, = +8$$
$$J, K, Q, A, = -4$$
$$\text{Total} = +4$$

As you can see, there were eight plus-value cards and four minus-value cards which resulted in a total count of +4. This means that there are now four more 10-value cards than low cards remaining in the deck and the advantage is with the player. Naturally, the higher the plus count, the more advantageous it is for the player and counters would be proportionally increasing their bets as the count got higher. The card counter would also be using the same basic strategy we spoke about previously, except for certain instances where a slight change would be called for.

On the other hand, if the count is negative, a card counter will always bet the minimum amount. Of course, they would prefer not to bet at all, but the casinos don't like you to sit at their tables and not bet so the counter has to bet something and the minimum is the least they can get by with.

There is one more important thing to explain about card counting and it's called the ***true count***. The true count is a measure of the count per deck rather than a ***running count*** of all the cards that have been played and to get the true count you simply divide the running count by the number of decks remaining to be played. As an illustration, let's say you're playing in a 6-deck game and the count is +9. You look at the shoe and estimate that 3 decks remain to be played. You then divide the count of +9 by 3 to get +3 which is the true count. As another example, let's say you're in an 8-deck game with a count of +12 and there are 6 decks left to be played. You divide +12 by 6 to get +2 which is the true count. To put it another way, a +2 count in a double-deck game with 1 deck left to be played is the same as a +4 count in a 4-deck game with 2 decks left to be played, which is the same as a +6 count is a 6-deck game with 3 decks left to be played, which is the same as a +12 count in an 8-deck game with 6 decks left to be played.

For the card counter it is crucial to always take the running count and then divide it by the number of decks remaining in order to get the true count because all betting and playing decisions are based on the true count rather than the running count.

Of course, if you're playing in a single-deck game the running count and the true count are initially the same. The more you get into the deck, however, the more weight is given to the running count because there is less than one deck remaining. So, if the running count was +3 and only a 1/2-deck remained you would calculate the true count by dividing +3 by 1/2 (which is the same as multiplying by 2/1, or 2) to get a true count of +6. As another example, if the running count was +2 and about 2/3 of the deck remained you would divide +2 by 2/3 (the same as multi-plying by 3/2 or, 1 and 1/2) to get +3.

As you can see, the count becomes much more meaningful as you get closer to the last cards in the deck and that's why casinos never deal down to the end. Instead, the dealer will insert a plastic card about 2/3 or 3/4 of the way in the deck and when that card is reached the dealer will finish that particular round and then shuffle the cards. How far into the deck(s) that plastic card is inserted is known as the *penetration point* and card counters always look for a dealer that offers good penetration. The card counter knows that the further into the deck(s) the plastic card is placed the more meaningful the true count will be and the more advantageous it will be for the card counter.

So, now that you know how those card counters keep track of the cards, what kind of advantage do you think they have over the casino? Well, not too much. Depending on the number of decks used, the rules in force, and the skill of the counter, it could be as much as 2% but that would be at the high end. Probably 1% would be closer to the actual truth. This means that for every $1,000 in bets that are made the card counter will win $10. Not exactly a huge amount but there are people out there who do make a living playing the game.

If you would like to learn more about blackjack, as well as more about card counting, be sure to take a look at the some of the ads in this book for ordering information on some very helpful books, newsletters, videos and computer software.

Rating Blackjack Games

by Arnold Snyder

We'll consider three distinct types of players in developing a rating system for blackjack games. These players are: gamblers, basic strategy players, and card counters.

For gamblers, the best games will be those which contain the fewest number of decks, with single decks being the best, and also the fewest player options. All other factors being equal, if you go from a single-deck game to a two-deck game, you will lose about 0.3% more of all the money you bet in the long run. A four-deck game will cost about 0.5% more than a single-decker. A six-deck or eight-deck shoe will cost about 0.6% more than a single-deck game.

In dollars and cents, assuming 100 hands per hour at $5 per hand, each 0.1% is equal to about 50¢ per hour. So a more practical way to look at it (at this betting level) is that the two-decker costs you an extra $1.50 per hour. The four-decker costs an extra $2.50 per hour. And the six or eight-decker will cost you an extra $3.00 per hour.

The Gambler's Considerations

Since we're defining the gambler as a player type who does not stick to perfect basic strategy, we can't really say what the total cost per hour of playing blackjack will be for this player. We'd have to precisely analyze those plays in which s/he was varying from basic strategy to make this determination.

As a general consideration, non-basic strategy players do better with fewer options because there are fewer opportunities to misplay hands. For example, it would be better for this type of player to play in games in which doubling down is limited to totals of hard 10 and 11 only. This is because totals of 10 and 11 are the most valuable double downs to make and it is usually correct to double down on these hands. If doubling down is allowed on any two cards, players who don't know basic strategy may frequently make costly errors.

The Basic Strategy Player

The second type of player, the basic strategy player, would also prefer the game with the fewest number of decks, but this player differs from the gambler in that s/he will find it most advantageous to play in games with the most player options allowed.

The most valuable options are: early surrender, doubling down on any two cards, and doubling after splits. Of slightly lesser value are regular (late) surrender and resplitting aces. Any restrictive rules, such as no resplitting pairs, will hurt the basic strategy player who knows how to take advantage of the rule(s).

Card Counters

For card counters only, two other factors are of prime importance in rating games: deck penetration and betting spread. By deck penetration, we mean how many of the cards will be dealt between shuffles. In a four-deck game, a dealer who deals out 3-1/2 decks will be far superior, from a card counters perspective, to a dealer who deals out only 2-1/2 decks between shuffles.

By betting spread, we mean how widely the player may vary their minimum and maximum bets. A table which allows a spread from $2 to $5 will prove more profitable to a counter than one which allows a spread from $3 to $5. Multi-action tables are better yet. If you can spread from one hand of $2 to three hands of $5 (or $15 total action), this would be even more to a card counter's advantage.

Note that deck penetration will have no effect whatsoever in the long run for players who are not card counters. Likewise, multi-action games, which allow a counter a greater betting spread, may tend to cause non-counters to overbet, and even to misplay hands.

So, before you pick the game, consider which player type you are. Non-counters should pick games in which they will lose the least. Card counters should pick the games where they will win the most.

Blackjack 101

by Henry Tamburin

The casino's edge over a typical unskilled player is 5 to 10 percent. Which means, over an extended period of time, the player has a high probability of losing money. That's unfortunate because blackjack players can significantly reduce the edge against them if they learn which are the best games to play and how to play each hand. Read on and learn how to beat the casinos at their own game, in this Blackjack 101 short course.

First things first. If you don't know the basic rules of casino blackjack you shouldn't be playing in a casino. This sounds trivial but you'd be surprised how many players play this game without a clue as to the objective of the game. Many honestly believe the goal is to get as close to 21 as possible. Others believe the best strategy is to follow the strategy of the dealer - after all he seems to be winning all the time.

To put it in simple terms the objective is to either beat the dealer by having your hand total higher than the dealer, or to have the dealer bust when your total is 21 or less. You want to try, if possible, not to exceed a total of 21. The reason for this has to do with how the casino creates its edge to begin with. It's real simple: you as a player go first and if your hand totals more than 21, guess what? That's right you lose, even if the dealer subsequently goes over 21 with his hand. Pretty neat rule for the house and something to keep in mind as a player.

OK let's get back to the rules. If you don't know what double down or pair splitting or insurance or surrender is all about, you better get a good book on blackjack and learn the basics before you risk any money in the casinos. At the very least pick up the free gaming guides in the casinos that explain all this.

All blackjack games are not created equal. Casino managers have a certain amount of latitude to modify the rules as they see fit. It's important you understand which rules are more favorable for the house and which ones favor the player.

Here is a rundown of the good rules for the player:

double down allowed on any two cards
double down allowed after pair splitting
multiple pair splitting allowed (even better if allowed with aces)
dealer stands on soft 17
the least number of decks the better (single or double is better than 4, which is better than 6, which is better than 8)
surrender allowed

Rule number one, if you are serious about winning, is: **given a choice, always play blackjack at the casino which offers the best rules**. You'll need every edge you can get and this one is important. So study the rules and go seek out the better games.

Your next task to cut the casino's edge is to learn the basic playing strategy. These strategies are developed by computer analysis of the game and represent mathematically correct strategy for each given playing situation. You won't win every hand following the basic strategy simply because in some situations no matter what hand you have the dealer's chances of beating you are very high. However, the basic strategy will allow you to make the best play to minimize your losses in unfavorable situations and, more importantly, allow you to maximize your profits when the advantage on a particular hand is in your favor.

You can find the basic strategy in most blackjack texts, including my *Blackjack: Take the Money and Run,* and it involves learning about 25 rules as to when to hit, stand, double, split or surrender. What I've done is to condense and simplify the most important strategy decisions into a set of nine easy-to-learn rules specifically for the casual player. Think of it as your first venue into learning winning blackjack playing strategies.

Memorize and use the rules below when you play blackjack and you will reduce the casino's edge to about one percent. Learn the complete basic strategy and you'll reduce the casino's advantage even more to about one-half of a percent (and I hope you commit to the latter).

Simplified Blackjack Playing Strategy

Your Hand	Playing Strategy vs Dealer's Up card
12 thru 16	stand on 2 thru 6, hit on 7 thru ace
17 thru 21	stand, except always hit soft 17 (A,6)
10 or 11	double on 2 through 9
soft 13 thru 17	always hit (except double all against 5,6)
soft 18 thru 21	always stand (except double soft 18 against 5,6)
8,8 and ace,ace	always split
5,5 and 10,10	never split
2,2;3,3;6,6;7,7;9,9	split on 2 thru 7 (except stand on 9,9 vs 7)
Never Take Insurance	

Do not, I repeat, do not play blackjack in a casino until you at least learn the above condensed basic strategy and, better yet, the complete strategy. If you insist on playing without learning the basic strategy, I suggest you stay home and instead just mail a check to the casino. Over time the results will be the same.

Henry Tamburin is the author of <u>Blackjack: Take the Money and Run</u>, <u>Reference Guide To Casino Gambling</u> and <u>The Ten Best Casino Bets</u>. He is also featured in the blackjack instructional video <u>Blackjack - Deal Me In.</u> Ordering information for his products can be found on page 66..

Roulette

by Steve Bourie

Virtually all American casinos use a double-zero roulette wheel which has pockets numbered from 1 to 36, plus 0 and 00 for a total of 38 pockets. This is in contrast to Europe where a single-zero wheel is used and the game has always been the most popular in the casino.

There are usually six seats at the roulette table and to help the dealer differentiate what each player is betting every player is assigned a different color chip which they purchase right at the table. Each table has its own minimum chip values and that information is usually posted on a sign at the table. As an example let's say a table has a $1 minimum chip value. This means that when you give the dealer your money the colored chips he gives you in return must have a minimum value of $1 each. So, if you gave the dealer $50 he would ask what value you wanted on the chips and if you said $1 he would give you 50 colored chips.

If you prefer, you could say you wanted the chips valued at $2 each and he would just give you 25 chips rather than 50. You can make the value of your colored chips anything you want and you'll notice that when the dealer gives you your chips he'll put one of your chips on the railing near the wheel with a marker on top to let him know the value of your chips. Later on when you're done playing at that table you must exchange your colored chips for regular chips before leaving. The colored chips have no value anywhere else in the casino so don't leave the table with them.

Besides the minimum chip value, there is also a minimum amount that must be bet on each spin of the wheel. Once again, the minimums are probably posted on a sign at the table and if it says $2 minimum inside and $5 minimum outside this means that if you are betting on any of the 38 numbers that pay 35-to-1 the total of all your bets must be $2. You could make two different $1 bets or one $2 bet, it doesn't matter except that the total of all your bets on the numbers must be at least $2. The $5 minimum outside means that any of the outside bets that pay 2-to-1, or even money, require that you bet $5 each time. On the outside bets you can't make a $3 bet and a $2 bet to meet the minimums - you have to bet at least $5 every time. After you've exchanged your cash for colored chips you're ready to place your first bet so, let's see what your options are:

You can make a ***straight*** bet where you only bet on one number and if it comes in you'll be paid 35-to-1. The casino advantage on this bet is 5.26% and by the time you're done with this roulette section I'm sure you'll be very familiar with that number.

Another choice you have is to do a *split*. This is where you put a chip on the line that separates two numbers. If either number comes up you'll be paid at 17-to-1. The casino advantage on this bet is 5.26%.

If you put a chip in an area that splits 4 numbers this is called a *corner* bet and if any one of those 4 numbers comes in you will be paid off at 8-to-1. The casino advantage on this bet is 5.26%.

If you put a chip at the beginning of a row of 3 numbers, this is called a *street* bet and if any one of those 3 numbers shows up you will be paid off at 11-to-1. The casino advantage on this bet is 5.26%.

You can also put a chip on the line between two streets so that you have a *double street* covered and if any one of those 6 numbers come in you'll be paid off at 5-to-1. The casino advantage on this bet is?... you guessed it...5.26%.

The only other bet you can make on the inside numbers is the *5- number* bet where you place one chip in the upper left corner of the number 1 box. If any one of those 5 numbers comes in you'll be paid off at 6-to-1 and what do you think the casino advantage is on this bet? Nope, I gotcha... it's 7.89%. Actually, this is the worst possible bet on the roulette table and the only bet you'll come across that doesn't have a 5.26% house edge on the double-zero roulette wheel. You should never make this bet.

One quick word here about "to" and "for" when discussing odds. Whenever the odds are stated as "to" this means that in addition to the stated payoff you also receive your original bet back. In other words, if you won your single number bet in roulette you would receive 35-to-1, which is a 35-chip payoff, plus you'd still keep your original one-chip bet, so you end up with 36 chips. Now if the odds are stated as "for" that means you do not receive back your original bet. If the odds in your single number bet were 35-*for*-1 you would still receive a 35-chip payoff but the casino would keep your original one-chip bet so you would only end up with 35 chips. The only place in a casino where the odds are always stated as "for" is in video poker. You might also come across it on a couple of craps bets where the odds are stated as "for-one" rather than "to-one" in order to give the casino a slightly better edge.

Now, getting back to our roulette examples, let's look at all of the outside bets that you can make and keep in mind that the house edge on all of these outside bets is...do you remember the number?...that's right...5.26%.

There are three bets you can make that will pay you even money, or 1-to-1, which means that if you win, you will get back one dollar for every dollar you bet:

Red or black - If you put a chip on red then a red number must come up in order for you to win. If the ball lands on a black number, 0 or 00 - you lose. The same thing goes for black - you lose if it comes in red, 0 or 00 and you win if the ball lands on a black number.

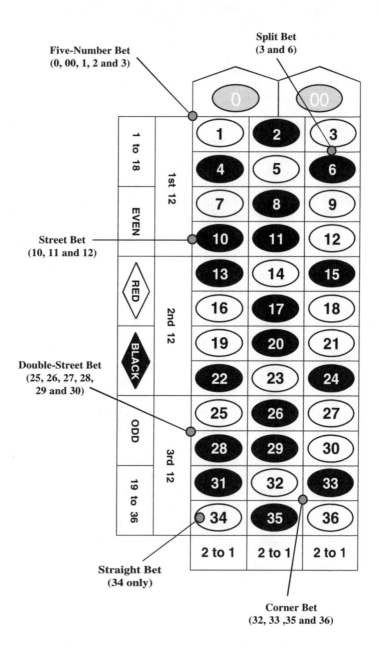

Five-Number Bet
(0, 00, 1, 2 and 3)

Split Bet
(3 and 6)

Street Bet
(10, 11 and 12)

Double-Street Bet
(25, 26, 27, 28,
29 and 30)

Straight Bet
(34 only)

Corner Bet
(32, 33 ,35 and 36)

Typical felt layout for placing bets on American double-zero roulette wheel

Odd or even - If you put a chip on odd then the ball must land on an odd number in order for you to win. If it lands on 0, 00, or an even number - you lose. If you bet on even, you win if an even number shows up and lose if the ball lands on 0, 00 or an odd number.

1 through 18 and 19 through 36 - If you bet on 1 through 18, then you win if a number from 1 through 18 comes in and you lose if the ball lands on 0, 00 or a number higher than 18. Similarly, if you bet on 19 through 36, you win if one of those numbers comes in and you lose on 0, 00 or any number lower than 19.

The only other bets left are the *dozens* and columns bets. If you look at the roulette betting layout you can see three areas that each correspond to 12-number sections on the table. The one marked 1st 12 covers the numbers from 1 to 12, the one marked 2nd 12 covers the numbers from 13 to 24 and the other one that's marked 3rd 12 covers the last section of numbers from 25 to 36. If you bet on the 1st 12 you would win if a number from 1 to 12 came in and you would lose if anything else came in, including 0 or 00. The same principle holds true for each of the other dozen bets where you would win if a number in that section came in and you would lose if anything else showed up. All dozens bets pay 2-to-1.

The last bet to look at is the *column* bet and that is also a bet that pays 2-to-1. There are three possible column bets you can make and you'll notice that each area corresponds to the numbers in the column directly above it. So, if you put a chip under the first column you will win if any of the numbers in that column come in and you will lose if any other number, including 0 or 00 shows up. Once again, the same rule is in effect for each of the other columns where you would win if the number appears in the column above your bet and you would lose if it doesn't.

All right, now you know all the possible bets and you know how to make them at the table. So, the next question is "How do you win?" and the answer to that is very simple - You have to get lucky! And that's the ONLY way you can win at roulette. As you found out earlier, every bet, except for the 5-number bet, which I'm sure you'll never make, has a house edge of?...that's right...5.26%. So, feel free to put your chips all over the table and then just hope that you're lucky enough to have one of your numbers come up. You see, it just doesn't matter what you do because you'll always have that same house edge of 5.26% working against you on every bet you make.

Now, you may have heard of a system for roulette where you should place your bets only on the numbers that are evenly spaced out around the wheel. For example, if you wanted to play only four numbers, you could bet on 1,2,31 and 32 because when you looked at a roulette wheel, you would notice that if you divided it into four equal parts, you would have a number that appears in each of the four sections. So, is this a good system? Well, actually it's no better and no worse than any other roulette system. The fact is that it's purely a matter of chance where the ball happens to land and it makes no difference whether the numbers you choose are right next to each other or evenly spaced out on the wheel. Each number has an equal chance to occur on every spin of the wheel and the house edge always remains at 5.26%.

You can probably tell that I wouldn't recommend roulette as a good game to play because there are other games that offer much better odds, but if you really insist on playing the game I have three good suggestions for you. #1 - Go to Atlantic City! In Atlantic City if you make an even-money outside bet, like red or black, odd or even, 1 through 18 or 19 through 36 and if 0 or 00 come up, the state gaming regulations allow the casino to take only half of your bet. Because you only lose half of your bet this also lowers the casino edge on these outside bets in half to 2.63%. This rule is only in effect for even-money bets so keep in mind that on all other bets the house edge still remains at that very high 5.26%.

The second suggestion I have for you also involves some travel and here it is: Go to Europe! The game of roulette began in Europe and many casinos over there use a single-zero wheel which makes it a much better game because the house edge on a single-zero roulette wheel is only 2.70%. To make it even better, they have a rule called "en prison" which is similar to the Atlantic City casino rule. If you make an even-money outside bet and the ball lands on 0 you don't lose right away. Instead, your bet is "imprisoned" and you have to let it ride on the next spin. Then, if your bet wins, you can remove it from the table. Because of this rule, the casino edge on this bet is cut in half to 1.35% which makes it one of the best bets in the casino and almost four times better than the same bet when it's made on a standard double-zero roulette wheel in the United States.

Now, if you're not into traveling and you don't think you can make it to Atlantic City or Europe, then you'll just have to settle for suggestion #3 which is: Win quickly! Naturally, this is easier said than done, but in reality, if you want to win at roulette the best suggestion I can give you is that you try to win quickly and then walk away from the table because the longer you continue to bet the longer that big 5.26% house edge will keep eating away at your bankroll. One major principle of gambling is that in order to win you must only play the games that have the lowest casino edge and, unfortunately, roulette is not one of them.

Before closing out this look at roulette, let's take a minute to examine one of the most famous betting systems of all time and the one that many people frequently like to use on roulette. It's called the Martingale system and it is basically a simple system of doubling your bet whenever you lose. The theory behind it is that sooner or later you'll have to win and thus, you will always come out ahead. As an example, let's say you're playing roulette and you bet $1 on red, if you lose you double your next bet to $2 and if you lose that then you double your next bet to $4 and if you lose that you double your next bet to $8 and so forth until you eventually win. Now, when you finally do win you will end up with a profit equal to your original bet, which in this case is $1. If you started the same system with a $5 bet, you would have to bet $10 after your first loss, $20 after your second loss and so forth, but whenever you won you would end up with a $5 profit.

In theory, this sounds like a good idea but in reality it's a terrible system because eventually you will be forced to risk a great amount of money for a very small profit. Let's face it, even if you only wanted to make a $1 profit on each spin of the wheel, sooner or later you will hit a major losing streak where you will have to bet an awful lot of money just to make that $1 profit. For example, if you go eight spins without a winner, you would have to bet $256 on the next spin and if that lost then you'd have to bet $512. Would you really want to risk that kind of money just to make $1? I don't think so. You may think that the odds are highly unlikely that you would lose that many bets in a row, but eventually it will happen and when it does you will suffer some astronomical losses. One other problem with this system is that eventually you won't be able to double your bet because you will have reached the casino maximum, which in most casinos is $500 on roulette. Just keep in mind that the Martingale system works best when it's played for fun on paper and not for real money in a casino. If it was truly a winning system it would have bankrupted the world's casinos years ago.

Craps Bets - Good, Bad & Ugly

by Henry Tamburin

Craps is a unique casino game because it contains some of the best, and also some of the worst, casino bets. It's important you know the difference if you are serious about winning.

The Good Bets

The best bets on the craps layout are the ones in which the casino's edge is 1.5% or less. Play smart and you can lower that edge to under 0.5%. A game this close over the short term can be beat!

The best bets are: pass line and don't pass, come and don't come, the odds bet, and a place bet on the 6 or 8. The casino's edge for the basic pass line or come bet (and opposite don't pass and don't come) is 1.4%. The place bet on the 6 and 8 is 1.5%. Although we can't lower the house edge on the place bet we can lower it on the pass and come (and opposite don't pass and don't come) by making the odds bet.

Nowadays, because of fierce casino competition for craps players, casinos allow players to make an odds bet equal to double, triple, five, 10 and even 20 times the amount of their pass line bet. Thus, a player who wagers $3 on the pass line could wager a maximum of $60 in odds. The casino's edge on this bet is reduced to about 0.1% Folks, it just doesn't get any lower than this unless you want to learn how to card count in blackjack. The following table shows the relationship of the casino's edge with the amount of odds.

Casino's Edge

pass line	1.4%
single odds	0.8%
double odds	0.6%
triple odds	0.5%
5 times odds	0.3%
10 times odds	0.2%
20 times odds	0.1%

One caveat, however, if you decide to bet 5, 10 or 20 times odds. Although this will reduce the casino's edge, it also will increase the amount of money you have on the layout. One roll of 7 and you'll lose the pass line and odds. Therefore, you need to have more of a bankroll when you start betting large amounts in odds. Or, you can start off betting single odds and then when you win, keep the size of the pass line bet the same but increase your odds bet to double. Win again and increase to triple odds and so forth. This technique for getting more money on the layout during a hot roll on a bet where the casino has no advantage is thoroughly explained in my book, *Craps: Take The Money and Run.*

The Bad Bets

These craps bets have a casino edge from 2.4 to 6.7%. Although this is not intolerable why make bets with this high of a casino edge when you can make the good bets with a lot lower casino edge?

The bad bets include (casino edge in parenthesis): lay 4 or 10 (2.4%); lay 5 or 9 (3.2%); place 5 or 9 (4.0%); lay 6 or 8 (4.0%); buy bets (4.8%); field (5.6%); and place 4 or 10 (6.7%).

The Ugly Bets

Now we come to the ugly or what I also call the sucker bets of craps. Why? Because here are the bets which command a casino's edge from 9.0% up to a stratospheric 16.7%. If you like throwing your money away, here are the bets for you: big 6 and 8 (9.1%); hardway 6 or 8 (9.1%); hardway 4 and 10 (11.1%); any craps (11.1%); 11 or 3 proposition (11.1%); 2 or 12 proposition (13.9%); and any seven (16.7%). You can also throw the hop bets, horn bets, world bets, and insurance type bets into this category of sucker bets.

It's no secret that to be a winner in craps you must make only those bets that have a low casino edge, increase your bet size as you win consecutive bets to take advantage of a hot roll, and learn when to take the money and run. This is the basics of winning craps play and to start, make only the best bets on the craps table and stay away from those bad and ugly bets. It is the key to being a consistent winning craps player.

Henry Tamburin is the author of the book Craps: Take The Money and Run and is featured in the video Craps - Rolling To Win. Ordering information for his books and videos can be found on page 66.

Casino Mistakes - Part I

by Steve Bourie

If you've read most of the stories in this section of the book it should be rather evident to you that casinos make their money by having an edge on every game they offer. In rare instances, however, mistakes are made on the part of the casinos and things don't work out the way they planned. What follows is a story about one of those instances in a Canadian casino. In part 2, noted gambling authority Stanford Wong relates the story of another incident at a Mississippi casino.

Casino de Montreal first opened for business in October 1993 and one of the games it offered was keno. Keno is a lottery-type game that involves the numbers from 1 to 80. Twenty numbers out of the 80 are selected randomly and players try to guess which numbers will be chosen. Players can guess anywhere from 1 to 20 numbers and the more numbers they guess correctly, the higher the payoff when they win.

The casino offered two types of keno games - mechanical and electronic. In the mechanical version the numbers were printed on 80 ping pong-type balls and were chosen by a blower system that mixed the balls and then allowed the balls to escape to a chute one-at-a-time so the numbers could be called out. The electronic version used a computer chip called a random number generator (RNG) to determine its 20 numbers. These electronic machines had been used in numerous Las Vegas casinos for years and had always proved reliable.

Daniel Corriveau was a freelance computer consultant who enjoyed using his skills to look for patterns in winning lottery numbers.When the new casino opened in his home province of Quebec he decided to turn his attention to the casino's keno game. Eventually, he thought he detected a pattern in the electronic version of the game and he went to the casino on April 10, 1994 to test out his theory. By the end of the evening he had hit 19 out of 20 numbers three consecutive times, plus some other number combinations for a total win of $620,000.

Knowing that it was statistically impossible to accomplish such a feat, the casino personnel immediately shut down the electronic game and decided not to pay Courriveau until they conducted an inquiry into what had happened. After all, they wanted to make sure that there wasn't some elaborate scheme underway to defraud them.

After conducting a full-scale police investigation, including a polygraph exam, the casino called a press conference 17 days later to announce that Courriveau had legitimately won his bets and presented him with a check for $620,000.

So, what happened? Did Courriveau really discover a winning program for predicting keno numbers? Well, not exactly. It turns out that there was a problem with the electronic version of the game. Although a RNG can literally produce hundreds of millions of different number combinations it always has to have a starting point, or seed, to begin its calculations. It then uses that number to do the math to come up with a new number which then becomes the seed for the next calculation. It then uses that number to do the math for the next calculation and that result becomes the seed for the next calculation. This process is repeated continuously. The one thing to keep in mind, however, is that because the calculations are always the same the RNG needs a different seed each time or else it will come up with the same numbers. In other words, if the starting seed doesn't change, the RNG will simply come up with the same results time after time.

As stated before, the electronic machines had a history of working fine in Las Vegas, but in Las Vegas the casinos are open 24 hours a day. In Montreal, however, the casino did not operate on a 24-hour basis and the machine was shut off at night. When the machine was turned on the next day it always started its calculations at the initial seed which was programmed into it. Since the seed never changed, the machine merely kept repeating the same pattern of numbers. Courriveau was lucky enough to spot the pattern but anyone probably could have done the same had they kept a history of the winning numbers. Today, the casino still offers keno, but only the mechanical version. The electronic keno game never re-opened after Courriveau's big win.

Casino Mistakes - Part II

by Stanford Wong

For one day in October 1994 Sic Bo was the most exciting game in any casino, anywhere. On October 25, I published a special issue of my newsletter, *Current Blackjack News*, explaining how to beat the game. Flat $100 bets had the expectation of winning $1,500 per hour. Ten of the people who received my newsletter by fax became professional sic bo players overnight. That made October 26 an exciting day for sic bo. Here are the details.

This is the content of the special issue of *Current Blackjack News* dated October 25, 1994: A professional sic bo player reveals his secret two-step approach for getting an edge at the game. Mississippi reporter Blair Guthrie has verified that the method works. The two steps to sic bo success are: 1 - Go to the Grand Casino in Biloxi. 2 - Bet on 4 and 17.

Sic bo is a game played with three dice, and customers can bet on the various number combinations. Normally the casino has an edge on every possible bet. An exception is bets on 4 and 17 at the Grand in Biloxi. Of the 6 x 6 x 6 or 216 permutations of three dice, there are three ways to make 4 and three ways to make 17. If there were no house edge, the payoff would be 71:1 on those two bets. The Grand pays 80:1. That is a 12.5% customer edge. You ought to get at least 60 games an hour. The maximum bet is $100.

If you bet $25 on 4 and $25 on 17 on each game, you will win $1,975 an average of twice per 72 games. You will lose $50 on each of the other 70 out of 72 games. That is a average net win of $450 per 72 games, which is just over an hour of sic bo.

I was not kidding about there being a professional sic bo player. I am sending him a year of Current Blackjack News to thank him for sharing his secret with us. Sic bo is risky. You can easily go for long stretches without winning a bet, and with twin $25 bets you will lose $3,000 or more an hour during those unlucky stretches.

October 26 - The table opened at 11 am. A couple of professional sic bo players arrived before 4 pm, but most arrived in the early evening. That probably reflects airline schedules rather than a preference for avoiding daytime sic bo. The players flew in from around the country, with several coming from Las Vegas. One fellow received his newsletter by fax in Minnesota, hopped into his car, and drove for 17 hours to reach the casino.

By late evening all the chairs were taken and new arrivals had to stand. Anyone could have played - you too could have gotten in on the giveaway had you been there. Long arms would have helped; those standing to make their bets had to reach over or between seated players. One sic bo pro to arrived at midnight to find no empty seats at the table. He could have stood and reached in to make his bets, but he wanted to sit down. Fortunately for him, one customer was happy to sell his seat for $40. The purchaser went on to win $8,000 in the next three hours.

One late arrival was so happy to find the game still open and the 80:1 payoffs still being made that he simply stood there enjoying the scene instead of hurrying to get his first bets down. He was intending to bet $75 per number, but the first game proceeded without him having a bet on it. The result on that game: The dice totaled 4, so being slow in getting his first bet down cost him $5,925. After that he made $75 bets for a while, and dropped back to $50 bets after a series of losses made him fear going bust. Every time he won he went back up to $75 bets for a while, and then dropped down to $50 bets. He lost all his $75 bets; all of his wins came with $50 bets. He ended up winning $2000, but would have been up much more had he been quicker getting his first bet down because then all his winners would have been on $75 bets.

Several players were betting the $100 max, but most were betting quarters ($25 chips). There were so many bets on the 4 and 17 that the chips overflowed the appropriate spaces on the layout. Bets in the areas around those two betting spots were understood by all to mean bets on those numbers.

Each time the dice totaled 4 or 17, a great cheer went up from the sic bo table. If you happened to be in the Grand at that time, you heard all the sic bo players and some of the floormen simultaneously shouting "Show time!" By late evening, each time one of those numbers rolled, the casino paid out almost $50,000. Payoffs were slow. The dealer would say "I'm going to pay this $25 bet now," count out $2,000, and then say, "Whose is this?" Someone would raise his hand and receive the payoff. There were no arguments; professional sic bo players are honorable people.

The players helped each other place bets too. One player at each end of the table acted as captain in charge of a betting square. (In sic bo, unlike roulette, all players use the same chips. If several people are betting the same amounts on the same numbers game after game, and on one game one player forgets to make the bet, if that number wins an argument might ensue.) The captains made sure that each player got his bet down each game. All the players were interested in keeping the game moving as quickly as possible.

The casino was unlucky. Numbers 4 and 17 each are expected to come up once per 72 games, but any given set of games can have too few or too many winners. On October 26 at the Grand in Biloxi, these two numbers came up more often than once per 72 games. Once the number 17 even came up on back to back games! The frequency with which these numbers won, combined with the large amounts being wagered on them, had the casino bosses concerned. By the end of the evening there were no less than seven supervisors in suits and ties observing the game and wondering why the casino was losing.

Normally the pace of sic bo is 60 to 75 games per hour. However, when 4 or 17 hit, it took the dealer up to 15 minutes to pay all the winning bets. After midnight the 4 and 17 hit about twice as often as expected, slowing the pace of the game to less than 30 games per hour.

The casino was losing, so several times more chips had to be brought to the table. A fill, as the procedure is called, was welcomed by the players as a chance to use the rest room without missing any betting opportunities.

The game closed at 3 am, its normal closing time, with the sic bo players being way, way ahead of the casino. I do not know the exact amount the players won, but a Grand casino insider estimates $180,000.

Besides lining up at the cashier, the players lined up at the rest room and restaurant. Minor bodily needs tend to be ignored when the cost of satisfying them is high. As soon as the game closed, such needs became urgent.

October 27 - The game was supposed to reopen at 11 am. The sic bo pros started drifting in around 10 am so as to be able to jump right in as soon as the game opened. Also coming in at 10: a team of possibly as many as a dozen casino employees to examine everything about the game. They took the dice shaker apart to examine it. They carefully examined the dice. They checked the electrical circuitry of the table to be sure that only winning numbers lit up. They seemed completely puzzled as to how the casino could have lost so much money the previous day.

At 11 am a dealer came to the sic bo game, and the chip tray was unlocked. Two minutes later the tray was locked up and the dealer disappeared. The would-be sic bo players asked what was happening, and were told that the opening was being delayed. The people who were waiting wanted very much for the table to open so that they could play some more sic bo. But they also enjoyed the fact that they had a 12.5% edge over the casino, and the casino had no inkling of what was going on.

At 1 pm a boss came over and said "I know you boys are waiting for game to open, but we are not opening it today." The players were not happy to hear that the game would remain closed, but they were impressed by the boss's graciousness.

Later the sic bo pros noticed a casino executive with a copy of my newsletter explaining how to beat the game. So it appeared that the casino finally knew why the players won at sic bo the previous day.

The sic bo table did not reopen that day, or the next day either. Apparently the casino folks rethought the wisdom of paying 80:1 for combinations that are expected to occur once in 72 games. The table remained closed until the casino obtained a new layout that promised only 60:1 on totals of 4 and 17, giving the casino a 15.3% edge on those bets.

Stanford Wong is a noted gambling expert and the author of numerous books on casino gambling. Ordering information for some of his books can be found on the next page. Wong has also created specialized software programs for video poker (see page 37) and for blackjack (see page 68).

Casino Myths & Superstitions

by Dewey Bryan

Here are some widely held beliefs about slots, video poker and blackjack that simply are not true. Acting on some of these myths can cost the player serious dollars. Others just raise the blood pressure to unhealthy levels. Subjecting them to the cold light of logic will improve your game.

Slot Myth: She just hit my jackpot! It's a familiar refrain. We're playing a machine and we decide to take a break. Someone jumps in and takes our place. We haven't gone 10 feet when ringing bells and clattering coins cause us to turn around and see our "replacement" scooping up coins from a big payout on "our" machine.

Slot Fact: It is highly unlikely that we would have hit that jackpot had we continued playing. Today's slot machines (and video poker games) are electronically controlled by a high speed random number generator. It selects the reel positions at the precise moment that we pull the handle or hit the spin button. To catch the same payout as the interloper, we would have had to put the reels in play at exactly the same instant the new player did.

Slot Myth: This slot machine is due. We hear this one all the time. "Someone played that Red, White and Blue machine for three hours and the 7's never hit. I tell you, that one is ready to pop!"

Slot Fact: Thinking that a machine that has not hit for some period of time is somehow "due" is one of the most costly mistakes a slots player can make. Every pull of the handle is an independent event. A slot machine does not "remember" that it has not lined up the 7's in the last three hours. If there are 10 ways to line up three 7's out of a total of 30,000 possibilities, our odds of catching three 7's is one in 3,000. There is nothing in the laws of probability to prevent a machine from going 6,000, or even 10,000 or more pulls without lining up three 7's. The odds of three 7's is 1 in 3,000 on each try.

The best way to think of a one-armed bandit that does not pay very often is that it is a tight machine. Shop around for one that rewards your play with small, steady wins.

Video Poker Myth: Video poker is like slots. A player has no idea how loose or tight they are.

This gambler knows that there are different types of machines, like Jacks or Better, Bonus, or Joker Poker. But once the type of game is selected, how loose a game might be is a mystery.

Video Poker Fact: Video poker differs in both the types of games offered and the payout schedules for each type of game. In fact, the payout schedule is posted right on each machine.

Video poker is a game of skill, while slots are games of chance. By playing video poker hands a certain way (a "basic strategy"), we can predict an expected frequency of final hands. Knowing the payout schedule and the expected frequency of hands lets us calculate the expected return for each payout schedule and type of machine. We could do the same thing with slot machines if casinos would just be kind enough to tell us how many of each symbol is on each reel and how many "stops" a slot machine makes.

This myth about video poker is a powerful one. Wander around any casino that has multiple payout schedules for the same type of game. It is almost certain that you will find someone playing an "inferior" machine when a better one is available a few feet away.

One word of caution: in order for the above to be true, a video poker machine must play as a truly random game. That is, these games must conform to the same laws of probability as if a "real" well shuffled single deck of cards was in use.

It is technically possible for a video poker machine to be "set" so that it is not truly random. Certain cards can be suppressed in certain situations, lowering (or eliminating) the player's probability of catching a paying combination. In well regulated gambling jurisdictions such as Nevada and Atlantic City, players are protected from such machines. But let the gambler beware--This is not the case in all jurisdictions.

Blackjack Myth: Third base controls the table. "The reason I'm losing is that idiot at third base keeps taking the dealer's bust card." Or, "I won't play unless I'm at third base. If someone who doesn't know how to play sits at third, it ruins the game for everyone."

Blackjack Fact: Poor play at third base, first base, or anywhere in the middle has no impact on the basic strategy player's or card counter's expectation. Mathematical blackjack simulations have shown that, no matter how crazy the play at third base, other players at the table are not adversely affected in their overall expectation.

Basic strategy and card counting depend on the overall randomness of the game, not the decisions of other players. As long as the game is random, i.e., players and the dealer have an equal chance of catching any one of the remaining cards in the deck, the actions of other players has no impact on your long term chances of winning or losing.

This myth is fueled by our own selective perception. We tend to notice those times when poor play at third base costs us and miss those instances when we are actually helped by moronic play.

Dewey Bryan is a contributing writer for gambling publications throughout the United States. He is also the former publisher of The Gambling Prospector, a monthly gambling newsletter.

ARIZONA

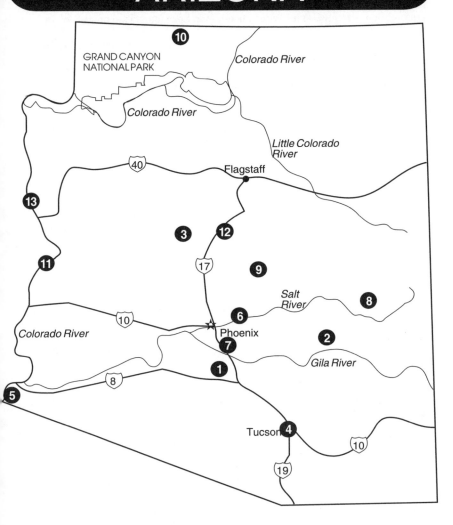

In mid-1993 Arizona's Governor Symington signed a compact with the state's tribes that allows them to offer slot machines on their reservations.

The compact does not allow for any table games but some casinos offer video versions of blackjack, craps and roulette. All Arizona casinos have slots, video poker and video keno. The minimum gambling age is 18 (21 if liquor is served). Unless otherwise noted all casinos are open 24 hours.

Apache Gold Casino
P.O. Box 1210
San Carlos, Arizona 85550
(520) 425-7692
Map Location: #2 (90 miles E. of Phoenix)

Toll-Free Number: (800) APACHE-3
Restaurants: 1   Liquor: Yes (Beer/Wine)
Casino Size: 10,000 Square Feet
Other Games: Poker, Keno, Video BJ
Casino Marketing: (800) APACHE-8
Fun Book: Available through local motels, RV parks and the chamber of commerce

Blue Water Casino
119 W. Riverside Drive
Parker, Arizona 85344
(520) 669-7777
Map Location: #11 (160 miles W. of Phoenix)

Toll-Free Number: (800) 747-8777
Restaurants: 1   Liquor: Yes
Other Games: Video BJ, Poker, Keno, Bingo

Bucky's Casino
530 E. Merritt
Prescott, Arizona 86301
(520) 776-1666
Map Location: #3 (91 miles S.W. of Flagstaff, Junction of Hwy. 69 & Hwy. 89)

Toll-Free Number: (800) 967-4637
Rooms: 161 Price Range: $99-$170
Restaurants: 2 (1 open 24 hours) Liquor: Yes
Other Games: Keno, Video BJ
Casino Marketing: (520) 771-0580
Special Features: Located in Prescott Resort Hotel and 1/4-mile from Yavapai Gaming Center. Free on-site shuttle service. Gas station with RV dump and mini-mart.

Casino of the Sun
7406 S. Camino De Oeste
Tucson, Arizona 85746
(520) 883-1700
Map Location: #4

Toll-Free Number: (800) 344-9435
Restaurants: 1 (open 24 hours) Liquor: No
Buffets: L-$3.95 D-$4.95
Other Games: Bingo, Keno, Poker, Video BJ
Special Features: Non-smoking slot room. Smoke shop. Gift shop.

Cliff Castle Casino
P.O. Box 4677
Camp Verde, Arizona 86322
(520) 567-6121
Map Location: #12 (50 miles S. of Flagstaff)

Toll-Free Number: (800) 381-SLOT
Room Reservation Number: (800) 524-6343
Rooms: 82 Price Range: $65-$88
Restaurants: 1 Liquor: Yes
Other Games: Poker,Video BJ, Video Craps, Video Roulette
Special Features: Casino is located in Best Western Cliff Castle Lodge.

Cocopah Casino
15136 S. Avenue B
Somerton, Arizona 85350
(520) 726-8066
Map Location: #5 (13 miles S.W. of Yuma)

Toll-Free Number: (800) 23-SLOTS
Restaurants: 1 Snack Bar Liquor: No
Hours: 6am-2am/24 hours (Fri/Sat)
Other Games: Bingo, Video BJ

Desert Diamond Casino
7350 S. Old Nogales Hwy.
Tucson, Arizona 85734
(520) 294-7777
Map Location: #4

Restaurants: 2 (1 open 24 hours)
Liquor: No
Casino Size: 45,000 Square Feet
Other Games: Poker, Keno, Bingo, Video BJ, Video Craps, Video Roulette

Fort McDowell Casino
P.O. Box 18359
Fountain Hills, Arizona 85269
(602) 837-1424
Map Location: #6 (25 miles N.E. of Phoenix)

Toll-Free Number: (800) THE-FORT
Restaurants: 3 (1 open 24 hours)
Buffets: B-$2.95 L-$4.95 D-$6.95/$7.95 (Tue)/$8.95 (Fri/Sat)   Liquor: No
Other Games: Poker, Keno, Bingo, Video BJ, Video Craps, Video Roulette
Special Features: 99¢ breakfast buffet from 12am-7am. Free valley-wide transportation (reservations required).

Gila River Casino - Lone Butte
1201 S. 56th Street
Chandler, Arizona 85226
(520) 796-7777
Map Location: #7 (25 miles S.E. of Phoenix)

Toll-Free Number: (800) WIN-GILA
Restaurants: 1 Deli (open 24 hours) Liquor: No
Casino Size: 8,500 Square Feet
Other Games: Video BJ

Gila River Casino - Wild Horse
5512 W. Wild Horse Pass
Chandler, Arizona 85226
(520) 796-7727
Map Location: #7 (25 miles S.E. of Phoenix)
Toll-Free Number: (800) WIN-GILA
Restaurants: 1 (open 24 hours) Liquor: No
Buffets: B-$1.99 L-$4.00 D-$6.00
Casino Size: 60,000 Square Feet
Other Games: Keno, Bingo, Video BJ,
              Video Craps, Video Roulette
Special Features: 99¢ breakfast buffet from
12am-7am.

Harrah's Phoenix Ak Chin Casino
15406 Maricopa Road
Maricopa, Arizona 85239
(602) 802-5000
Map Location: #1 (35 miles S. of Phoenix)

Toll-Free Number: (800) HARRAHS
Restaurants: 3 (1 open 24 hours)
Buffets: B-$4.95 L-$5.95/$6.95 (Sat-Sun)
D-$8.95/$9.95 (Fri-Sun)
Liquor: Yes
Casino Size: 30,000 Square Feet
Other Games: Poker, Bingo, Video BJ,
              Video Craps, Video Roulette
Fun Book: Only given to bus groups
Special Features: Breakfast buffet is $1.99 if
you present a Harrah's Gold Card. Two bars.
Live entertainment. Native-American crafts
store and smoke shop.

Hon Dah Casino
P.O. Box 3250
Pinetop, Arizona 85935
(520) 369-0299
Map Location: #8 (190 miles N.E. of Phoenix)

Toll-Free Number: (800) WAY-UP-HI
Restaurants: 1 (open 24 hours) Liquor: Yes
Other Games: Poker, Keno, Video BJ
Fun Book: Available through local motels
              and chamber of commerce
Special Features: 120-space full-service RV
park. Convenience store. Gas station.

Mazatzal Casino
P.O. Box 1820
Payson, Arizona 85547
(602) 474-6044
Map Location: #9 (90 miles N.E. of Phoenix)

Toll-Free Number: (800) 777-7529
Restaurants: 2 (1 open 24 hours) Liquor: No
Casino Size: 35,000 Square Feet

Other Games: Poker, Keno, Bingo, Video BJ
Fun Book: Only given to bus groups or as
              part of Stay & Play packages.
Special Features: Offers discounted Stay &
Play packages with some local motels. Pack-
age includes: discounted room price, Fun
Books, breakfast for 2 in full-service restau-
rant, plus free shuttle to and from motel.
Sports bar. Video arcade. Gift shop.

Paradise Casino
540 Quechan Drive
Yuma, Arizona 85364
(619) 572-7777
Map Location: #5 (244 miles W. of Tucson)

Toll-Free Number: (888) 777-4946
Restaurants: 1 (open 24 hours) Liquor: No
Other Games: Poker, Keno, Bingo, Video BJ
Special Features: Cappuccino bar.

Pipe Spring Resort & Casino
HC 65, Box 3
Fredonia, Arizona 86022
(801) 559-6537
Map Location: #10 (200 miles N.W. of Flag-
staff)

Restaurants: 1 Deli Liquor: No
Hours: 9am-10pm/1:30am (Fri/Sat)
Casino Size: 5,000 Square Feet
Special Features: 48-space RV park with full
hook-ups.

Spirit Mountain Casino
8555 S. Highway 95
Mohave Valley, Arizona 86440
(520) 346-2000
Map Location: #13 (15 miles S. of Bullhead
City)

Restaurants: 1 Snack Bar Liquor: Yes

Yavapai Gaming Center
1505 E. Highway 69
Prescott, Arizona 86301
(520) 445-5767
Map Location: #3 (91 miles S.W. of Flagstaff)

Toll-Free Number: (800) SLOTS-44
Restaurants: 1 Snack Bar Liquor: No
Other Games: Poker, Keno, Bingo, Video BJ
Special Features: Located 1/4-mile from
Bucky's Casino. Free shuttle bus service.

CALIFORNIA

California's Indian casinos are embroiled in a legal dispute with the state concerning what kind of electronic gaming devices are allowed on their lands. As of late 1996 almost all of the tribes were offering video poker, video keno, video slots and video pull tabs. The major difference between these machines and those found in a regular casino is that these machines will accept cash but they do not pay out in cash. Instead, when you are ready to cash out the machine will print a receipt which must be cashed by one of the floor attendants or cashed at the casino cage. The state believes that these video machines are illegal but an agreement has been worked out that allows the tribes to keep them in operation until a federal court decision settles the issue.

Many California Indian casinos also offer a player-banked version of blackjack. Under this system one player at the table acts as the banker and the casino takes a commission from all of the players (including the banker) for dealing the cards and monitoring the game. Each casino sets its own rates so be aware that the commissions will vary. In some casinos, such as Fantasy Springs, the commission is a flat 50¢ per hand (on $3 and $5 tables) or $1 (on $10 and up tables). In others, such as Jackson Indian Bingo & Casino, it is based on the size of the bet: 25¢ for bets from $1 to $9.00; 50¢ for bets from $9.25 to $30.00; $1 for bets from $30.25 to $100.00; $2 for bets from $100.25 to $200; and $3 for bets from $200.25 to the casino maximum of $300. Most California card rooms also offer some form of player-banked blackjack.

Unless otherwise noted, all casinos are open 24 hours and offer video slots, video poker, video poker and video pull tabs. Optional games offered include: blackjack (BJ), baccarat (B), Poker (P), pai gow poker (PGP), Caribbean Stud Poker (CSP), bingo (BG) and simulcasting (S). The minimum gambling age is 18. Although most of the casinos have toll-free numbers be aware that many of those numbers will only work for calls made within California.

Barona Casino & Bingo
1000 Wildcat Canyon Road
Lakeside, California 92040
(619) 443-2300
Map Location: #1 (15 miles N.E. of San Diego)

Toll-Free Number: (888) 7-BARONA
Restaurants: 1 Liquor: No
Buffets: L-$3.99 D-$4.99
Other Games: BJ, P, BG (Fri-Sun), S
Special Features: Groups receive a Fun-Pak that includes 50% off buffet, 15% off gift shop and $5 in video machine play.

Black Bart Casino
P.O. Box 1177
Willits, California 95490
(707) 459-7330
Map Location: #11 (120 miles N.W. of Sacramento)

Restaurants: 1 Deli Liquor: No
Hours: 10am-2am/24 hours (Fri/Sat)
Casino Size: 3,000 Square Feet
Other Games: BJ

Cache Creek Indian Bingo & Casino
14455 Highway 16
Brooks, California 95606
(916) 796-3118
Map Location: #2 (35 miles N.W. of Sacramento)

Toll-Free Number: (800) 452-8181
Restaurants: 1 Liquor: No
Other Games: BJ, P, BG (Thu-Mon), PGP, CSP

Casino Morongo
49750 Seminole Drive
Cabazon, California 92230
(909) 849-3080
Map Location: #3 (90 miles E. of Los Angeles)

Toll-Free Number: (800) 252-4499
Restaurants: 2 Liquor: Yes
Casino Size: 85,000 Square Feet
Other Games: BJ, P, CSP, BG

Cher-Ae Heights Casino
P.O. Box 635
Trinidad, California 95570
(707) 677-3611
Map Location: #4 (300 miles S.E. of Sacramento)

Toll-Free Number: (800) 684-BINGO
Restaurants: 1 Snack Bar   Liquor: No
Hours: 11am-2am/24 Hours (Wed-Sun)
Other Games: BJ, P, BG (Wed-Sun)

Chicken Ranch Bingo
16929 Chicken Ranch Road
Jamestown, California 95327
(209) 984-3000
Map Location: #5 (100 miles S.E. of Sacramento)

Toll-Free Number: (800) 752-4646
Restaurants: 1 Snack Bar   Liquor: No
Hours: 10am-10pm/1am (Thu-Sun)
Casino Size: 35,000 Square Feet
Other Games: Only Video Machines and Bingo

Chumash Casino
3400 Hwy. 246
Santa Ynez, California 93460
(805) 686-0855
Map Location: #13 (25 miles N.W. of Santa Barbara)

Toll-Free Number: (800) 728-9997
Restaurants: 1 Liquor: No
Hours: 10am-2am/24 Hours (Fri/Sat)
Other Games: BJ, P, Bingo (Wed/Fri-Sun)

Colusa Casino & Bingo
P.O. Box 1267
Colusa, California 95932
(916) 458-8844
Map Location: #6 (75 miles N. of Sacramento)

Toll-Free Number: (800) 655-U-WIN
Restaurants: 1 Snack Bar Liquor: No
Other Games: BJ, P, BG (Tue/Fri-Sun)

Elk Valley Casino
2500 Howland Hill Road
Crescent City, California 95531
(707) 464-1020
Map Location: #7 (84 miles N. of Eureka)

Restaurants: 1 Snack Bar Liquor: No
Other Games: BJ, P, BG
Special Features: Weekly poker, blackjack and video poker tournaments.

Fantasy Springs Casino
82-245 Indio Springs Drive
Indio, California 92203
(619) 342-5000
Map Location: #8 (125 miles E. of Los Angeles)

Toll-Free Number: (800) 827-2WIN
Restaurants: 2 (1 open 24 hours) Liquor: Yes
Other Games: BJ, P, CSP, BG, S

Havasu Landing Casino & Resort
P.O. Box 1976
Havasu Lake, California 92363
(619) 858-4593
Map Location: #18 (200 miles E. of Los Angeles)

Restaurants: 1 Liquor: Yes
Other Games: Video BJ
Special Features: Campground rentals (800) 307-3610. Mobile homes on lake available for daily rental (619) 858-5410.

Jackson Indian Bingo & Casino
12222 New York Ranch Road
Jackson, California 95642
(209) 223-1677
Map Location: #9 (60 miles S.E. of Sacramento)

Toll-Free Number: (800) 822-WINN
Restaurants: 1 Liquor: No
Other Games: BJ, P, PGP, CSP, BG

Palace Indian Gaming Center
P.O. Box 308
Lemoore, California 93245
(209) 924-7751
Map Location: #10 (50 miles S. of Fresno)

Toll-Free Number: (800) 942-6886
Restaurants: 1 Liquor: No
Hours: 10am-2am/24 Hours (Fri/Sat)
Casino Size: 17,500 Square Feet
Other Games: Video BJ, BG (Thu-Tue)

Robinson Rancheria Bingo & Casino
1545 E. Highway 20
Nice, California 95464
(707)275-9000
Map Location: #11 (100 miles N.W. of Sacramento)

Toll-Free Number: (800) 809-3636
Restaurants: 1 Liquor: No
Casino Size: 37,500 Square Feet
Other Games: BJ, P, BG (Wed-Sun)
Special Features: Weekly tournaments.

San Manuel Indian Bingo & Casino
5797 N. Victoria Avenue
San Bernardino, California 92346
(909) 864-5050
Map Location: #12 (65 miles E. of Los Angeles)

Toll-Free Number: (800) 359-BINGO
Restaurants: 2 Liquor: No
Casino Size: 75,000 Square Feet
Other Games: BJ, P, BG

Soboba Casino
2333 Soboba Road
San Jacinto, California 92583
(909) 654-2883
Map Location: #3 (90 miles E. of Los Angeles)

Toll-Free Number: (800) 618-7774
Restaurants: 1 Liquor: No
Other Games: BJ, P, PGP

Spa Casino
140 N. Indian Canyon Drive
Palm Springs, California 92262
(619) 323-5865
Map Location: #3 (115 miles E. of Los Angeles)

Toll-Free Number: (800) 258-2WIN
Room Reservations: (800) 854-1279
Rooms: 230 Price Range: $54-$114
Restaurants: 1 Liquor: Yes
Casino Size: 15,000 Square Feet
Other Games: BJ, P
Special Features: Hotel features hot mineral spa, massages and facials.

Spotlight 29 Casino
46200 Harrison Place
Coachella, California 92236
(619) 775-5566
Map Location: #8 (130 miles E. of Los Angeles)

Restaurants: 1 Liquor: Yes
Buffets: L-$3.95 D-$5.95
Other Games: BJ, P, CSP, BG

Sycuan Gaming Center
5469 Dehesa Road
El Cajon, California 92019
(619) 445-6066
Map Location: #14 (10 miles E. of San Diego)

Toll-Free Number: (800) 272-4646
Restaurants: 1 Liquor: No
Buffets: B-$1.99 L-$7.95 D-$6.95
Other Games: BJ, P, PGP, CSP, BG, S

Table Mountain Casino
8184 Table Mountain Road
Friant, California 93626
(209) 822-2485
Map Location: #15 (15 miles N. of Fresno)

Toll-Free Number: (800) 541-3637
Restaurants: 2 Liquor: No
Other Games: BJ, P, PGP, BG (Wed-Sun)

Viejas Casino & Turf Club
5000 Willows Road
Alpine, California 91901
(619) 445-5400
Map Location: #16 (25 miles E. of San Diego)

Toll-Free Number: (800) 847-6537
Restaurants: 2 Liquor: Yes
Buffets: B-$1.99 L-$4.95 D-$5.95
Other Games: BJ, B, P, PGP, CSP, BG, S

Win-River Casino
2100 Redding Rancheria Road
Redding, California 96001
(916) 243-3377
Map Location: #17 (163 miles N. of Sacramento)

Toll-Free Number: (800) 280-8946
Restaurants: 1 Snack Bar Liquor: No
Other Games: BJ, P, BG (Wed-Sun)

COLORADO

Colorado offers "limited gaming" in the mountain towns of Black Hawk, Central City and Cripple Creek. There are also two Indian casinos (which abide by Colorado's limited gaming rules) in Ignacio and Towaoc. Gambling is limited in two aspects: one, only electronic games (including slots, video poker, video blackjack and video keno) and the table games of poker and blackjack are allowed. Two, a single wager cannot exceed $5.

The rules for poker are such that a raise is considered a separate bet. Three raises per round are allowed. On the last round, two players may go "head-to-head" with an unlimited number of raises. Nine varieties of poker are approved for casino play. Texas Hold 'Em, 7-Card Stud and Omaha are the most popular choices.

Blackjack wagers are limited to a $5 maximum, with most casinos allowing a $2 or $3 minimum bet. However, doubles and splits are considered separate bets. Colorado casinos employ Vegas Strip rules and most allow doubling after splits. Since pairs may be split three times (to make up to four hands) it is theoretically possible to bet $40 on what began as a single $5 wager!

Multiple Action blackjack is also available in Colorado. Multiple action allows a player to place up to three bets (of up to $5 each) on a single blackjack hand. This hand is then played for three rounds against the same dealer up-card. Several Colorado casinos offer Multiple Action blackjack.

While bets are limited to $5, jackpots certainly are not. Colorado has Quartermania, which offers a linked progressive jackpot among many casinos in the three gaming towns. The Quartermania jackpot begins at $200,000. Megabucks, a linked $1 progressive, is also available in Colorado. The beginning jackpot on Megabucks machines is $1 million.

Here's information, as supplied by Colorado's Division of Gaming, showing the slot machine payback percentages for each city's casinos for the one year period from July 1, 1995 through June 30, 1995:

	Black Hawk	Central City	Cripple Creek
5¢ Slots	**90.88%**	89.76%	90.62%
25¢ Slots	**93.69%**	92.95%	93.23%
$1 Slots	94.44%	**95.11%**	94.51%
$5 Slots	94.53%	94.58%	**94.82%**
All Slots	**93.94%**	93.78%	93.56%

These numbers reflect the percentage of money returned on each denomination of machine and encompass all electronic machines including video poker and video keno. The best returns for each category are highlighted in bold print and you can see that Black Hawk offered the best returns on 5¢ and 25¢ machines. Central City returned the most on $1 machines and Cripple Creek offered the best return on $5 machines. Overall, Black Hawk returned the most on its machines, but only by a very slight margin.

The two major free gaming oriented magazines are the Colorado Gambler and the Rocky Mountain News Gaming Guide. Both are free, and available in most casinos in Colorado. Look in them for ads for casino coupons or fun books. The Denver Post Weekend section (published every Friday) also contains coupons and fun book offers for the casinos in Black Hawk and Central City.

Black Hawk

Map Location: #1 (35 miles west of Denver. Take U.S. 6 through Golden to Hwy 119. Take Hwy 119 to Black Hawk. Another route is I-70 West to exit 244. Turn right onto Hwy. 6. Take Hwy 6 to 119 and into Black Hawk.)

There are no hotel/casinos in Black Hawk. The nearest lodging is at Harvey's Wagon Wheel Casino, 3/4-mile up Gregory St. in Central City (see Central City listings for particulars). Another alternative is the Gold Dust Lodge, located on Hwy. 119 about 1.5 miles from Black Hawk casinos. The Gold Dust features 23 remodeled rooms with private baths, TV and telephones, starting at $55 per night.

The casinos in Black Hawk and Central City are located one mile apart. The Central City Tramway offers shuttle service between the two towns. The cost is 50¢ per ride (each way). Harrah's and Bullwhackers also provide free shuttle service between their casinos in each town.

There are bus tour programs (Ace Express, People's Choice) operating between Denver and Black Hawk/Central City. These tour programs are usually affiliated with one or two casinos that will reimburse a portion of the tour charge and provide coupons and fun books. The Colorado Central Station also sponsors bus service to its casino. All bus programs are bargain priced (less than $10) with casinos reimbursing most or all of the cost of the ride. Check the "Weekend" section of the Friday Denver Post and Rocky Mountain News for bus tour ads and for casino ads that feature coupons.

Most Black Hawk casinos have "captive" parking lots. Parking itself is free, but the parking ticket must be validated hourly. Failure to validate, or leaving the casino, will generate a parking fee of as high as $3 per hour. Black Hawk has a large public lot called Miner's Mesa. The parking fee is $5, which includes a free shuttle into town. Casinos occasionally run promotions which reimburse the $5 charge.

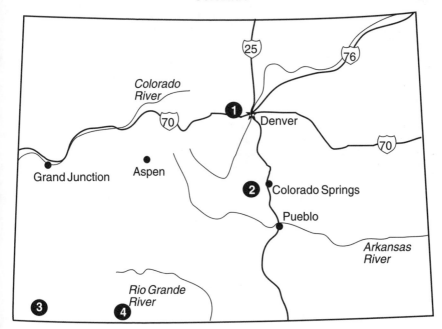

Black Hawk Station
141 Gregory Street
Black Hawk, Colorado 80422
(303) 582-5582

Restaurants: 1 (snack bar)
Other Games: Blackjack
Special Features: Live entertainment, free drinks for players, three-coin 25¢ video poker.

Bronco Billy's Sports Bar & Casino
125 Gregory Street
(303) 582-3311

Restaurants: 1
Other Games: Blackjack
Senior Discount: If 50, or older, every Wed get free lunch, prize drawings 10am-5pm
Special Features: Most ads include an offer for their fun book. Frequent sports related promotions. $2.95 complete prime rib dinner. 49¢ breakfast 8am-10am daily.

Bull Durham
110 Main Street
(303) 582-0810

Restaurants: 1 (snack bar)
Other Games: Blackjack
Fun Book: Coupons sometimes given at door
Special Features: Free drinks for $1 slot and table players.

Bullwhackers Black Hawk Casino
101 Gregory Street
(303) 764-1600

Toll-Free Number: (800) GAM-BULL
Restaurants: 1
Casino Size: 36,000 Square Feet
Other Games: Blackjack, Poker
Senior Discount: Tuesday get double points in slot club, plus $3.99 dinner specials
Special Features: Cash back slot club. Video arcade. Large, free parking (with validation) lot. Frequent in-casino promotions.

Bullwhackers Silver Hawk
100 Chase Street
(303) 764-1400

Toll-Free Number: (800) GAM-BULL
Restaurants: 1
Casino Size: 12,000 Square Feet
Other Games: Blackjack
Special Features: Cash back slot club. Video arcade. Large, free parking (with validation) lot. Frequent in-casino promotions. Italian restaurant with daily specials and personal pan pizzas.

Colorado Central Station Casino
340 Main Street
(303) 582-3000

Rooms: 5 Price: $55
Restaurants: 2
Other Games: Blackjack, Poker
Fun Book: Available through bus programs.
    Coupons sometimes handed out at door.
Special Features: Hotel rooms are bed &
breakfast. Free valet parking (with validation). Cash back slot club. Live entertainment. Burger King restaurant. Pizza and Mexican specialties. Frequent promotions.

Crook's Saloon & Casino
200 Gregory Street
(303) 582-5094

Restaurants: 1
Special Features: Free on-site parking (with
validation). Video arcade.

Eureka!
211 Gregory Street
(303) 582-1040

Restaurants: 1
Other Games: Blackjack
Fun Book: Coupons sometimes handed
        out at door
Special Features: 50¢ strawberry margarita.
$1 shrimp cocktail. Lucky Dragon Chinese
restaurant.

Fitzgeralds Casino
101 Main Street
(303) 582-6162

Toll-Free Number: (800) 538-5825
Restaurants: 1
Other Games: Blackjack, Poker
Special Features: Cash back slot club. Cov-
ered parking. Frequent in-casino promotions.

Gilpin Hotel Casino
111 Main Street
(303) 582-1133

Restaurants: 2
Other Games: Blackjack, Poker,
            Simulcast Racing
Casino Marketing: (303) 278-1114
Special Features: Live entertainment. Cash
back slot club. Closed-circuit showings of
sports events. Frequent slot tournaments. 200-
space lot offers free valet parking (with validation).

Gold Mine Casino
Highway 119
(303) 582-0711

Restaurants: 1
Other Games: Blackjack
Casino Size: 11,500 Square Feet
Casino Marketing: (303) 277-1055
Special Features: Cash back slot club. Free
parking (with validation).

Golden Gates Casino
261 Main Street
(303) 582-1650

Restaurants: 1 (snack bar)
Other Games: Blackjack
Special Features: Free valet parking (with
validation).

Gregory Street Casino
380 Gregory Street
(303) 582-1006

Restaurants: 1 (snack bar)
Other Games: Blackjack

Harrah's Black Hawk
131 Main Street
(303) 777-1111

Toll-Free Number: (800) HARRAHS
Restaurants: 1
Other Games: Blackjack
Special Features: Live entertainment. Free
on-site parking (with validation).

Jazz Alley Casino
321 Main Street
(303) 582-1125

Restaurants: 1
Buffet: Weekends only
Other Games: Blackjack
Special Features: Cash back slot club. Free
valet parking (with validation).

Otto's Casino at the Black Forest Inn
260 Gregory Street
(303) 642-0415

Restaurants: 2
Other Games: Blackjack
Senior Discount: Specials every Wed
Special Features: Free on-site parking (with
validation). Black Forest Inn offers fine dining. Daisy's Arcade is a self-contained video
arcade across the street from Otto's, featuring
video games and a snack bar. Frequent in-
casino promotions.

Red Dolly Casino
530 Gregory Street
(303) 582-1100

Restaurants: 1
Other Games: Blackjack
Special Features: Free on-site parking (with validation). 10 oz. top sirloin steak dinner for $2.49.

RichMan Casino
101 Richman Street
(303) 582-0400

Restaurants: 1 (snack bar)
Other Games: Blackjack
Special Features: Free valet parking (with validation).

Rohling Inn
160 Gregory Street
(303) 582-3063

Restaurants: 1
Special Features: Only open Fri-Sun, except during summer. Cash back slot club.

Silver Hawk Casino
Highway 119
(303) 582-3547

Restaurants: 1
Other Games: Blackjack
Special Features: Cash back slot club. Pizza & Pasta restaurant. Free parking (with validation).

Wild Card Saloon & Casino
112 Main Street
(303) 582-3412

Restaurants: 1 (snack bar)
Other Games: Blackjack
Special Features: Convenience store located in the casino.

Central City

Map location: #1 (same as Black Hawk). Central City is located one mile from Black Hawk. Turn left at the second stoplight on Hwy. 119 and proceed up Gregory Street.

Harvey's Wagon Wheel Hotel/Casino is the only hotel in the Black Hawk/Central City area. See Harvey's listing in this section for particulars. There are a few bed & breakfasts, including the Gregory Inn (7 rooms, $55-$155, 303-582-5561), Lee Mansion (4 rooms, $75-$125, 303-582-5517) and Central City Manor (3 rooms, $45-$65, 303-582-0752).

Some casinos (Teller House, Lady Luck) have captive parking lots. There are several small private parking lots in the immediate area. The parking fee is usually $5. Some casinos will reimburse this fee after a one-hour stay in their casino. Public Parking is provided via lots A, B, C and D. There is a $5 parking charge for the close-in A and B lots. Parking in the outlying lots is free, with free shuttle service to and from the casinos.

Central City is experimenting with a city-wide valet parking system. The fee is $5, which is reimbursed by several casinos.

Bullwhackers Central City Casino
130 Main Street
Central City, Colorado 80427
(303) 271-2500

Toll-Free Number: (800) GAM-BULL
Restaurants: 1
Buffets: L-$5.99 D-$5.99
Casino Size: 32,000 Square Feet
Other Games: Blackjack
Senior Discount: Monday get double points
              in slot club, plus $3.99 dinner specials
Fun Book: Given when you ride
              on Ace Express
Special Features: Slot club with cash back and member discounts. Frequent giveaways and in-casino promotions

Central Palace Casino
132 Lawrence Street
(303) 477-7117

Toll-Free Number: (800) 822-7466
Restaurants: 2
Other Games: Blackjack
Special Features: Full-service mesquite grill restaurant plus lunch & dinner buffet, snack bar and deli. Friday night "Seafood Extravaganza." Meeting facilities available.

Coyote Creek Casino
98 Lawrence Street
(303) 582-1900

Restaurants: 1
Other Games: Blackjack
Special Features: Exclusively single-deck blackjack. One single deck multi-action game. Video arcade. Gift shop.

Doc Holliday Casino
101 Main Street
(303) 582-1619

Restaurants: 1
Other Games: Blackjack
Special Features: Single-deck blackjack. Video arcade. Taco Bell Express restaurant.

Dostal Alley Saloon & Gaming Emporium
#1 Dostal Alley
(303) 582-1610

Restaurants: 1
Special Features: Valet parking (fee reimbursed by participating casinos).

Famous Bonanza/Lucky Strike
107 Main Street
(303) 582-5914

Restaurants: 1
Other Games: Blackjack, Poker
Special Features: Restaurant features Mexican specialities. Video arcade

Golden Rose Casino
102 Main Street
(303) 582-5060

Toll-Free Number: (800) 929-0255
Restaurants: 2
Buffet: L-$6.95 D-$7.95
Other Games: Blackjack

Harrah's Central City
131 Main Street
(303) 582-1171

Restaurants: 2
Other Games: Blackjack
Special Features: Live entertainment.

Harvey's Wagon Wheel Casino
321 Gregory Street
(303) 231-9200

Toll-Free Reservations: (800) HARVEYS
Rooms: 117 Price Range $65-$85
Suites: 10 Price Range $115-$125
Restaurants: 2
Other Games: Blackjack, Poker
Special Features: Live entertainment. Bar with lounge area. Tony Roma's restaurant. Cash back slot club. Frequent in-casino promotions, including hourly cash giveaways for slot club members. Live entertainment. The "Infinity Mine" collapses every 30 minutes. Bus program from several Denver locations. Free valet parking.

Lady Luck Casino
120 Main Street
(303) 582-1603

Restaurants: 1
Other Games: Blackjack
Special Features: Slot club with cash awards, occasional in-casino promotions. Special programs for seniors. Free parking (with validation). Free shuttle service to and from the Lady Luck's lot.

Papone's Palace Casino
118 Main Street
(303) 582-5820

Other Games: Blackjack
Special Features: 25¢ draft beer

Teller House Casino
120 Eureka Street
(303) 582-3200

Restaurants: 1
Special Features: Cash back slot club. Free parking (with validation).

Cripple Creek

Map Location: #2 (47 miles west of Colorado Springs. Take exit 141 at Colorado Springs off I-25. Go west on Hwy. 24 to the town of Divide. Turn left onto Hwy. 67 and go 18 miles to Cripple Creek.)

With 159 rooms and 45,000-square-feet of casino space the Double Eagle Hotel & Casino is Cripple Creek's newest and largest hotel/casino.

Cripple Creek has several other hotel/casinos. See the listings in this section for particulars. There is also a 67-room Holiday Inn Express, located 1/4-mile from the casinos, which offers a rate of $99 per night. Free shuttle service is provided to and from the casinos. For reservations, call 1-800-HOLIDAY.

Many Cripple Creek casinos hand out coupons and fun books at their doors. Also check the ads in the Colorado Springs Gazette Telegraph, the Pueblo Chieftain and the free tourist magazines.

The Cripple Creek Shuttle Service and Pueblo Shuttle service are two bus tour programs providing service from Colorado Springs to Cripple Creek. The Midnight Rose Hotel & Casino has its own shuttle service called the Ramblin' Express. Shuttle service fares are usually reimbursed by the casinos.

Most parking in Cripple Creek is either free or reimbursed by the casino. A few lots have validation systems similar to Black Hawk/Central City. Check at the lot for each particular casino's parking rules.

Aspen Mine & Casino
166 E. Bennett Avenue
Cripple Creek, Colorado 80813
(719) 689-0770

Restaurants: 2
Other Games: Blackjack
Fun Book: Coupons handed out at door
Special Features: Casino entrance features a two-story mock-up of a Colorado mine. Full-service Chinese restaurant and Subway Sandwich shop on 2nd floor. Live entertainment.

Black Diamond Casino
425 E. Bennett Avenue
(719) 689-2898

Restaurants: 1 (snack bar)
Fun Book: Look for ads in free magazines, coupons sometimes handed out at door
Special Features: $1 daily drink specials. 99¢ shrimp cocktail. Real gold vein in wall (upstairs).

Brass Ass Casino
264 E. Bennett Avenue
(719) 689-2104

Restaurants: 1 (snack bar)
Fun Book: Coupons handed out at door

Bronco Billy's Sports Bar & Casino
233 E. Bennett Avenue
(719) 689-2142

Restaurants: 2
Other Games: Blackjack
Fun Book: Most Bronco Billy's ads include an offer for their fun book
Special Features: Several TV screens tuned to sports all the time. 49¢ breakfast from 8am to 10pm. Full-service restaurant and Taco John's Express.

Colorado Grande Casino & Restaurant
300 E. Bennett Avenue
(719) 689-3517

Restaurants: 1
Special Features: Cash back slot club. Free parking (with validation).

Crapper Jack's Casino
404 E. Bennett Avenue
(719) 689-9467

Restaurants: 1
Special Features: Restaurant features rotisserie chicken specials.

Creeker's Casino
272 E. Bennett Avenue
(719) 689-3239

Restaurants: 1
Buffet: L-$5.95 D-$5.95
Other Games: Blackjack
Fun Book: Coupons handed out at door
Special Features: Cash back slot club.

Double Eagle Hotel & Casino
442 E. Bennett Avenue
(719) 689-7234

Toll-Free Reservations: (800) 711-7234
Rooms: 151 Price Range: $99-$119
Suites: 8   Price Range: $129-$159
Restaurants: 1
Other Games: Blackjack
Special Features: Cripple Creek's newest and largest hotel/casino. Valet parking. Meeting rooms available.

Gold Rush Hotel & Casino/Gold Digger's Casino
209 E. Bennett Avenue
(719) 689-2646

Toll-Free Number: (800) 235-8239
Rooms: 14 Price Range: $99-$109
Restaurants: 2
Other Games: Blackjack
Special Features: Gold Digger's and Gold Rush are adjacent properties interconnected to form one casino. Hotel is affiliated with Best Western. All rooms have TV, telephone and private bath. Golden Grille restaurant. Video arcade located next to casino.

Imperial Casino Hotel
123 N. Third Street
(719) 689-2922

Toll-Free Number: (800) 235-2922
Rooms: 27 Price Range: $45-$125
Suites: 2 Price Range: $100-$125
Restaurants: 2
Other Games: Blackjack
Fun Book: Coupons handed out at door
Special Features: 9 rooms available with private bath. Authentic Victorian melodrama runs through summer months in the Gold Bar Room Theatre. Live entertainment.

Independence Hotel & Casino
151 E. Bennett Avenue
(719) 689-2925

Rooms: 8 Price Range: $60-$80
Restaurants: 1
Special Features: All rooms have queen bed, private bath, and phone. Free parking (with validation).

Johnny Nolon's Casino
301 E. Bennett Avenue
(719) 689-2080

Restaurants: 3
Other Games: Blackjack
Fun Book: Look for ads in free magazines
Special Features: Full-service restaurant with nightly specials. Maxwell Street Deli and 1896-era ice cream parlor & soda fountain.

Jubilee Casino & Carnival
351 Myers Avenue
(719) 689-2519

Toll-Free Number: (800) WIN-HERE
Restaurants: 1
Casino Size: 15,075 Square Feet
Other Games: Blackjack, Poker
Fun Book: Look for ads in free magazines, coupons sometimes handed out at door
Special Features: Video arcade and children's carnival on second floor of casino.

Loose Caboose
400 E. Bennett Avenue
(719) 689-2935

Restaurants: 1

Lucky Lola's
251 E. Bennett Avenue
(719) 689-2994

Restaurants: 1

Maverick's Casino & Steak House/Glitter Gulch Casino
411 E. Bennett Avenue
(719) 689-2737

Restaurants: 2
Other Games: Blackjack
Fun Book: Coupon handed out at door
Special Features: Maverick's and Glitter Gulch are adjacent properties interconnected to form one casino. $4.99 complete steak dinner. 99¢ Bar-B-Que beef sandwich or hot dog at bar. Snack bar in Glitter Gulch. Cash and other bonuses for rare blackjack hands. Free parking.

Midnight Rose Hotel & Casino
256 E. Bennett Avenue
(719) 689-2865

Toll-Free Number: (800) 635-5825
Rooms: 19 Price Range: $89-$109
Restaurants: 2
Buffet: L-$5.95 D-$6.95
Other Games: Blackjack, Poker
Fun Book: Ask at cashier's cage
Special Features: All rooms have TV, phone and private bath. Wendy's, Pizza Hut and Baskin Robbins downstairs. Full-service restaurant (with daily specials) upstairs. Ramblin' Express shuttle service from Colorado Springs, Pueblo, Canon City and Castle Rock. $5 parking charge reimbursed after one-hour stay in casino.

Old Chicago Casino
419 E. Bennett Avenue
(719) 689-7880

Restaurants: 1
Other Games: Blackjack
Special Features: Cash back slot club. $2.95 soup & salad bar. Big screen TV's for sports watching. More than 50 varieties of beer. Video arcade. Free parking.

Palace Hotel & Casino
172 E. Bennett Avenue
(719) 689-2993

Rooms: 16 Price Range: $45-$70
Restaurants: 1
Other Games: Blackjack
Fun Book: Look for ads in free magazines
Special Features: 3 rooms available with private bath. $4.99 prime rib or rib eye steak dinner.

Silver Spur Casino
443 E. Bennett Avenue
(719) 689-2898

Restaurants: 1 Snack Bar
Special Features: Most Silver Spur ads include an offer for their free fun book. Also, ask at cashier's cage and mention this guide.

Treasure Mountain Casino
239 E. Bennett Avenue
(719) 689-3557

Restaurants: 1 (snack bar)
Fun Book: Coupons sometimes handed out at door

Virgin Mule
259 E. Bennett Avenue
(719) 689-2734

Restaurants: 1 (snack bar)

Womack's Golden Horseshoe Hotel & Casino
210-212 E Bennett Avenue
(719) 689-0333

Rooms: 8 Price Range: $62-$84
Restaurants: 1
Other Games: Blackjack
Fun Book: Coupons handed out at door
Special Features: 6 rooms available with private bath (no TV or telephone). Cash back slot club. Parking fee reimbursed by casino.

Ute Mountain Casino
3 Weeminuche Drive
Towaoc, Colorado 81334
(303) 565-8800
Map Location: #3 (425 miles S.W. of Denver, 11 miles S. of Cortez on Hwys. 160/666).

Toll-Free Number: (800) 258-8007
Restaurants: 1 Liquor: No
Buffets: L-$5.95 D-$6.95
Casino Size: 32,000 Square Feet
Hours: 8am-4am Daily
Other Games: Blackjack, Poker, Keno, Bingo (Fri-Tue)
Casino Marketing: (800) 258-8007
Fun Book: Given at local motels/RV parks
Special Features: 100-space RV park.

Indian Casinos

Sky Ute Lodge & Casino
Highway 172 North
Ignacio, Colorado 81137
(970) 563-3000
Map Location: #4 (345 miles S.W. of Denver; 20 miles S.E. of Durango).

Reservation Number: (800) 876-7017
Rooms: 36   Price Range: $45-$110
Restaurants: 2 Liquor: Yes
Buffets: B-$4.99/$8.99 (Sun) L-$5.99 D-$6.99/$8.99 (Fri)
Hours: 24 Hours Daily
Other Games: Blackjack, Poker, Keno, Bingo (Wed-Sun)
Casino Marketing: (800) 876-7017
Special Features: Liquor is not served in the casino, only in the restaurant.

CONNECTICUT

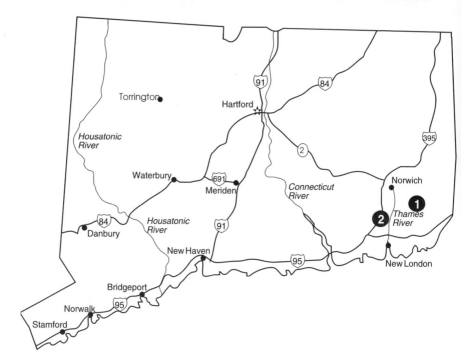

Foxwoods was New England's first casino. It is also the largest Indian casino in the United States and according to *Business Week* it is also "the most profitable gambling operation in the U.S., if not the world." The slot machines alone bring in more than $1.5 million a day in gross profit.

The Mashantucket Pequot Tribe which operates Foxwoods had to sue the state to allow the casino to open. They argued that since the state legally permitted "Las Vegas Nights," where low-stakes casino games were operated to benefit charities, then the tribe should be entitled to do the same. Eventually, they won their case before the U.S. Supreme Court and began construction of their casino which was financed by a Malaysian conglomerate (after 22 U.S. lenders turned down their loan requests).

When the casino first opened in February 1992, slot machines were not permitted. In January 1993 a deal was made between Governor Weicker and the Pequots which gave the tribe the exclusive right to offer slot machines in return for a yearly payment of $100 million, or 25% of the gross slot revenue - whichever is greater. The agreement was subject to cancellation, however, if the state allowed slot machines anywhere else in Connecticut.

In early 1994 the Mohegan tribe signed a compact with the state that allows it to offer casino gambling at its reservation in Uncasville (map location #2). The Pequots gave permission for the Mohegans to have slot machines in their casino and in return the state lowered the Pequots yearly payment requirements to $80 million, or 25% of the gross revenue - whichever is greater. The same payment schedule also applies to the Mohegans. The payment schedules are subject to cancellation, however, if the state legalizes any other form of casino gambling. The Mohegan casino opened in October 1996.

For those interested in the payback on Foxwoods' slot machines, we offer the following information from Connecticut's Division of Special Revenue regarding slot payback percentages for the fiscal year ending June 30, 1996:

Denomination	PAYBACK
25¢	91.1%
50¢	92.0%
$1.00	92.9%
$5.00	94.3%
$10.00	95.2%
$25.00	95.4%
$100.00	95.6%

These figures reflect the total percentages returned by each denomination of slot machine from July 1, 1995 through June 30, 1996. Foxwoods' total win on its slot machines during that year was slightly more than $594 million and of that amount 25%, or about $148.5 million, was paid to the state.

Keep in mind that the casino does not pay any tax on its table games and, therefore, it is not required to report the profits on that part of its operation. A rough estimate of the table game wins, however, is possible.

Since the average casino generates about 65% of its profits from its slot machines, it can be estimated that Foxwoods' total combined (slots and table games) win is about $915 million. After subtracting the slot winnings of $594 million this leaves a table games win of about $321 million.

The minimum gambling age at both properties is 18 for bingo and 21 for the casino. Both casinos are also open 24 hours.

The games offered at Foxwoods are: blackjack, craps, roulette, baccarat, mini-baccarat, big six wheel, bingo, poker, pai gow poker, Caribbean Stud Poker, keno, pull tabs, red dog and chuck-a-luck. There is also a simulcast facility with pari-mutuel betting.

Foxwoods Resort Casino
Route 2
Ledyard, Connecticut 06339
(860) 885-3000
Map Location: #1 (45 miles S.E. of Hartford; 12 miles N. of I-95 at Mystic). From I-95 take exit 92 to Rt. 2-West, casino is 7 miles ahead. From I-395 take exit 79A to Rt. 2A follow to Rt. 2-East, casino is 2 miles ahead.

Toll-Free Number: (800) PLAY-BIG
Reservation Number: (800) FOXWOODS
Rooms: 592   Price Range: $175-$250
Suites: 108   Price Range: $200-$525
Restaurants: 10 (2 open 24 hours)
Buffets: B-$4.99 L-$10.95 D-$10.95
Casino Size: 139,000 Square Feet
Casino Marketing: (800) 99-SLOTS
Special Features: Two hotels with pool, spa, health club and beauty salon. Turbo Ride: a 48-seat computer-controlled large-screen-movie adventure ride. Cinedrome: a 360-degree theater and nightclub. 1,500-seat theatrical showroom with musical revues and headliner entertainment. Gift shops. "Wampum Card" earns complimentaries for players.

The games offered at Mohegan Sun are: blackjack, craps, roulette, baccarat, mini-baccarat, big six wheel, bingo, poker, pai gow poker, Caribbean Stud Poker and keno.

Mohegan Sun Casino
Mohegan Sun Boulevard
Uncasville, Connecticut 06382
(860) 848-5677

Toll-Free Number: (888) 226-7711
Restaurants: 20 (2 open 24 hours)
Buffets: B-$5.95 L-$9.95 D-$9.95
Casino Size: 150,000 Square Feet
Casino Marketing: (888) 99-SLOTS
Special Features: Restaurants include three fine dining, a New York-style deli, a buffet, a coffee shop and a food court with specialty food outlets. 6,000-square-foot Kid's Quest-supervised children's activity center.

DELAWARE

Delaware's three pari-mutuel facilities all offer slot machines. The machines first went into operation on December 29, 1995.

Technically, the machines are video lottery terminals (VLT's) because they are operated in conjunction with the Delaware Lottery. Unlike VLT's in other states, however, Delaware's machines pay out in cash. The VLT's also play other games including: video poker, video keno and video blackjack. The minimum gambling age is 21.

According to figures from the Delaware Lottery for the seven month period from January 1, 1996 through July 28, 1996 the VLT's at Delaware Park returned 92.0% while the VLT's at Dover Downs returned 90.2%. No figures were available for the Midway Slots location when this book went to press.

Delaware Park
777 Delaware Park Boulevard
Stanton, Delaware 19804
(302) 994-2521
Map Location: #1

Hours: 8am-2am/1pm-2am (Sun)
Special Features: Live thoroughbred racing. Simulcasting.

Dover Downs
1131 N. Dupont Highway
Dover, Delaware 19901
(302) 674-4600
Map Location: #2

Toll-Free Number: (800) 441-7223
Hours: 8am-2am/1pm-2am (Sun)
Special Features: Live harness racing from November through April. Daily simulcasting.

Midway Slots & Simulcast
P.O. Box 310
Delaware State Fairgrounds
U.S. 13 South
Harrington, Delaware 19952
(302) 398-4920
Map Location: #3 (20 miles S. of Dover)

Toll-Free Number: (888) 88-SLOTS
Hours: 8am-2am/1pm-2am (Sun)
Special Features: Live harness racing from early September through early November at Harrington Raceway. Daily simulcasting.

FLORIDA

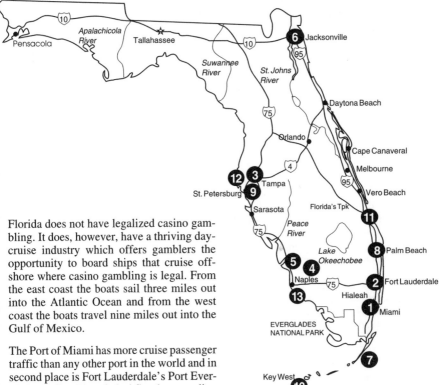

Florida does not have legalized casino gambling. It does, however, have a thriving day-cruise industry which offers gamblers the opportunity to board ships that cruise offshore where casino gambling is legal. From the east coast the boats sail three miles out into the Atlantic Ocean and from the west coast the boats travel nine miles out into the Gulf of Mexico.

The Port of Miami has more cruise passenger traffic than any other port in the world and in second place is Fort Lauderdale's Port Everglades. In Port Everglades' fiscal year ending September 30, 1995, there were 2.2 million cruise passenger boardings. Of that amount 1.4 million - or almost 64% - were boardings on the daily gambling cruise ships.

There are a variety of boats in operation ranging from the 1,300-passenger Discovery cruise ship all the way down to the yacht-sized SunCruz Casino boat in Key Largo which carries 150 passengers.

Generally, you will find that the larger ships have more of a variety of things to do besides the gambling, but the cost will be a little higher because of added port/service charges. All of the ships that sail from the major ports, such as Port Everglades and the Port of Miami, will add port/service charges to the quoted cruise price. Usually, there is also a charge to park your car at those locations. Since late 1994 many smaller ships have

begun operations and because they don't dock at the large ports they usually don't have port/service charges added to their cruise prices. Also, most of them offer free parking. You will find that almost all of the ships (especially in the Miami/Ft. Lauderdale area) are constantly running price specials so don't be surprised if you call and are quoted a price lower than the regular brochure rates listed here.

All ships offer: slots, video poker, blackjack, craps, roulette and Caribbean Stud Poker. Some casinos also offer: baccarat (B), mini-baccarat (MB), sports book (SB), poker (P), Pai Gow Poker (PGP), Let It Ride (LIR), bingo (BG) and the big 6 wheel (B6). Each boat sets its own minimum gambling age; on some boats it is 21 and on others it's 18.

The nearest Caribbean casinos are in the Bahamas. There are two in Grand Bahama: Bahamas Princess Resort & Casino (800) 223-1818 and Lucayan Beach Resort & Casino (800) 772-1226. The two casinos share a jet charter service which operates two flights daily from the Fort Lauderdale airport. One flight leaves at 9am and returns at 5:15pm. The other flight leaves at 6:30pm and returns at 12:45am. Grand Bahama Island is 90 miles from Fort Lauderdale and the flight takes 20 minutes. The cost is $49 (plus departure taxes of $43) and includes $20 in matchplay money, round-trip taxi transportation and a $10 food credit. Look in the coupon section in the back of this book for a special 2-for-1 offer from the Lucayan Beach Resort & Casino.

The other two casinos are in the Bahamian capital of Nassau which is on New Providence Island: Nassau Marriott Resort & Crystal Palace Casino (800) 222-7466 and Atlantis, Paradise Island (800) 321-3000. Technically, Atlantis is on Paradise Island and not in Nassau because you have to cross a bridge in downtown Nassau to get to the property.

There is daily scheduled jet service on several airlines to the Nassau airport from both Miami and Fort Lauderdale. Nassau is 150 miles from Miami and the flying time is 45 minutes. Additionally, USAir Express has several daily prop-plane flights to the Paradise Island airport from Miami and Fort Lauderdale. Flying time is one hour to Paradise Island.

Fort Lauderdale

Map Location: #2

Discovery Cruise Line
1850 Eller Drive
Port Everglades, Florida 33316
(954) 525-7800

Reservation Number: (800) 93-SHIPS
Gambling Age: 18
Ship's Registry: Panama
Food Service: Buffet Included
Schedule:
Bahamas Cruises
7:45am - 11:00pm (M/W/Sun)
6:45am - 8:30pm (Fri)

Other Cruises
10:00am - 4:30pm (Tu/Th/Sat)
7:15pm - 12:15am (Tu/Th/Sat)
10:45pm - 3:00am (Fri)
1:15am - 5:15am (Sat)
Prices:
Bahamas Cruises
Adult $99.99 (Fri)/$129.99 (Sun/M/W)
Sen'r $69.99 (Fri)/$79.99(Sun/M/W)
Child $10.00 (Fri)/$39.99(Sun/M/W)

Day Cruises
Adult $49.99
Sen'r $49.99
Child $ 5.00

Dinner Cruises
Adult $49.99 (Tu/Th)/$59.99 (Sat)
Sen'r $39.99 (Tu/Th)/$59.99 (Sat)
Child $29.99 (Tu/Th/Sat)

Late Night Cruises
Adult $29.99 (Fri)
Adult $19.99 (Sat)
Service Charges: Bahamas-$49, Others-$19
Parking: $7.00
Other Games: P, BG
Special Features: 1,300-passenger *Discovery Dawn* sails from Port Everglades in Fort Lauderdale. Seven course dinner upgrade available. Bahamas "Cruise 'n Stay" hotel packages available. Private cabin rentals available. Bahamas cruise is to Freeport.

Maxamillion Casino Cruises
Bahia Mar Yachting Center
Fort Lauderdale, Florida 33316
(954) 462-0246 or (888) PLAY-MAX

EXPECTED TO OPEN BY EARLY 1997

Monte Carlo Casino Cruiser
101 N. Riverside Drive, Suite-210
Pompano Beach, Florida 33062
(954) 785-5100

Reservation Number: (954) 781-7810
Gambling Age: 21
Ship's Registry: U.S.A.
Food Service: A la Carte Snack Bar
Schedule:
11:30am - 4:30pm (Mon-Fri)
12:00pm - 5:00pm (Sat/Sun)
7:30pm - 12:30am (Sun-Thu)
7:30pm - 1:30am (Fri/Sat)

Price: $14.95 Day/$19.95 Evening
Port Charges: None
Other Games: MB
Parking: Free
Special Features: 400-passenger, 2-deck *Monte Carlo* departs from Sands Harbor Hotel/Marina/Restaurant on A1A and Atlantic Blvd. in Pompano Beach. Free hors d'ouevres. Live entertainment. Must be 21 or older.

SeaEscape
140 S. Federal Highway
Dania, Florida 33004
(954) 925-9700

Reservation Number: (800) 327-2005
Gambling Age: 18
Ship's Registry: Bahamas
Food Service: Buffet Included
Schedule:
   Bahamas Cruises
   8:00am - 9:15pm (Sun)
   8:00am - 9:30pm (M/W)
   7:00am - 7:00pm (Fri)

   Other Cruises
   10:00am - 4:00pm (Tu/Th/Sat)
   7:30pm - 12:30am (Tu/Th)
   10:30pm - 3:00am (Fri)
   8:00pm - 1:30am (Sat)

Prices:
   Bahamas Cruises
   Adult $99.00 (Fri)
   Child $39.00 (Fri)

   Adult $119.00 (Sun/M/W)
   Child $39.00 (Sun/M/W)

   Day Cruises
   Adult $49.00
   Child Free

   Dinner Cruises
   Adult $39.00 (Tu/Th)
   Child $39.00 (Tu/Th)

   Adult $49.00 (Sat)
   Child $49.00 (Sat)

   Late Night Cruise
   Adult $29.00 (Fri)
   Child $29.00 (Fri)
Port Charges: Bahamas-$49, Others-$19
Parking: $7
Other Games: B, P, PGP, BG, SB,
            Super Pan, Aruba Rum 32
Special Features: 900-passenger *Ukraina* sails

from Port Everglades in Fort Lauderdale. Children under 12 pay only port charges ($19) on day cruises (one per full-fare paying adult). Full-service dinner upgrade available. Bahamas "Land and Sea" hotel packages available. Private cabin rentals available. Bahamas cruise is to Freeport.

SunCruz Casino Hollywood
647 E. Dania Beach Blvd.
Dania, Florida 33004
(954) 929-3800

Reservation Number: (800) 474-DICE
Gambling Age: 18
Ship's Registry: U.S.A.
Food Service: A la Carte Snack Bar
Schedule:
   11:30am - 4:30pm (Mon-Fri)
   12:00pm - 5:00pm (Sat/Sun)
   7:30pm - 12:30am (Sun-Thu)
   7:30pm - 1:30am (Fri/Sat)
Price: $10
Port Charges: None
Parking: Free
Other Games: MB, P, SB, LIR, Lotto
Special Features: 600-passenger, 3-deck boat departs from Martha's Restaurant on A1A in Hollywood. Free hors d'ouevres served on boat. One free drink included with admission. Must be 18 or older.

Vegas Express Cruise Lines
336 E. Dania Beach Blvd.
Dania, Florida 33004
(954) 927-8473

Reservation Number: (800) 9-VEGAS-9
Gambling Age: 21
Ship's Registry: U.S.A.
Food Service: A la Carte Snack Bar
Schedule:
   10:30am - 4:00pm (Tue-Fri)
   11:00am - 4:30pm (Sat/Sun)
   7:00pm - 12:30am (Sun-Thu)
   7:00pm - 1:00am (Fri/Sat)
Price: $10
Port Charges: None
Parking: Free
Fun Book: Only to groups
Other Games: B, P, SB, LIR
Special Features: 375-passenger *Vegas Express* sails from behind Tugboat Annie's Restaurant in Dania. $5 walk-up fee added at ticket window for passengers without a reservation. Must be 18 or older.

Fort Myers

Map Location: #5 (40 miles N. of Naples)

Europa SeaKruz
645 San Carlos Blvd.
Ft. Myers Beach, Florida 33931
(941) 463-5000

Reservation Number: (800) 688-PLAY
Gambling Age: 21
Ship's Registry: Panama
Food Service: Included
Schedule: 10:00am - 4:00pm (M-Sat)
            11:00am - 5:30pm (Sun)
            6:30pm -12:30am (M-Th)
            6:30pm - 1:00am (F/Sat)
            7:00pm -12:30am (Sun)
Prices: $27/$32 (Fri/Sat)
Port Charges: None   Parking: Free
Other Games: BG, Lotto, Oasis Stud Poker
Special Features: 340-passenger *Europa Star*
sails from Snug Harbor on Fort Myers Beach.
Price includes buffet on day cruises and sit-
down dinner on evening cruises. Children 4 to
12 sail for $12; kids 3 or younger are free.

Fort Pierce

Map Location: #11 (60 miles N. of Palm
Beach)

Princess Yacht Lines
Port of Fort Pierce
Fort Pierce, Florida 34982
(561) 462-1732

SCHEDULED TO OPEN BY EARLY 1997

Jacksonville

Map Location: #6

La Cruise Casino
4738 Ocean Street
Atlantic Beach, Florida 32233
(904) 241-7200

Reservation Number: (800) 752-1778
Gambling Age: 18
Ship's Registry: Panama
Food Service: A la Carte Snack Bar
Schedule: 11:00am - 4:00pm (Tu-Th/Sat)
            1:00pm - 6:00pm (Sun)
            7:00pm -12:00am (Tu-Sat)
Price: $18

Port Charges: None   Parking: Free
Other Games: P, SB, P, B6
Special Features: 450-passenger *La Cruise*
sails from Mayport Village. $10 seafood
buffet offered in land-based pavilion on every
cruise. All passengers must be 18 or older.

Key Largo

Map Location: #7 (50 miles S. of Miami)

SunCruz Casino Key Largo
99701 Overseas Highway
Key Largo, Florida 33037
(305) 451-0000

Reservation Number: (800) 843-5397
Gambling Age: 18
Ship's Registry: U.S.A.
Food Service: A la Carte Snack Bar
Schedule:
    Departs   2:00pm (daily)
    Shuttle   5:00pm (daily)
    Shuttle   7:00pm (daily)
    Shuttle   9:00pm (daily)
    Shuttle   11:00pm (daily)
    Shuttle   12:30am (F/Sat)
    Returns   2:00am (Sun-Th)
    Returns   3:00am (F/Sat)
Prices: $7 (2 and 5pm), $11 (7:00 or later)
Port Charges: None   Parking: Free
Other Games: SB, Lotto
Senior Discount: 2-for-1, if 55 or older
Special Features: 150-passenger yacht de-
parts from Key Largo's Holiday Inn. The boat
stays offshore and a water taxi shuttles pas-
sengers back and forth according to the above
schedule. Free hors d'ouevres served on boat.
One free drink included with admission. Chil-
dren under 7 are free; 8 and older pay full fare.

Key West

Map Location: #10 (90 miles S. of Miami)

Dixie Duck Showboat & Casino
631 Greene Street
Key West, Florida 33040
(305) 294-3004

Reservation Number: (305) 294-3004
Gambling Age: 18
Ship's Registry: U.S.A.
Food Service: A la Carte Snack Bar
Schedule: 7:00pm - 10:30pm (Daily)

Price: $15/$19.95 (Nov-June)
Port Charges: None   Parking: Free
Other Games: No Video Poker
Special Features: 200-passenger *Dixie Duck* sails from Conch Harbor. Fare includes $5 table match play coupon and free draft beer or wine during casino hours. All passengers must be 18 or older.

Marco Island

Map Location: #13 (15 miles S. of Naples)

Casino Cruises
P.O. Box 2027
Marco Island, Florida 34146

Reservation Number: (800) 310-5665
Gambling Age: 21
Ship's Registry: U.S.A.
Food Service: A la Carte Snack Bar
Schedule: 10:00am - 4:00pm (Daily)
            6:00pm -12:00am (Daily)
Price: $18
Port Charges: None   Parking: Free
Other Games: P, BG
Special Features: 350-passenger *Royal Princess* sails from pier 81 on Marco Island. All passengers must be 21 or older.

Miami

Map Location: #1

Discovery Cruise Line
Port of Miami
Miami, Florida
(305) 525-7800

Reservation Number: (800) 93-SHIPS
Gambling Age: 18
Ship's Registry: Panama
Food Service: Buffet Included
Schedule:

Bahamas Cruises
8:00am - 11:00pm (M/Tu/Th)
6:45am - 8:30pm (F/Sat)

Other Cruises
10:00am - 4:30pm (Wed)
10:00am - 3:00pm (Sun)
7:15pm - 12:15am (Wed)
4:30pm - 8:30am (Sun)
10:00pm - 2:45am (Fri)
10:00pm - 2:45am (Sat)

Prices:
Bahamas Cruises
Adult $99.99 (Fri/Sat)
Sen'r $69.99 (Fri/Sat)
Child $10.00 (Fri/Sat)

Adult $129.99 (M/Tu/Th)
Sen'r $ 79.99 (M/Tu/Th)
Child $ 39.99 (M/Tu/Th)

Day Cruises
Adult $49.99
Sen'r $49.99
Child $ 5.00

Dinner Cruises
Adult $49.99
Sen'r $39.99
Child $29.99

Late Night Cruises
Adult $39.99
Sen'r $39.99
Child $29.99
Service Charges: Bahamas-$49, Others-$19
Parking: $8
Other Games: P, BG
Special Features: 1,000-passenger *Discovery Sun* sails from the Port of Miami. Seven course dinner upgrade available. Bahamas "Cruise 'n Stay" hotel packages available. Private cabin rentals available. Bahamas cruise is to Freeport.

Europa SeaKruz
300 Alton Road, Pier A
Miami Beach, Florida 33139
(305) 538-8300

Reservation Number: (800) 688-PLAY
Gambling Age: 21
Ship's Registry: Panama
Food Service: Buffet (extra charge)
Schedule & Prices:
  1:30pm - 5:30pm (M-F) $19.95
  12:30pm - 5:30pm (Sat/Sun) $19.95
  7:30pm -11:30am (Sun-Th) $19.95
  7:30pm -12:30am (F/Sat) $24.95
Port Charges: None   Parking: Free
Other Games: MB, P, SB, LIR, BG, Lotto
Special Features: 350-passenger *Europa Sun* sails from Miami Beach Marina. Optional lunch buffet is $5, dinner buffet is $9. $20 in casino play rebated to each paying customer on all cruises ($10 in slot tokens and $10 in table game matchplay). Must be 21 or older to sail.

Tropicana Casino Cruises
905 S. America Way
Miami, Florida 33132
(305) 447-9999

Reservation Number: (800) 965-3999
Gambling Age: 21
Ship's Registry: Bahamas
Food Service: Buffet (extra charge)
Schedule:
    11:00am - 4:00pm (Sat/Sun)
    7:30pm - 12:00am (Wed/Thu)
    7:30pm - 1:00am (Fri/Sat)
    6:00pm - 11:30pm (Sun)
Price: $10
Port Charges: None   Parking: $8
Other Games: MB, BG
Special Features: 650-passenger *M/V Tropicana* sails from the Port of Miami. Children 12 and younger sail for free (except port charges) on all cruises. Optional lunch or dinner buffet is $10. Sunday brunch is $15. Children pay same fare as adult.

Palm Beach

Map Location: #8

Palm Beach Cruise Line
157 E. Port Road
Riviera Beach, Florida 33404
(407) 845-7447

Reservation Number: (800) 841-7447
Gambling Age: 18
Ship's Registry: Panama
Food Service: Meals Included
Schedule & Prices:
    Bahamas Cruise
    8:30am -12:00am (Tu/Th) $79
    8:30am -12:00am (Sat) $89
    Coastal Cruises
    10:00am - 4:00pm (Mon/Wed) $39
    10:00am - 4:00pm (Fri) $39
    11:00am - 5:00pm (Sun) $49
    7:00pm -12:00am (Mon/Wed) $39
    7:00pm - 1:00am (Fri) $49
Port Charges: Bahamas-$36, Others-$15
Parking: $5
Other Games: P
Special Features: 620-passenger *Viking Princess* sails from the Port of Palm Beach. Private cabin rentals available. "Bahamas Great Escapes" hotel packages available. Bahamas cruise sails to Freeport.

Port Richey

Map Location: #12 (23 miles N.W. of Tampa)

SunCruz Casino Port Richey
7917 Bayview Avenue
Port Richey, Florida 34668
(813) 848-3423

Reservation Number: (800) 464-DICE
Gambling Age: 18
Ship's Registry: U.S.A.
Food Service: Ala Carte Snack Bar
Schedule: 11:00am - 5:00pm (Daily)
             7:00pm - 12:00am (Daily)
Price: $5
Port Charges: None   Parking: Free
Other Games: P, SB, LIR
Special Features: 350-passenger, 3-deck boat departs from Hooter's Restaurant. $5 in table matchplay given to all paying passengers. Must be 18 or older.

St. Petersburg

Map Location: #9

Empress Cruise Lines
450 34th Street North
St. Petersburg, Florida 33713
(813) 895-3325

Reservation Number: (800) 486-8600
Gambling Age: 18
Ship's Registry: U.S.A.
Food Service: Buffet Included
Schedule & Prices:
    11:00am - 5:00pm (Daily) $26.00
    7:00pm -12:00am (Sun-Th) $26.00
    7:00pm - 1:00am (Fri) $26.00
    7:00pm - 1:00am (Sat) $38.00
Port Charges: None   Parking: Free
Other Games: SB
Special Features: 470-passenger *Majestic Empress* sails from Kingfish Wharf at John's Pass on Treasure Island. Children 3 to 12 sail for $13 on any cruise; 2 or younger are free.

Empress Cruise Lines
198 Seminole Street
Clearwater, Florida
(813) 895-3325

Reservation Number: (800) 486-8600
Gambling Age: 18
Ship's Registry: U.S.A.
Food Service: Buffet Included

Schedule & Prices:
  10:30am - 4:30pm (Daily) $26.00
  6:30pm -11:30am (Sun-Th) $26.00
  6:30pm -12:30am (Fri) $26.00
  6:30pm -12:30am (Sat) $38.00
Port Charges: None   Parking: Free
Other Games: SB
Senior Discount: 55 or older pay $10 for
                 Mon-Fri day cruises or
                 Sun,Mon,Tue,Thu eves
Special Features: 470-passenger *Crown Empress* sails from Clearwater Bay Marina. Children 3 to 12 sail for $13 on any cruise; 2 or younger are free.

Europa SeaKruz
150 153rd Avenue
Madeira Beach, Florida 33708
(813) 393-5110

Reservation Number: (800) 688-PLAY
Gambling Age: 21
Ship's Registry: U.S.A.
Food Service: Buffet Included
Schedule & Prices:
  10:00am - 4:00pm (M-F) $39.95
  11:00am - 5:00pm (Sat/Sun) $39.95
  6:30pm -12:00am (Sun-W) $39.95
  6:30pm -12:30am (Th) $39.95
  6:30pm - 1:00am (Fri/Sat) $49.95
  1:15am - 6:15am (Sat) $39.95
Service Charge: $15
Parking: $3
Other Games: MB, P, SB, BG, Lotto
Fun Book: Only offered to groups
Senior's Discount: Offered periodically. Ask for details.
Special Features: 439-passenger Europa Sky sails from John's Pass Village in Madeira Beach. Weekend day cruises offer free onboard child care.

Indian Casinos

Florida has four Indian gaming locations. The Seminoles have three and the fourth is on the Miccosukee reservation. As of September 1996 the only games permissible at these locations were bingo, video pull tabs and low-limit poker games with a maximum pot of $10. There is no compact in effect and the state has gone to court to shut down the Indian gaming operations.

In turn, the Seminole tribe has made a formal appeal to U. S. Secretary of the Interior Bruce Babbitt to allow full-scale casino gambling on their reservations.

All Indian casinos offer high-stakes bingo, video pull tabs and poker games with a maximum pot of $10. All are open 24 hours and the minimum gambling age is 18.

Miccosukee Indian Gaming
500 S.W. 177 Avenue
Miami, Florida 33194
(305) 222-4600
Map Location: #1

Toll-Free Number: (800) 741-4600
Restaurants: 2 (1 open 24 hours)
Liquor: Yes
Special Features: Live entertainment and dancing nightly in Cypress Lounge. Pay-per-view boxing events shown free of charge.

Seminole Poker Casino
4150 N. State Road 7
Hollywood, Florida 33021
(954) 961-3220
Map Location: #2 (5 miles S. of Fort Lauderdale)

Toll-Free Number: (800) 323-5452
Restaurants: 1 Snack Bar Liquor: No

Seminole Indian Casino
5223 N. Orient Road
Tampa, Florida 33610
(813) 621-1302
Map Location: #3

Toll-Free Number: (800) 282-7016
Restaurants: 1 Cafeteria Liquor: No

Seminole Indian Casino
506 South 1st Street
Imokalee, Florida 33934
(941) 658-1313
Map Location: #4 (35 miles N.E. of Naples)

Toll-Free Number: (800) 218-0007
Restaurants: 2 (1 open 24 hours)
Liquor: Yes
Special Features: No Bingo on Mon and Tues

GEORGIA

There are two gambling cruise ship operations in Georgia and both sail three miles out into international waters where casino gambling is permitted.

Atlantic Star Cruise Lines
P.O. Box 2117
Tybee Island, Georgia 31328
(912) 786-7827
Map Location: #2 (20 miles E. of Savannah)

Reservation Number: (912) 786-7827
Gambling Age: 21
Ship's Registry: U.S.
Buffets: Included
Schedule & Prices:
   1:00pm - 5:30pm (Sat/Sun) $24.00
   7:00pm - 11:30pm (Sun-Th) $24.00
   7:00pm - 11:30pm (F/Sat) $35.00
Port Charges: None   Parking: Free
Games Offered: Blackjack, Craps, Slots
Special Features: 100-passenger *Atlantic Star* sails from Lazaretto Creek Marina on Tybee Island. No one under 21 permitted to board.

Golden Isles Cruise Lines
One St. Andrews Court
Brunswick, Georgia 32034
(912) 265-3558
Map Location: #1 (75 miles S. of Savannah)

Reservation Number: (800) 842-0115
Gambling Age: 18
Ship's Registry: Panama
Buffets: Included
Schedule & Prices:
   11:00am - 4:00pm (Sat) $19.96
   1:00pm - 6:00pm (Sun) $35.00
   7:00pm - 12:00am (Tue-Thu) $25.00
   7:00pm - 1:00am (Fri/Sat) $35.00
Port Charges: None   Parking: Free
Games Offered: Blackjack, Craps, Roulette, Caribbean Stud Poker, Let It Ride, Slots
Special Features: 350-passenger *Emerald Princess* sails from Brunswick Landing Marina. Children only permitted on day cruises, they must be 8 or older and pay full fare.

ILLINOIS

Illinois was the second state to legalize riverboat casinos. There are 10 licenses issued for the entire state, but each licensee is allowed to have up to two boats. Riverboat casinos began operating in September 1991 with the launching of the first boat, the Alton Belle.

Most cruises begin boarding 1/2-hour before departure time and disembark within 1/2-hour after returning. The casino opens when boarding begins and remains open after docking until everyone disembarks. This allows a maximum gambling time, on most boats, of three hours. If, due to bad weather, the boat does not cruise then a dockside gaming session is held and the same admission charges (if any) apply. By state law no one is allowed to enter the casino 1/2-hour after gaming begins. This means that even if the boat is not leaving the dock, you must arrive prior to the scheduled departure time or you will not be permitted to board. Be aware that most boats will require you to have advance reservations on weekends and holidays so be sure to call ahead and ask about their policy before going to the boat.

For those interested in which casinos provide the best returns on their slot machines we offer the following statistics from the Illinois Gaming Board for the 1995 calendar year beginning January 1, 1995 and ending December 31, 1995:

CASINO	PAYBACK
Casino Queen	94.4%
Grand Victoria	94.2%
Empress	94.0%
Harrah's	94.0%
Hollywood	94.0%
Alton Belle	93.9%
Rock Island	93.0%
Par-A-Dice	92.6%
Silver Eagle	92.0%
Players	91.0%

These figures reflect the total percentages returned by each casino for all of their slot machines. As you can see, the Casino Queen returned the most to its slot machine players, while Players Riverboat returned the least. Although these numbers are only for 1995, they pretty much remain the same from year-to-year with Casino Queen at the top, Players Riverboat at the bottom and the others somewhere in between.

Unless otherwise noted, all casinos offer: slots, video poker, big six wheel, blackjack, craps, roulette and Caribbean Stud Poker. Some casinos also offer: Let It Ride (LIR), baccarat (B), mini-baccarat (MB) and video keno (VK). The minimum gambling age is 21.

Alton Belle Riverboat Casino
219 Piasa Street
Alton, Illinois 62002
(618) 474-7500
Map Location: #1 (260 miles S.W. of Chicago. 25 miles N. of St. Louis, MO)

Reservation Number: (800) 336-SLOT
Restaurants: 2
Buffets: B-$3.95 L-$5.95 D-$9.95
Schedule: 11 Cruises Daily
Times: 7am, 9am, 11am, 1pm, 3pm, 5pm, 7pm, 9pm, 11pm, 1am, 3am
Prices: All cruises are free
Casino Size: 19,300 Square Feet
Other Games: VK
Casino Marketing: (800) 500-VIP1
Fun Book: Only given to groups
Special Features: 1,200-passenger modern yacht that cruises the Mississippi River. Off track betting parlor located in land-based pavilion.

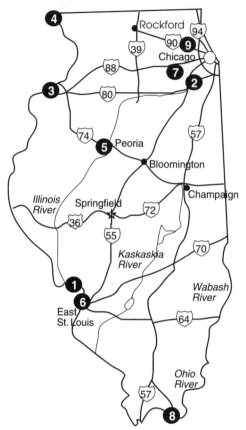

Casino Queen

200 S. Front Street
E. St. Louis, Illinois 62201
(618) 874-5000
Map Location: #6 (290 miles S.W. of Chicago)

Reservation Number: (800) 777-0777
Buffets: B-$1.95/$6.95 (Sun)
           L-$4.95 D-$9.95
Schedule: 11 Cruises Daily
Times: 9am, 11am, 1pm, 3pm, 5pm, 7pm,
       9pm, 11pm, 1am, 3am, 5am
Prices: All cruises are $2
Casino Size: 25,000 Square Feet
Other Games: B, VK
Senior Discount: 9am, 11am and 1pm cruises are free on Wednesdays, if 50 or older. Also receive free danish, coffee, juice, 2- f o r - 1 breakfast or lunch and 50% off in gift shop.
Special Features: Old-Fashioned, 1,500-passenger paddle wheeler that cruises the Mississippi river. Buffets are served on the boat. Prime rib table-service dinner is offered on the 5pm, 7pm and 9pm cruises for $9.95.

Empress Casino Joliet

2300 Empress Drive
Joliet, Illinois 60436
(815) 744-9400
Map Location: #2 (43 miles S.W. of Chicago)

Reservation Number: (888) 4-EMPRESS
Rooms: 85 Price Range: $80-$100
Suites: 17 Price Range: $120-$150
Restaurants: 2
Buffets: B-$3.99 L-$11.95 D-$16.95
Schedule: 7 Cruises Daily (8 on Empress II)
Times (I): 9:30am, 12:30pm, 3:30pm,
          6:30pm, 9pm, 12am, 3am
Times (II): 8:30am, 10:30am, 1:30pm, 4:30pm,
          7:30pm, 10:30pm, 1:30am, 4:30am
Prices: All cruises are free
Casino Size: 19,000 Square Feet - Empress I
Casino Size: 27,000 Square Feet - Empress II
Other Games: MB, VK, Simulcasting
Senior Discount: Free breakfast buffet on
     8:30am or 9:30am cruise, if 55 or older
Special Features: 1,000-passenger Empress I and 1,500-passenger Empress II are modern yachts that cruise the Des Plaines River.

Grand Victoria Casino
250 S. Grove Avenue
Elgin, Illinois 60120
(847) 888-1000
Map Location: #9 (41 miles N.W. of Chicago)

Reservation Number: (847) 888-1000
Restaurants: 3
Buffets: B-$5.99 (Sun) L-$8.88 D-$12.99
Schedule: 8 Cruises Daily (9 on Fri/Sat)
Times: 9am, 11:30am, 2pm, 4:30pm, 7pm,
10pm, 12:30am, 3am, 5am (Fri/ Sat)
Prices: All cruises are free, however, you must call for reservations and guarantee them with a credit card. If you don't show up, or if you don't cancel your reservation at least four hours ahead, you will be charged $10 for each ticket you reserved.
Casino Size: 29,850 Square Feet
Other Games: VK
Casino Marketing: (847) 468-7000
Fun Book: Only given to groups
Special Features: 1,200-passenger paddle wheeler-replica that cruises the Fox River. Live entertainment Wed-Sun 6pm-12am.

Harrah's Joliet Casino
150 N. Scott Street
Joliet, Illinois 60431
(815) 740-7800
Map Location: #2 (43 miles S.W. of Chicago)

Reservation Number: (800) HARRAHS
Restaurants: 2
Buffets: B-$3.99 L-$7.95 D-$12.95
Schedule:
Northern Star: 10:30am, 1:30pm, 4:30pm,
7:30pm, 10:30pm, 1:30am
Southern Star II: 9am, 12pm, 3pm, 6pm,
9pm, 12am, 3am
Prices: All cruises are free
Casino Size: 13,440 Square Feet (S. Star II)
Casino Size: 17,000 Square Feet (N. Star)
Other Games: MB, VK - Southern Star II
Other Games: MB, Video BJ - Northern Star
Casino Marketing: (800) HARRAHS
Special Features: Complimentary soda and juice. Northern Star is a 1,000-passenger modern mega-yacht. Southern Star II is an 1880s stern wheeler replica. Both cruise the Des Plaines River. Each boat has a deli on board. Pavilion houses 210-seat buffet, steak house, sports bar and lounge with live entertainment.

Hollywood Casino - Aurora
1 New York Street Bridge
Aurora, Illinois 60506
(708) 801-1234
Map Location: #7 (41 miles W. of Chicago)

Reservation Number: (800) 888-7777
Restaurants: 3
Buffets: B-$4.99 L-$7.99 D-$11.99
Schedule:
City of Lights I: 10am, 1pm, 4pm, 7pm,
10pm, 12:30am, 2:30am, 4:30am
City of Lights II: 8:30am, 11:30am, 2:30pm,
5:30pm, 8:30pm, 11:30pm
Prices: All cruises are free
Casino Size: 11,000 Square Feet (C of L I)
Casino Size: 21,000 Square Feet (C of L II)
Other Games: MB
Casino Marketing: (708) 801-7203
Senior Discount: 2-for-1 breakfast or lunch buffet on Thursday, if 55 or older
Special Features: 675-passenger *City of Lights I* and 1,200-passenger *City of Lights II* are paddlewheel-replica boats that cruise the Fox River. All restaurants are in land-based pavilion. Headliner entertainment offered at nearby Paramount Arts Center.

Jumer's Casino Rock Island
18th St. - Mississippi Riverfront
Rock Island, Illinois 61201
(309) 793-4200
Map Location: #3 (170 miles W. of Chicago)

Reservation Number: (800) 477-7747
Restaurants: 1 on boat adjacent to casino
Buffets: L-$4.95 D-$7.95
Schedule: 8 Cruises Daily (9 on Fri/Sat)
Times: 9am, 11am, 1pm, 3pm, 5pm, 7pm,
9pm, 11pm, 1am (Fri/Sat)
Prices: All cruises are free
Parking: Free
Casino Size: 8,100 Square Feet
Casino Marketing: (309) 793-4200 ext-245
Special Features: 1,200-passenger old-fashioned paddle wheel boat that cruises the Mississippi River. Free hors d'oeuvres, coffee, juice and soft drinks. $1 mixed drinks. Casinos on 3 decks. Restaurant is on the Effie Afton which is another boat docked next to the casino.

Par-A-Dice Riverboat Casino
21 Blackjack Boulevard
East Peoria, Illinois 61611
(309) 698-7711
Map Location: #5 (170 miles S.W. of Chicago)

Reservation Number: (800) PAR-A-DICE
Rooms: 204 Price Range: $67-$85
Suites 13 Price Range: $99-$275
Buffets: B-$4.95 L-$6.95 D-$9.95
Schedule: 9 Cruises Daily
Times: 9am, 11pm, 1pm, 3pm, 5pm,
       7pm, 9pm, 11pm, 1am
Prices: $4/$7 Sat or Holiday
Parking: $2
Casino Size: 33,000 Square Feet
Other Games: MB, VK, LIR
Casino Marketing: (800) PAR-A-DICE
Fun Book: Given upon departure from boat
Senior Discount: If 55, or older, all cruises are
       free on Monday. At all other times $2
       discount on cruise.
Special Features: 1,600-passenger modern
boat that cruises the Illinois River. 2 restaurants and banquet facilities. All rooms are at
on-property Hampton Inn.

Players Riverboat Casino
207 S. Ferry Street
Metropolis, Illinois 62960
(618) 524-2628
Map Location: #8 (Across from Paducah,
KY. Take exit 37 on I-24)

Reservation Number: (800) 935-7700
Hotel Reservations: (800) 550-9777
Rooms: 110 Price Range: $69-$90
Suites: 10 Price Range: $100-$150
Restaurants: 2
Buffets: B-$3.99 L-$4.99 D-$7.99
Schedule: 8 Cruises Daily (9 on Fri/Sat)
Times: 9am, 11am, 1pm, 3pm, 5pm, 7pm,
9pm, 11pm, (1am on Fri/Sat)
Prices: All cruises are free
Other Games: VK
Casino Size: 29,000 Square Feet
Casino Marketing: (800) 929-5905
Special Features: 1,300-passenger side
wheeler-replica that cruises the Ohio River.
Both restaurants are in land-based pavilion -
Merv Griffin's Landing. On-property hotel
offers complimentary daily breakfast bar.
350-seat theater is adjacent to hotel.

Silver Eagle Casino
19731 Route 20 West
East Dubuque, Illinois 61025
(815) 747-2455
Map Location: #4 (180 miles N.E. of Chicago. 10 miles W. of Galena, IL)

Reservation Number: (800) SILVER-1
Restaurants: 1 deli
Schedule: 6 Cruises Daily (7 on Fri/Sat)
Times: 12pm, 2pm, 4pm, 6pm,
       8pm, 10pm, 12am (Fri/Sat)
Prices: All cruises are free
Casino Size: 9,250 Square Feet
Casino Marketing: (815) 747-2455
Special Features: 1,000-passenger modern
yacht that cruises the Mississippi River. Restaurant and gift shop in on-shore pavilion. 3
gaming decks, plus an observation deck.

INDIANA

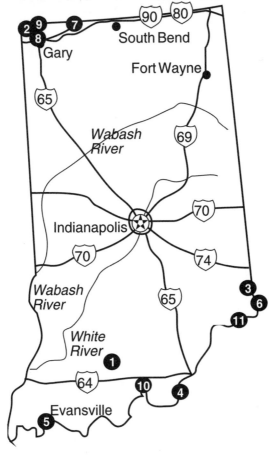

Although the governor vetoed riverboats for his state, the Indiana legislature voted to override him and in June 1993 Indiana became the sixth state to allow riverboat gambling.

The terms of Indiana's law allow for 11 riverboats in the state - five on Lake Michigan, one on Patoka Lake (map location #1) and five along the Ohio River. The boats are required to cruise and there are no bet or loss limits imposed on gamblers.

As of September 9, 1996 four casinos were in operation and five more licenses had been issued. Of the remaining two locations one boat is scheduled for Patoka Lake and the

other will be located in either Crawford County (map location #10) or Switzerland County (map location #11). The Indiana Gaming Commission was scheduled to announce its decision on the final location in January 1997.

When the first Lake Michigan boats opened in June 1996 it was discovered that if the boats cruised the lake they would be in violation of the Johnston Act, a federal law which prohibits the use or transportation of gambling machines in territorial waters of the U.S. Because of this problem the Lake Michigan boats have not been cruising and have been conducting dockside gaming sessions instead. These sessions have the same time limits as the cruises and once a session begins the doors to the casino are closed and no one is allowed to enter until boarding begins for the next session. You are, however, permitted to leave at any time during a dockside session. As of September 1996 legislators were working to find a solution to the conflict with the Johnston Act that would allow the Lake Michigan boats to cruise.

For those interested in which casinos offer the best return on their slot machines, we offer the following information from the Indiana Gaming Commission regarding average slot payout percentages for the two-month period from June through July 1996:

CASINO	PAYBACK
Majestic Star	93.38%
Trump Casino	93.35%
Empress Casino	92.96%
Casino Aztar	92.35%

These figures reflect the total percentages returned by each casino for all of their electronic machines including slot machines, video poker, video keno, etc. As you can see, the Majestic Star returned the most to its slot machine players, while Casino Aztar returned the least.

Most cruises on Indiana riverboats are for one or two hours. Boarding begins 1/2 hour before the scheduled cruise time and you can gamble as soon as you get on the boat. Upon returning you have another 1/2 hour to gamble before the next boarding begins.

Be aware that most boats will require you to have advance reservations on weekends and holidays so be sure to call ahead and ask about their policy before going to the boat.

Unless otherwise noted, all casinos offer: blackjack, craps, roulette, slots, video poker, video keno and Caribbean Stud Poker. Optional games include: baccarat (B), mini-baccarat (MB) and Let It Ride (LIR). The minimum gambling age is 21.

Argosy Casino - Lawrenceburg
204 Short Street
Lawrenceburg, Indiana 47025
(812) 539-8000
Map Location: #3 (95 miles S.E. of Indianapolis)

EXPECTED TO OPEN BY EARLY 1997

Caesars Riverboat Casino
231 S. Fifth Street
Louisville, Kentucky 40202
(502) 589-6060
Boat will be located in Bridgeport
Map Location: #4

EXPECTED TO OPEN BY MID-1997

Casino Aztar
700 N.W. Riverside Drive
Evansville, Indiana 47708
(812) 433-4100
Map Location: #5 (168 miles S.W. of Indianapolis)

Reservation Number: (800) 342-5386
Restaurants: 5
Schedule: 9 Cruises Daily
Times: 9:30am, 11:30am, 1:30pm, 3:30pm, 5:30pm, 7:30pm, 10:30pm, 1:30am, 3:30am
Prices: $3/$5 for 7:30 and 10:30
Parking: $1 per hour (5 hours free with casino validation)
Casino Size: 35,000 Square Feet
Special Features: 2,800-passenger old fashioned paddle wheeler that cruises the Ohio River.

Empress Casino Hammond
825 Empress Drive
Hammond, Indiana 46320
(219) 473-0978
Map Location: #2 (15 miles E. of Chicago)

Reservation Number: (800) 888-4-EMPRESS
Restaurants: 3
Buffets: B-$4.95 L-$6.95 D-$9.95
Schedule: 10 Cruises (Sessions) Daily
Boarding Times: 8am, 10am, 12pm, 2pm, 4pm, 6pm, 8pm, 10pm, 12am, 2am
Prices: All cruises are free
Casino Size: 35,000 Square Feet
Other Games: MB, LIR
Special Features: 2,500-passenger modern yacht that cruises Lake Michigan. Sign up for Player's Club and get 15% discount in restaurants and gift shop.

Grand Victoria Casino & Resort
600 Grand Victoria Drive
Rising Sun, Indiana 47040
(812) 438-1234
Map Location: #6 (100 miles S.E. of Indianapolis)

Reservation Number: (800) GRAND-11
Restaurants: 1

Schedule: 8 Cruises Daily
Times: 9:30am, 12pm, 2:30pm, 5pm, 7:30pm, 10:30pm, 12:30am, 1am, 3:30am
Prices: $5, except 7:30 and 10:30 which are $7/$9 (Fri/Sat)
Casino Size: 45,000 Square Feet
Other Games: LIR
Fun Book: Given with slot club registration
Special Features: 2,700-passenger old-fashioned paddle wheeler that cruises the Ohio River. Hotel expected to open by late 1997.

Indiana Blue Chip Hotel & Riverboat Casino
1215 Potter Drive
West Lafayette, Indiana 47906
(317) 463-1585
Map Location: #7 (40 miles E. of Chicago)

Boat will be located in Michigan City
EXPECTED TO OPEN BY MID-1997

Trump Casino
1 Buffington Harbor
Gary, Indiana 46406
(219) 977-7100
Map Location: #8 (15 miles E. of Chicago)

Reservation Number: (888) 218-7867
Restaurants: 2 (1 Deli on boat)
Buffets: B-$4.95 L-$7.95 D-$11.95
Schedule: 10 Cruises (Sessions) Daily
Boarding Times: 9am, 11am, 1pm, 3pm, 5pm, 7pm, 9pm, 11pm, 1am, 3am

Prices: All cruises are free
Casino Size: 37,000 Square Feet
Other Games: MB
Special Features: 2,300-passenger modern yacht that cruises Lake Michigan.

Majestic Star Casino
1 Buffington Harbor
Gary, Indiana 46406
(219) 977-7920
Map Location: #8 (15 miles E. of Chicago)

Reservation Number: (888) 888-2B-LUCKY
Restaurants: 2 (1 Snack Bar on boat)
Buffets: B-$4.99 L-$7.99 D-$11.99
Schedule: 10 Cruises (Sessions) Daily
Boarding Times: 8am, 10am, 12pm, 2pm, 4pm, 6pm, 8pm, 10pm, 12am, 2am
Prices: All cruises are free
Other Games: B
Special Features: 1,300-passenger modern yacht that cruises Lake Michigan.

Showboat Marina Casino
P.O. Box 777
East Chicago, Indiana 46312
(219) 392-1111
Map Location: #9 (5 miles E. of Chicago)

EXPECTED TO OPEN BY MID-1997

IOWA

Iowa was the first state to legalize riverboat gambling. The boats began operating on April Fools Day in 1991 and passengers were originally limited to $5 per bet with a maximum loss of $200 per person, per cruise. Because of these restriction several boats later moved on to Mississippi which offered 24-hour, no-limit, dockside gambling.

In September 1991 the first of 10 riverboats began operating in the bordering state of Illinois and these boats did not have the restrictive $5 bet limits or loss limits. The increased competition from these boats cut deeply into the profitability of the Iowa boats and in early 1994 the Iowa legislature voted to eliminate the restrictions. They also agreed to allow the boats to remain open 24 hours with only one daily two-hour cruise required. Additionally, a provision was added to allow slot machines to be placed at the state's four pari-mutuel facilities. All of this, however, was subject to voter approval in county-wide referendums. The measures passed in all of the affected counties except Black Hawk where it failed on two separate occasions. Waterloo Greyhound Park is the only track in that county and they are the states's only pari-mutuel facility without slot machines. They ceased operations on July 13, 1996 but may re-open at a later date. Iowa is also home to three Indian casinos.

Here's information, as supplied by the Iowa Racing and Gaming Commission, showing the slot machine payback percentages for all locations for the fiscal year beginning July 1, 1995 through June 30, 1996:

LOCATION	PAYBACK
Bluffs Run	93.9%
Harvey's	93.9%
President	93.7%
Dubuque Greyhound	93.4%
Lady Luck	93.4%
Ameristar	93.2%
Mississippi Belle II	93.0%
Dubuque Diamond Jo	93.0%
Prairie Meadows	92.5%
Miss Marquette	91.4%
Catfish Bend	91.7%
Belle of Sioux City	90.9%

These figures reflect the total percentages returned by each riverboat casino or pari-mutuel facility for all of its electronic machines including: slots, video poker, video keno, etc. As you can see, Bluffs Run and Harvey's returned the most to their players, while the Belle of Sioux City returned the least.

Admission to all riverboat casinos is free. Most boats cruise from June through October and remain dockside from November through May although there might be slight differences in those schedules among the different boats.

Unless otherwise noted, all riverboats and Indian casinos offer: blackjack, roulette, craps, slots, and video poker. Some casinos also offer: Poker (P), Caribbean Stud Poker (CSP), Let It Ride (LIR), big six (B6), mini-baccarat (MB), Pai Gow Poker (PGP) and video keno (VK). The minimum gambling age is 21.

Ameristar Casino Council Bluffs
2200 River Road
Council Bluffs, Iowa
(712) 328-8888
Map Location: #8

Toll-Free Number: (800) 700-1012
Restaurants: 2 (1 open 24 hours)
Buffets: B-$9.95 (Sun) L-$5.95
          D-$7.95/$9.95 (Sat/Sun)
Casino Size: 27,000 Square Feet

Cruise Schedule: One cruise 7:30am-9:30am daily. Boat then remains dockside and stays open 24 hours.
Other Games: CSP, LIR
Casino Marketing: (712) 328-8888
Senior Discount: If 55, or older, ask for special $39 value coupon book
Special Features: 1,700-passenger paddle wheeler that cruises the Missouri River.

Belle of Sioux City
100 Chris Larsen Park
Sioux City, Iowa 51102
(712) 255-0080
Map Location: #3

Toll-Free Number: (800) 424-0080
Restaurants: 1
Buffets: L-$5.95 D-$7.95
Cruise Schedule: Opens 8:30 am. One cruise daily 9am-11am. Boat then remains open dockside until 3am/5am (Fri/Sat).
Other Games: P, CSP, LIR
Casino Marketing: (800) 424-0080
Fun Book: Only given to groups
Special Features: 1,200-passenger old-fashioned stern wheeler that cruises the Missouri River.

Catfish Bend Casino
902 Riverview Drive
Fort Madison, Iowa 52627
(319) 372-2946
Map Location: #9 (180 miles S.E. of Des Moines)

Toll-Free Number: (800) 372-2WIN
Restaurants: 1 Deli
Cruise Schedule: Opens 8am. One cruise 10am-12pm Monday through Friday. Boat then remains open dockside and until 2am/24 hours (Wed-Sun)
Other Games: P
Casino Marketing: (800) 372-2WIN
Special Features: 600-passenger paddle wheeler that cruises the Mississippi River. $5 admission charge per hour for anyone under 21. Docks in Burlington, Iowa from November through April.

Dubuque Diamond Jo Casino
3rd Street Ice Harbor
Dubuque, IA 52004
(319) 583-7005
Map Location: #7

Toll-Free Number: (800) LUCKY-JO
Restaurants: 2

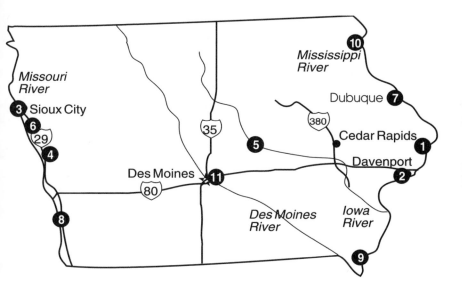

Buffets: B-$7.95 (Sun) L-$6.95
            D-$9.95/$11.95 (Fri/Sat)
Schedule: Opens 7am. One cruise 7:30am-
    9:30am Monday through Friday. Boat then
    remains open dockside until
    2am/4am (Wed/Thu)/24 hours (Fri/Sat).
Other Games: P, CSP, LIR
Casino Marketing: (800) LUCKY-JO
Special Features: 650-passenger old-fashioned
steamboat replica that cruises the Mississippi
River. Deli on boat. Buffet in land-based
pavilion. Free child-care area for children 3
and older (capacity of 5 children).

Harvey's Casino Hotel
One Harvey's Boulevard
Council Bluffs, Iowa 51501
(712) 329-6000
Map Location: #8

Toll-Free Number: (800) HARVEYS
Rooms: 240 Price Range: $95
Suites: 11 Price Range $195-$295
Restaurants: 2 (1 open 24 hours)
Buffets: B-$2.99 L-$5.99 D-$7.99
Schedule: One cruise Mon-Fri 7:30am-
        9:30am. Boat then remains open
        dockside 24 hours.
Casino Size: 26,000 Square Feet
Other Games: CSP, LIR, MB
Fun Book: Available at visitor centers
Special Features: 1,700-passenger paddle
wheel-replica that cruises the Missouri River.
Hotel is located on property.

Lady Luck Casino Bettendorf
1821 State Street
Bettendorf, Iowa 52722
(319) 359-7280
Map Location: #2

Toll-Free Number: (800) 724-5825
Restaurants: 1
Buffets: B-1.99/$9.95 (Sun)
            L-$6.95 D-$9.95
Schedule: One cruise 7:30am-9:30am Mon-
          Fri. Boat then remains dockside
          and stays open 24 hours.
Other Games: P, CSP, LIR, MB, PGP, VK
Senior Discount: Free buffet Tue/Thu from
               7am to 6pm, if 55 or older
Fun Book: Go to Mad Money booth
Special Features: 2,000-passenger old-fash-
ioned paddle wheeler that cruises the Missis-
sippi River. Supervised video arcade on 3rd
floor for minors under 21.

Mississippi Belle II
Showboat Landing
Clinton, Iowa 52733
(319) 243-9000
Map Location: #1 (83 miles E. of Cedar
Rapids)

Toll-Free Number: (800) 457-9975
Restaurants: 1

Buffets: L-$5.95 D-$7.95/$9.95 (Fri/Sat)
Schedule: Opens 9am. One cruise 1pm-3pm
    Mon-Fri. Boat then remains dockside
    and stays open until 2am/4am (Fri/Sat).
Casino Size: 10,577 Square Feet
Other Games: VK, CSP
Special Features: 1,000-passenger old-fashioned paddle wheeler that cruises the Mississippi River. Supervised play area for children
ages 3-12. Live entertainment. $5 admission
charge for anyone under 21.

Miss Marquette Riverboat Casino
P.O. Box 460
Marquette, Iowa 52158
(319) 873-3531
Map Location: #10 (60 miles N. of Dubuque)

Toll-Free Number: (800) 4-YOU-BET
Restaurants: 1
Buffets: B-$3.95 L-$4.95 D-$7.59
Schedule: One cruise daily from 11am-1pm.
    Boat then remains dockside and
    stays open 24 hours.
Casino Size: 30,000 Square Feet
Other Games: CSP, B6, VK
Fun Book: Distributed by local hotels
Special Features: 1,200-passenger paddle
wheeler that cruises the Mississippi River.
Restaurant and family arcade are located on
land-based pavilion.

President Riverboat Casino
130 West River Drive
Davenport, Iowa 52801
(319) 328-8000
Map Location: #2 (80 miles S.E. of Cedar
Rapids)

Toll-Free Number: (800) BOAT-711
Restaurants: 2 (1 open 24 hours)
Buffets: B-$2.49 L-$4.95 D-$6.95
Schedule: One cruise 7:30am-9:30am Mon-
    Fri. Boat then remains dockside
    and stays open 24 hours.
Casino Size: 32,000 Square Feet
Other Games: P, CSP, B6, VK
Casino Marketing: (800) BOAT-711
Senior Discount: Go to Captain's Club and
    ask to join the Silver Club, if 55 or older
Special Features: 2,200-passenger paddle
wheel replica that cruises the Mississippi
River. Restaurants are on a barge which is
docked adjacent to The President. Nearby
Blackhawk Hotel (800) 553-1173 offers spe-
cial gaming packages.

Indian Casinos

Casino Omaha
at Blackbird Bend
Onawa, Iowa 51040
(712) 423-3700
Map Location: #4 (30 miles S. of Sioux City,
60 miles N. of Omaha, 4 miles W. of I-29 at
exit 112)

Toll-Free Number: (800) 858-UBET
Restaurants: 1 Deli Liquor: Yes
Buffets: L-$4.99 D-$4.99/$7.85 (Fri/Sat)
Hours: 8am-2am/24 Hours (Fri/Sat)
Other Games: P, VK
Casino Size: 30,000 Square Feet
Casino Marketing: (800) 858-UBET, ext. 111
Fun Book: Only given to groups
Special Features: Free continental breakfast
Mon-Fri from 8am-10am. Present proof of
date of birth for free gift during your birthday
month.

Mesquaki Bingo & Casino
1504 305th Street
Tama, Iowa 52339
(515) 484-2108
Map Location: #5 (40 miles W. of Cedar
Rapids)

Toll-Free Number: (800) 728-4263
Restaurants: 1 Liquor: No
Buffets: B-$3.95 L-$5.95 D-$6.95
Hours: 24 Hours Daily
Other Games: P, CSP, Keno,
    Bigo, Simulcasting

Winnavegas
330th Street
Sloan, Iowa 51055
(712) 428-9466
Map Location: #6 (20 miles S. of Sioux City)

Toll-Free Number: (800) 468-9466
Rooms: 50 Price Range: $35-$60
Restaurants: 1 Liquor: Yes
Buffets: B-$3.45 L-$5.45 D-$7.25
Hours: 24 Hours Daily
Other Games: P, CSP, LIR, MB, Keno, Bingo
Senior Discount: 20% off buffets, if 62 or
    older. 96¢ lunch Tue from 11am-3pm
    with Player's Card which can be
    obtained at front desk.
Fun Book: Only given to groups

Pari-Mutuels

Bluffs Run Casino
2701 23rd Avenue
Council Bluffs, Iowa 51501
(712) 323-2500
Map Location: #8 (102 miles S. of Sioux City)

Toll-Free Number: (800) BET-2-WIN
Restaurants: 4
Buffets: B-$2.99 L-$4.95 D-$7.95
Casino Size: 50,000 Square Feet
Hours: 24 Hours Daily
Other Games: Only slot machines
Special Features: Live dog racing (Tue-Sun). Horse race simulcasting.

Dubuque Greyhound Park & Casino
1855 Greyhound Park Drive
Dubuque, Iowa 52001
(319) 582-3647
Map Location: #7

Toll-Free Number: (800) 373-3647

Restaurants: 1
Buffets: B-$9.95 (Sun) L-$6.95
 D-$8.95/$10.95 (Fri)
Hours: 9am-2am/24 hours (Fri/Sat)
Other Games: Only slot machines
Special Features: Live dog racing (Wed-Sun) during season which runs from late April through late October.

Prairie Meadows Track & Casino
1 Prairie Meadows Drive
Altoona, Iowa 50009
(515) 967-1000
Map Location: #11 (5 miles E. of Des Moines)

Toll-Free Number: (800) 325-9015
Restaurants: 1
Buffets: B-$3.95
Hours: 24 Hours Daily
Other Games: Only slot machines
Special Features: Live thoroughbred and quarter-horse racing (Mon/Thu-Sat) during season which runs from April through August. Simulcasting of dog and horse racing all year.

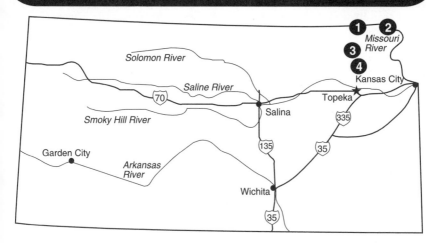

There are four Kansas Indian tribes with compacts that were approved in late 1995: the Sac and Fox, the Kickapoo of Kansas, the Prairie Band Potawatomi and the Iowa Tribe of Kansas and Nebraska. All of the compacts allow for blackjack, craps, roulette, baccarat, poker, wheel of fortune, keno, slots and video poker.

As of September 1996 one casino was open and two more were expected to open by early 1997. Only the Iowa Tribe of Kansas and Nebraska (map location #2) had no plans to open a casino during 1997.

The Potawatomi Tribe is planning a 63,000-square-foot casino and a 100-room hotel that will be managed by Harrah's. That facility is not expected to open until late 1997 and until that time they will be operating a temporary casino at their bingo hall. The temporary casino is expected to open by early 1997.

As this book went to press the Kickapoos' Golden Eagle Casino was the only property in operation and it offered the following games: blackjack, craps, slots and video poker. The minimum gambling age is 21.

Golden Eagle Casino
Rt. 1, Box 149
Horton, Kansas 66439
(913) 486-6601
Map Location: #3 (45 miles N. of Topeka)

Toll-Free Number: (888) 464-5825
Restaurants: 1   Liquor: No
Buffets: D-$6.95

Prairie Band Potawatomi Bingo
Rt. 2, Box 50A
Mayetta, Kansas 66509
(913) 966-2801
Map Location: #4 (17 miles N. of Topeka)

EXPECTED TO OPEN BY EARLY 1997

Sac and Fox Casino
P.O. Box 11
Hiawatha, Kansas 66434
(913) 742-3337
Map Location: (#1)

EXPECTED TO OPEN BY EARLY 1997

LOUISIANA

Video poker is permitted at Louisiana truck stops, racetracks/OTB's and bars/taverns. There is no limit to the number of machines permitted at racetracks and off-track betting locations, however, truck stops are allowed no more than 50, while bars and taverns are permitted a maximum of three.

Louisiana was the fourth state to approve riverboat gambling and its 1991 gambling law allows a maximum of 15 boats statewide with a limit of six in any one parish. In 1992 a provision was added for one land-based casino in New Orleans.

The law requires that all boats be newly built within Louisiana and it does not allow for existing boats to be adapted to offer casino gambling. Also, all boats must be paddlewheel driven and replicas of old-fashioned turn-of-the-century models. All boats are also required to cruise, except those located along the Red River which are exempt because those waters were deemed too dangerous to continually navigate. A section of the state's law, however, allows the captain to order any boat to remain dockside if he believes that the sailing conditions present any kind of danger to the vessel, passengers or crew. Until early 1995 many of the riverboats used this loophole to avoid cruising and al-

most all of them offered 24-hour dockside gaming. This eventually led to a more stringent enforcement by gaming authorities and now all riverboats (except those on the Red River) must go on 90-minute cruises. All cruises are free (except for Flamingo Casino New Orleans) and boarding is scheduled 45 minutes before each cruise, however, passengers can actually begin boarding as soon as the boat returns from its previous cruise which is about an hour-and-a-half before the next scheduled cruise.

Casino gambling has not been completely successful in Louisiana. There was a major failure in New Orleans in June 1995 when the River City casino complex closed after only two months of operation. The complex contained two riverboats (Grand Palais and Crescent City) and could not generate enough business to remain open. Also, the state's only, non-Indian, land-based casino in New Orleans, operated by Harrah's Jazz Co., declared bankruptcy and shut its doors in November 1995 because its revenues were drastically below expectations.

There has also been an anti-gambling sentiment developing within Louisiana and a statewide referendum was scheduled for November 1996 that could outlaw video poker as

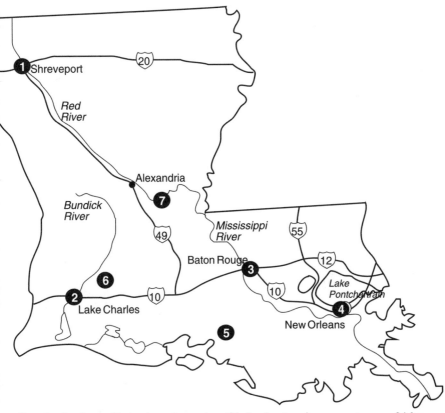

well as the riverboats. Voters in each county will get to decide whether or not they want riverboat casinos. If the referendum passes in a particular county it means that a currently operating boat in that county would have to close when its current license expires.

As of September 1996 there were 14 riverboat casinos in operation in 12 different locations (the two Lake Charles locations each have two boats) and the state's gaming commission was reviewing applications to award the 15th license.

No information can be given on the slot machine percentage paybacks for Louisiana's casinos because that information is not released by the state's gaming commission. The state does require, however, that the machines in the casinos be programmed to pay back no less than 80% and no more than 99.9%. For video gaming machines at locations other than casinos the law requires a minimum return of 80% and a maximum return of 94%.

All riverboat casinos operate on a 24-hour basis and the games offered are: slots, video poker, craps, blackjack and roulette. Optional games include: baccarat (B), mini-baccarat (MB), poker (P), Caribbean Stud Poker (CSP), Pai Gow Poker (PGP) and Let It Ride (LIR). The minimum gambling age is 21.

Belle of Baton Rouge
103 France Street
Baton Rouge, Louisiana 70802
(504) 378-6000
Map Location: #3

Toll-Free Number: (800) 266-2692
Restaurants: 4 (1 on boat)
Buffets: L-$7.95 D-$10.95
Schedule: 8 cruises daily
Times: 8am, 11am, 2pm, 5pm,
       8pm, 11pm, 2am, 5am
Casino Size: 29,000 Square Feet
Other Games: P, CSP, LIR
Casino Marketing: (800) 676-4VIP
Fun Book: Only given to groups

Senior Discount: If 50, or older, 15% off in restaurants and gift shop. Ask to join Belles and Beaus Senior Club.
Special Features: 1,500-passenger paddle wheeler that cruises the Mississippi River. Land-based entertainment pavilion houses buffet restaurant, retail shops and lounge with live entertainment.

Bally's Belle of Orleans
1 Stars & Stripes Boulevard
New Orleans, Louisiana 70126
(504) 248-3200
Map Location: #4

Toll-Free Number: (800) 57-BALLY
Restaurants: 1 (Snack bar on boat)
Buffets: B-$5.95/$16.95 (Sun)
  L-$9.95/$10.95 (Fri) D-$13.95/$15.95 (Fri)
Schedule: 8 cruises daily
Times: 6am, 9am, 12pm, 3pm,
    6pm, 9pm, 12am, 3am
Casino Size: 30,000 Square Feet
Other Games: MB, P, CSP, PGP, LIR
Fun Book: Only given to groups
Special Features: 1,200-passenger paddle wheeler that cruises Lake Pontchartrain. Buffets restaurant and lounge are located in land-based terminal.

Boomtown Casino Westbank
4132 Peters Road
Harvey, Louisiana 70058
(504) 366-7711
Map Location: #4 (a suburb of New Orleans)

Toll-Free Number: (800) 366-7711
Restaurants: 2 (1 snack bar on boat)
Schedule: 8 cruises daily
Times: 7:45am, 10:45am, 1:45pm, 4:45pm,
    7:45pm, 10:45pm, 1:45am, 4:45am
Casino Size: 30,000 Square Feet
Other Games: P, CSP, LIR
Casino Marketing: (800) 366-7711
Fun Book: Given when you join the slot club
Special Features: 1,600-passenger paddle wheeler that cruises on the Harvey Canal. 88,000-square-foot land-based terminal features restaurant, arcade with children's games and a lounge with live entertainment.

Casino Magic - Bossier City
P.O. Box 71115
Bossier City, Louisiana 71171
(318) 746-0711
Map Location: #1 (Across the Red River From Shreveport)

Toll-Free Number: (800) 5-MAGIC-5
Restaurants: 1
Schedule: 24 hours daily
Other Games: CSP, LIR
Special Features: 1,200-passenger paddle wheeler that stays dockside on the Red River.

Casino Rouge
1717 River Road North
Baton Rouge, Louisiana 70802
(504) 381-7777
Map Location: #3

Toll-Free Number: (800) 44-ROUGE
Restaurants: 2 (1 snack bar on boat)
Buffets: B-$13.95 (Sun) L-$7.95 D-$11.95/
$10.95 (Fri)
Schedule: 8 cruises daily
Times: 8am, 11am, 2pm, 5pm,
    8pm, 11pm, 2am, 5am
Casino Size: 28,146 Square Feet
Other Games: P, CSP, LIR
Special Features: 1,500-passenger paddle wheeler that cruises the Mississippi River. Land-based terminal features 2 restaurants and supervised children's play area.

Flamingo Casino New Orleans
610 S. Peters Street
New Orleans, Louisiana 70130
(504) 587-7777
Map Location: #4

Toll-Free Number: (800) 587-LUCK
Restaurants: 1 snack bar on boat
Schedule: 8 cruises daily
Times: 8:45am, 11:45am, 2:45pm, 5:45pm,
    8:45pm, 11:45pm, 2:45am, 5:45am
Admission: Free with Louisiana driver's license, Flamingo Magic Player's Club Card or Hilton Riverside guest/room key. Other guests are $5 but free once a Player's Club Card is obtained on-board (at no cost)
Parking: Park at Hilton and casino will reimburse parking charges (up to 4 hours). Free valet parking at Hilton
Casino Size: 20,000 Square Feet
Other Games: MB, P, CSP, PGP, LIR
Casino Marketing: (800) 587-LUCK
Special Features: 1,200-passenger paddle wheeler that cruises on the Mississippi River. Located at Poydras St. Wharf adjacent to the New Orleans Hilton Riverside (800-HILTONS) and Riverwalk Marketplace. Walking distance to French Quarter, convention center and the Superdome. Free self-parking. Non-smoking gaming areas. Live Dixieland jazz.

Harrah's Shreveport
315 Clyde Fant Parkway
Shreveport, Louisiana 71101
(318) 424-7777
Map Location: #1

Toll-Free Number: (800) HARRAHS
Restaurants: 3 (1 open 24 hours)
Buffet: B-$3.95 L-$5.95 D-$7/95
Schedule: 24 hours daily
Casino Size: 30,000 Square Feet
Other Games: MB, CSP, LIR
Casino Marketing: (318) 424-7777
Senior Discount: If 55, or older, receive
$1 off buffets
Special Features: 1,650-passenger paddle wheeler that remains dockside on the Red River.

Horseshoe Casino Hotel
711 Horseshoe Boulevard
Bossier City, Louisiana 71111
(318) 742-0711
Map Location: #1 (across the Red River from Shreveport)

Toll-Free Number: (800) 895-0711
Rooms: 180 Price Range: $60-$79
Suites: 21 Price Range: $100-$150
Restaurants: 2 (1 open 24 hours)
Buffets: B-$5.95 (Sat/Sun) L-$6.95
D-$8.95/$10.95 (Mon/Tue)
Schedule: 24 hours daily
Other Games: MB, CSP, LIR
Casino Size: 30,000 Square Feet
Casino Marketing: (800) 895-0711
Fun Book: Only offered to groups
Special Features: 4-story, 2,250-passenger paddle wheeler that remains dockside on the Red River. Rooms are at nearby LeBossier Hotel and free shuttle service is offered. $1,000,000 free pull slot machine (limit - two pulls per person, per day), must be a member of Winner's Circle Club (membership is free).

Isle of Capri Casino & Hotel
711 Isle of Capri Boulevard
Bossier City, Louisiana 71111
(318) 678-7777
Map Location: #1 (across the Red River from Shreveport)

Toll-Free Number: (800) THE-ISLE
Room Reservations: (800) 221-4095
Rooms: 200 Price Range: $49-$65
Suites: 45 Price Range: $59-$85
Restaurants: 3 (1 open 24 Hours)
Buffets: B-$2.49 L-$4.99 D-$7.99

Schedule: 24 hours daily
Prices: Free
Casino Size: 30,000 Square Feet
Other Games: MB, P, PGP, CSP, LIR
Casino Marketing: (318) 678-7400
Fun Book: Only given to groups
Special Features: 1,650-passenger paddle wheeler that remains dockside on the Red River. Live entertainment every day. Hotel is located two miles away and free shuttle service is offered.

Isle of Capri Casino - Lake Charles
100 Westlake Avenue
Westlake, Louisiana 70669
(318) 430-0711
Map Location: #2 (220 miles W. of New Orleans)

Toll-Free Number: (800) THE-ISLE
Restaurants: 2 (1 snack bar on boat)
Buffets: B-$3.99 L-$5.99 D-$7.99
Schedule: Two boats each cruise 8 times daily
Crown Times: 6:30am, 9:30am, 12:30pm,
3:30pm, 6:30pm, 9:30pm, 12:30am, 3:30am
Grand Palais Times: 8am, 11am, 2pm, 5pm,
8pm, 11pm, 2am, 5am
Other Games: MB, P, CSP, LIR
Senior Discount: If 55, or older,
2-for-1 buffet
Fun Book: Sign up at the slot club booth
Special Features: Two 1,200-passenger paddle wheelers (Crown and Grand Palais) that cruise Lake Charles. With two boats there is never a wait to board because when one is out, the other is in. Land-based terminal has two restaurants.

Players Island Casino
800 Bilbo Street
Lake Charles, Louisiana 70601
(318) 437-1500
Map Location: #2 (220 miles W. of New Orleans)

Toll-Free Number: (800) 977-PLAY
Restaurants: 3 (1 open 24 Hours)
Rooms: 132 Price Range: $75-$120
Suites: 2 Price Range: $185
Buffets: B-$5.99 L-$7.99
D-$10.99/$11.99 (Thu-Sat)
Schedule: Two boats each cruise 8 times daily
Players Riverboat Times: 9am, 12pm, 3pm,
6pm, 9pm, 12am, 3am, 6am
Star Casino Times: 10:30am, 1:30pm, 4:30pm,
7:30pm, 10:30pm, 1:30am, 4:30am, 7:30am

Other Games: MB, P, CSP
Casino Marketing: (800) 625-BOAT
Special Features: Players Island includes two boats - Players Riverboat is a 1,700-passenger paddle wheeler and Star Casino is a 1,460-passenger paddle wheeler. Both cruise Lake Charles. Free hourly pirate show with special effects and life-size characters. Free valet parking. Showroom with headliner entertainment. Rooms are at Players Hotel adjacent to the riverboats. Rooms are also available at nearby Holiday Inn (800-367-1814).

Treasure Chest Casino
5050 Williams Boulevard
Kenner, Louisiana 70065
(504) 443-8000
Map Location: #4 (a suburb of New Orleans)

Toll-Free Number: (800) 298-0711
Restaurants: 2
Buffets: B-$5.99/$18.99 (Sun) L-$8.99
        D-$12.99/$16.99 (Fri/Sat)
Schedule: 8 cruises daily
Times: 8am, 11am, 2pm, 5pm,
        8pm, 11pm, 2am, 5am
Parking: Free
Casino Size: 25,000 Square Feet
Other Games: P, CSP, LIR
Casino Marketing: (800) 298-0711
Special Features: 1,900-passenger paddle wheeler that cruises on Lake Pontchartrain. Free valet parking. Snack bar is located on barge adjacent to riverboat.

Indian Casinos

Cypress Bayou Casino
P.O. Box 519
Charenton, Louisiana 70523
(318) 923-7284
Map Location: #5 (75 miles S. of Baton Rouge)

Toll-Free Number: (800) 284-4386
Restaurants: 3
Casino Size: 50,000 Square Feet
Casino Hours: 10am-2am/4am (Fri/Sat)
Casino Marketing: (800) 284-4386
Special Features: Land-based casino. Free valet parking. Bocats Lounge features two 800-gallon freshwater aquariums.

Grand Casino Avoyelles
711 Grand Boulevard
Marksville, Louisiana 71351
(318) 253-1946
Map Location: #7 (30 miles S.E. of Alexandria)

Toll-Free Number: (800) WIN-1-WIN
Restaurants: 2 (1 open 24 hours)
Buffets: L-$6.99 D-$7.99/$8.99 (Sun)
Casino Size: 100,000 Square Feet
Other Games: B, MB, P, PGP, CSP, LIR
Casino Marketing: (800) WIN-1-WIN
Special Features: Land-based casino. Free general and valet parking. Kids Quest - supervised children's activity center (6 weeks to 12 years). Video arcade. Hotel expected to be constructed by summer 1996.

Grand Casino Coushatta
777 Coushatta Drive
Kinder Louisiana 70648
(318) 738-7300
Map Location: #6 (35 miles N.E. of Lake Charles)

Toll-Free Number: (800) 584-7263
Restaurants: 2 (1 open 24 hours)
Buffets: L-$6.99 D-$9.99
Casino Size: 71,000 Square Feet
Other Games: MB, P, PGP, CSP, LIR
Casino Marketing: (800) 584-7263
Special Features: Land-based casino. Free general and valet parking. Kids Quest - supervised children's activity center (6 weeks to 12 years). Video arcade for teens. Food court.

MARYLAND

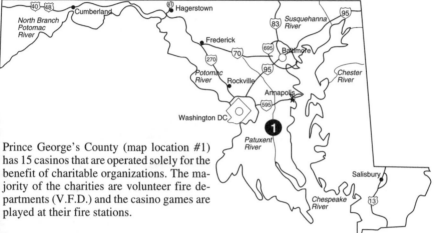

Prince George's County (map location #1) has 15 casinos that are operated solely for the benefit of charitable organizations. The majority of the charities are volunteer fire departments (V.F.D.) and the casino games are played at their fire stations.

The law limits each casino to operate no more than two days per week and the hours of operation are also restricted. Additionally, all casino personnel must be volunteers who have worked for the charitable organization for a minimum of two years.

In late 1995 the law was modified to increase the number of casinos to 21. Additionally, the number of days each casino is allowed to operate was increased to three. As of September 1996, however, no additional licenses had been granted and the original two-day limit was still in effect. According to state officials, the new licenses and the three-day operating limit are expected to be in effect by early 1997.

No slot machines or dice games are permitted. The maximum bet allowed is $500 and the maximum payout on any one bet is limited to $1,000. The games offered include: blackjack (BJ), roulette (R), baccarat (B), minibaccarat (MB), poker (P), Caribbean Stud Poker (CSP), pai gow poker (PGP) and Let It Ride (LIR). The maximum bet limit shown in each listing refers only to blackjack, as the other game limits are lower.

The majority of the casinos do not serve liquor and all have limited food service operations which usually consist of a small kitchen. Most do not have dining areas and in most cases the food is served right at the gaming tables. The minimum gambling age is 21.

Accokeek V.F.D.
1611 Livingston Road
Accokeek, Maryland
(301) 283-2730 or 283-4456

Hours: Sun 2pm-11pm, Mon 12pm-11pm
Games: BJ, R, P, CSP
Max. Bet: $100
Liquor: Yes

Bladensburg V.F.D.
4213 Edmonston Road
Bladensburg, Maryland
(301) 209-9333

Hours: Wed 12pm-11pm, Thu 12pm-11pm
Games: BJ, R, MB, P, PGP
Max. Bet: $500
Liquor: No

Branchville V.F.D.
4905 Branchville Road
College Park, Maryland
(301) 345-8423

Hours: Tue 12pm-11pm, Wed 12pm-11pm
Games: BJ, R, P, LIR
Max. Bet: $250
Liquor: No

Crescent Cities Jaycees at Silver Hill F.D.
3900 Silver Hill Road
Suitland, Maryland
(301) 899-3150

Hours: Fri 4:30pm-2am, Sat 2pm-2am
Games: BJ, R, B, P, CSP
Max. Bet: $300   Liquor: Yes (Beer Only)

Hillside V.F.D.
at Clinton V.F.D.
9025 Woodyard Road
Clinton, Maryland
(301) 868-1333

Hours: Tue 12pm-11pm, Wed 12pm-11pm
Games: BJ, R, CSP, PGP
Max. Bet: $50   Liquor: Beer Only

Hyattsville V.F.D. at Knights of Columbus
3611 Stewart Road
Forestville, Maryland
(301) 736-2908

Hours: Mon 12pm-11pm, Tue 12pm-11pm
Games: BJ, R, MB, P, PGP
Max. Bet: $500   Liquor: No

Kentland V.F.D. at Elks Club
6700 Kenilworth Avenue
Riverdale, Maryland
(301) 277-7261 (Sunday)
(301) 736-1978 (Friday)

Hours: Fri 12pm-2am, Sun 2pm-11pm
Games: BJ, R, P
Max. Bet: $300   Liquor: No

Landover Hills Boys & Girls Club
at Landover Hills F.D.
4601 68th Avenue
Landover Hills, Maryland
(301) 773-6077

Hours: Fri 12pm-2am, Sat 12pm-2am
Games: BJ, R, P
Max. Bet: $25   Liquor: No

Laurel Boys & Girls Club at Phelps Center
701 Montgomery Street
Laurel, Maryland
(301) 490-6570

Hours: Thu 12pm-11pm, Sat 12pm-2am
Games: BJ, R, P
Max. Bet: $25   Liquor: No

Marlboro Boys & Girls Club
at Brandywine V.F.D.
14201 Brandywine Road
Brandywine, Maryland
(301) 372-8181

Hours: Thu 12pm-11pm, Fri 12pm-2am
Games: BJ, R, P, CSP, LIR
Max. Bet: $100   Liquor: Yes

Marlboro V.F.D.
14815 Pratt Street
Upper Marlboro, Maryland
(301) 952-0938

Hours: Thu 12pm-11pm, Sat 12pm-2am
Games: BJ, R, P, CSP, LIR
Max. Bet: $100   Liquor: Yes

Prince George's Jaycees at Glendale V.F.D.
11900 Glendale Boulevard
Glendale, Maryland
(301) 805-9400

Hours: Thu 3pm-11pm, Fri 3pm-2am
Games: BJ, R, P
Max. Bet: $100   Liquor: No

P. G. Temple at Beltsville V.F.D.
4911 Prince George's Avenue
Beltsville, Maryland
(301) 937-4343

Hours: Fri 12pm-2am, Sat 12pm-2am
Games: BJ, B, R, P, PGP
Max. Bet: $150   Liquor: No

Ritchie V.F.D. at Oxon Hill V.F.D.
7600 Livingston Road
Oxon Hill, Maryland
(301) 839-2054

Hours: Tue 12pm-11pm, Wed 12pm-11pm
Games: BJ, R, P, CSP, PGP
Max. Bet: $300   Liquor: No

Riverdale V.F.D.
at Knights of Columbus
9300 Baltimore Avenue
College Park, Maryland
(301) 220-1727

Hours: Sun 2pm-11pm, Mon 12pm-11pm
Games: BJ, R, P
Max. Bet: $300   Liquor: No

MICHIGAN

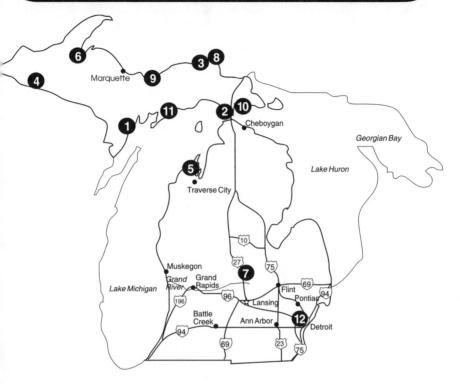

Michigan's largest and most popular casino is actually in Canada. It's Casino Windsor in Ontario which is just across the river from downtown Detroit. Casino Windsor first opened May 17, 1994 and a riverboat (Northern Belle Casino) was later added to accommodate the overflow crowds which the casino drew. Both casinos are operated by a consortium of three companies: Caesars World, Inc., Circus Circus Enterprises and Hilton Hotels Corp. A larger casino, along with a hotel, is expected to open by late 1997.

All winnings are paid in Canadian currency and the minimum gambling age is 19. Both casinos are open 24 hours and offer the following games: blackjack, roulette, baccarat, mini-baccarat, big six wheel, pai-gow poker, Caribbean Stud Poker and Let It Ride. Dice games are prohibited by Canadian law.

Casino Windsor
445 Riverside Drive West
Windsor, Ontario N9A 6T8
(519) 258-7878
Map Location: #12

Toll-Free Number: (800) 991-7777
Restaurants: 1
Casino Size: 50,000 Square Feet
Special Features: Three-level casino. Third floor is the Canadian Club for premium table players. Free shuttle service from remote self-parking lots.

Northern Belle Casino
350 Riverside Drive East
Windsor, Ontario N9A 6T8
(519) 258-2141
Map Location: #12

Restaurants: 1
Casino Size: 23,000 Square Feet
Special Features: 1,500-passenger paddle wheeler that remains dockside on the Detroit

River. 18,000-square-foot landbase contains food court, currency exchange, entertainment area, gift shop and tourism information kiosk.

There are 12 Indian casinos in Michigan. Since the majority of the casinos are small, most of the dining facilities are more like snack bars rather than restaurants. The largest casino is the Kewadin Casino, Sault Ste. Marie with 28 blackjack tables.

The Indian tribes are not required to release information on their slot machine percentage paybacks, but according to Pat Lane at the Michigan Racing Commission, which is responsible for regulating the tribe's slots, "the machines must meet the minimum standards for machines in Nevada or New Jersey." In Nevada the minimum return is 75% and in New Jersey it's 83%. Therefore, the Michigan Indian casinos must return at least 75% in order to comply with the law.

Unless otherwise noted all Indian casinos in Michigan offer the following games: blackjack, slots and video poker. Other games offered include: craps (C), roulette (R), baccarat (B), mini-baccarat (MB), poker (P), Caribbean Stud Poker (CSP), Let It Ride (LIR), keno (K) and bingo (BG). The minimum gambling age is 21 if liquor is served, otherwise it is 18.

Bay Mills Resort & Casino
Lakeshore Drive, Box 249
Brimley, Michigan 49715
(906) 248-3715
Map Location: #3 (12 miles S.W. of Sault Ste. Marie)

Toll-Free Number: (800) 386-2250
Rooms: 67   Price Range: $69-$190
Suites: 4   Price Range: $190
Restaurants: 2   Liquor: Yes
Buffets: B-$4.95 L-$6.95
            D-$8.95/$9.95 (Fri)/$10.95 (Sat)
Hours: 24 Hours Daily
Casino Size: 15,000 Square Feet
Other Games: C, K, CSP
Senior Discount: If 55, or older, room rate
            discounted Sun-Thu
Special Features: Free shuttle service to King's Club and Kewadin casinos.

Chip-In Casino
P.O. Box 351
Harris, Michigan 49845
(906) 466-2941
Map Location: #1 (13 miles W. of Escanaba on Hwy. 41)

Toll-Free Number: (800) 682-6040
Rooms: 27   Price: $48.50
Restaurants: 1   Liquor: Yes
Buffets: B-$6.25 (Sun) L-$6.25 D-$6.25
Table Game Hours: 9am-2am/4am (Fri/Sat)
Slot Hours: 24 Hours Daily
Casino Size: 15,000 Square Feet
Other Games: C, K, CSP, BG
Special Features: Bus tour customers receive $20 coin match and $10 match play. Local motels offer casino packages.

Kewadin Casino, Christmas
102 Candy Cane Lane
Christmas, Michigan 49862
(906) 387-5475
Map Location: #9 (40 miles E. of Marquette)

Toll-Free Number: (800) KEWADIN
Restaurants: 1 Deli   Liquor: Yes
Table Game Hours: 4pm-12am
            10am-1am (Fri/Sat)
Slot Hours: 9am-2am Daily
Casino Size: 3,060 Square Feet
Other Games: CSP
Special Features: Beer and wine served. Free shuttle service from local motels.

Kewadin Casino, Hessel
3 Mile Road
Hessel, Michigan 49745
(906) 484-2903
Map Location: #10 (20 miles N.E. of St. Ignace)

Toll-Free Number: (800) KEWADIN
Restaurants: 1 Deli   Liquor: Yes
Table Game Hours: 4pm-2am/3pm-2am (Fri/Sat)
Slot Hours: 9am-2am Daily
Casino Size: 6,500 Square Feet
Special Features: Beer and wine served. Free shuttle service from local motels.

Kewadin Casino, Manistique
Rte 1, Box 15330, U.S. 2
Manistique, Michigan 49854
(906) 341-5510
Map Location: #10 (95 miles S.E. of Marquette)

Toll-Free Number: (800) KEWADIN
Restaurants: 1 Deli   Liquor: Beer/Wine
Table Game Hours: 4pm-12am
                               9am-1am (Fri/Sat)
Slot Hours: 9am-1am Daily
Casino Size: 3,060 Square Feet
Other Games: CSP
Special Features: Free shuttle service.

Kewadin Casino, Sault Ste. Marie

2186 Shunk Road
Sault Ste. Marie, Michigan 49783
(906) 632-0530
Map Location: #8

Toll-Free Number: (800) KEWADIN
Room Reservations: (800) KEWADIN
Rooms: 52   Price Range: $98-$159
Restaurants: 2 (1 open 24 hours)   Liquor: Yes
Buffets: B-$5.99 L-$5.99
               D-$7.99/$11.99 (Fri/Sat)
Hours: 24 Hours Daily
Casino Size: 85,123 Square Feet
Other Games: C, R, P, PGP, CSP, LIR, K, BG
Casino Marketing: (906) 635-4968
Fun Book: Only given to bus groups
Special Features: Clarion Hotel is attached to casino. Free valet parking. Free shuttle service. Live entertainment nightly.

Kewadin Casino, St. Ignace

3039 Mackinaw Trail
St. Ignace, Michigan 49781
(906) 643-7071
Map Location: #2 (50 miles S. of Sault Ste. Marie)

Toll-Free Number: (800) KEWADIN
Restaurants: 1 Deli   Liquor: Yes
Hours: 24 Hours Daily
Casino Size: 56,168 Square Feet
Other Games: C, R, P, PGP, CSP, LIR, K
Fun Book: Only given to bus groups
Special Features: Local motels/hotels offer casino packages and free shuttle service.

Kings Club Casino

Rte 1, Box 313
Brimley, Michigan 49715
(906) 248-3227
Map Location: #3 (12 miles S.W. of Sault Ste. Marie)

Toll-Free Number: (800) 575-5493
Restaurants: 1 Deli   Liquor: Yes
Casino Size: 7,400 Square Feet
Hours: 10am-2am Daily
Other Games: Only Slots

Lac Vieux Desert Casino

446 Watersmeet
Watersmeet, Michigan 49969
(906) 358-4226
Map Location: #4 (49 miles S.E. of Ironwood)

Toll-Free Number: (800) 583-3599
Rooms: 96   Price Range: $70-$130
Suites: 15   Price Range: $100-$130
Restaurants: 1   Liquor: Yes
Table Game Hours: 10am-4am Daily
Slot Hours: 24 Hours Daily
Other Games: C, R, B, MB, P, CSP,
                         PGP, LIR, K, BG
Casino Marketing: (906) 358-4423
Senior Discount: If 55, or older, get 2 free rolls of nickels with $10 coin buy-in on Tuesdays from 10am to 6pm
Fun Book: Only given to groups or hotel guests

Leelanau Sands Casino

2521 N.W. Bayshore Dr.
Sutton's Bay, Michigan 49682
(616) 271-4104
Map Location: #5 (4 miles N. of Sutton's Bay)

Toll-Free Number: (800) 922-2946
Room Reservations: (800) 930-3008
Rooms: 51   Price Range: $60-$95
Restaurants: 1   Liquor: Yes
Buffets: B-$4.00 L-$6.00 D-$12.00
Casino Size: 32,000 Square Feet
Hours: 8am-2am/3am (Fri/Sat)
              9am-2am (Sun)
Other Games: C, R, CSP, K
Senior Discount: If 55, or older, every Tuesday receive $30 for $15 coupon, complimentary cocktail and $1 breakfast or lunch
Fun Book: Given at local motels/hotels
Special Features: Rooms are at nearby GTB Motel which is within walking distance of casino. Internet site offers specials - www.casino2win.com

Ojibwa Casino

Rte 1, Box 284A
Baraga, Michigan 49908
(906) 353-6333
Map Location: #6 (30 miles S. of Houghton)

Room Reservations: (800) 323-8045
Rooms: 40   Price Range: $55
Restaurants: 1   Liquor: Yes
Buffets: B-$6.95 (Sun)
               D-$11.95 (Fri)/$8.95 (Sat)

Table Game Hours: 11am-2am/4am (Fri/Sat)
Slot Hours: 9am-2am/24 Hours (Fri/Sat)
Other Games: C, R, CSP, LIR, BG
Casino Marketing: (800) 323-8045
Fun Book: Only given to bus groups

Soaring Eagle Casino
2395 S. Leaton Road
Mount Pleasant, Michigan 48858
(517) 772-8900
Map Location: #7 (65 miles N. of Lansing)

Toll-Free Number: (800) 283-0558
Restaurants: 1 Snack Bar Liquor: No
Table Game Hours: 10am-2am Daily
Slot Hours: 24 Hours Daily
Other Games: C, R, P, BG
Special Features: Casino, card room and bingo hall are in separate facilities within 1/2-mile of each other. Card room (517) 772-0827. Bingo Hall (517) 773-2998.

MINNESOTA

All 16 Minnesota casinos are located on Indian reservations. They are either operated by the tribes themselves, or in conjunction with management companies. Under a compact reached with the state the only type of slot machines permitted are the electronic video variety. Therefore, you will not find any mechanical slots that have traditional reels - only video screens. A few casinos do not serve alcoholic beverages and of those that do some may enforce a two-drink maximum.

Minnesota casinos vary in size starting with the intimate Lake of the Woods operation with eight blackjack tables all the way up to the massive Mystic Lake complex with its two casinos and 128 blackjack tables.

The Minnesota Indian tribes are not required to release information on their slot machine percentage paybacks. According to the terms of the compact between the state and the tribes, however, the minimum and maximum payouts are regulated as follows: video poker and video blackjack - 83% to 98%, slot machines - 80% to 95%, keno - 75% to 95%. Each tribe is free to set its machines to pay back anywhere within those limits.

The hours of operation are listed for those casinos that are not open on a 24-hour basis. Unless otherwise noted, all casinos offer: video slots, video poker, video keno and blackjack. The minimum gambling age is 18 (21 if liquor is served).

Black Bear Casino & Hotel
1789 Highway 210
Carlton, Minnesota 55718
(218) 878-2327
Map Location: #1 (130 miles N. of Twin Cities)

Toll-Free Number: (888) 771-0777
Reservation Number: (800) 553-0022
Rooms: 158 Price Range: $49-$139
Suites: 60 Price Range: $89-$139
Restaurants: 2 (open 24 hours) Liquor: Yes
Other Games: Bingo, Video Craps
Fun Book: Only given to hotel guests
Senior Discount: 10% discount on room rate,
               if 50, or older
Special Features: Hotel is connected to casino by a skywalk.

Firefly Creek Casino
Route 2, Box 96
Granite Falls, Minnesota 56241
(612) 564-2121
Map Location: #2 (110 miles W. of Twin Cities. Five minutes S.E. of Granite Falls on Highway 67 E.)

Restaurants: 1 Liquor: Yes
Casino Size: 26,000 Square Feet
Hours: 8am-2am/24 hours (Fri/Sat)
Other Games: Bingo

Fond-du-Luth Casino
129 E. Superior Street
Duluth, Minnesota 55802
(218) 722-0280
Map Location: #3 (150 miles N.E. of Twin Cities)

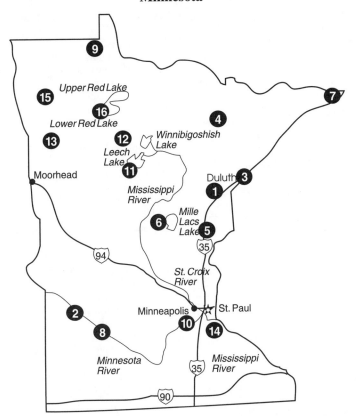

Toll-Free Number: (800) 873-0280
Restaurants: 1 Snack Bar Liquor: Yes
Casino Hours: 10am-2am/24 hours (Fri/Sat)
Other Games: Bingo
Special Features: One hour free parking in lot adjacent to casino.

Fortune Bay Casino

1430 Bois Forte Road
Tower, Minnesota 55790
(218) 753-6400
Map Location: #4 (245 miles N. of Twin Cities. 24 miles N.E. of Virginia, MN on the S. shore of Lake Vermilion)

Toll-Free Number: (800) 992-7529
Restaurants: 1 Liquor: Yes
Buffets: L-$4.95 D-$9.95
Casino Hours: 24 Hours Daily
Other Games: Bingo (Wed-Sun), Keno
Casino Marketing: (800) 992-7529
Senior Discount: Sunday bingo sessions discounted, if 55 or, older
Special Features: Located on shore of Lake Vermilion. 118-room hotel to open early 1997.

Grand Casino Hinckley

777 Lady Luck Drive
Hinckley, Minnesota 55037
(612) 384-7777
Map Location: #5 (76 miles N. of Twin Cities. One mile E. of I-35's Hinckley exit on Route 48)

Toll-Free Number: (800) GRAND-21
RV Reservations: (800) 995-GRAND
Hotel Reservations: (800) HOTEL-17
Rooms: 154 Price Range: $69-$89
Suites: 50 Price Range: $79-$144
Restaurants: 4 (all open 24 hours)
Liquor: Yes
Buffets: L-$6.99 D-$8.99/$12.95 (Tue)
Casino Size: 90,000 Square Feet
Other Games: Video Horse Racing, Video Blackjack, Video Craps, Video Roulette
Casino Marketing: (800) GRAND-76
Special Features: 224-pad RV park with full hook-up. Kid's Quest - supervised children's activity center. Video arcade. Free live entertainment nightly. Weekly Blackjack tournaments. 18-hole championship golf course.

Grand Casino Mille Lacs
777 Grand Avenue
Onamia, Minnesota 56359
(612) 532-7777
Map Location: #6 (90 miles N. of Twin Cities. On Highway 169 on the W. shore of Lake Mille Lacs)

Toll-Free Number: (800) 626-LUCK
Reservation Number: (800) HOTEL-17
Rooms: 175 Price Range: $69-$89
Suites: 20 Price Range: $79-$144
Restaurants: 3 (2 open 24 hours) Liquor: No
Buffets: L-$5.99 D-$7.99
       Brunch-(12am-7am Sat/Sun) $2.99
Casino Size: 120,000 Square Feet
Other Games: Bingo, Video Horse Racing,
       Video Blackjack/Craps/Roulette
Casino Marketing: (800) GRAND-76
Special Features: Weekly blackjack tournament. Free bus transport for groups of 30 or more. Kid's Quest - supervised children's activity center. Video arcade.

Grand Portage Lodge & Casino
P.O. Box 233
Grand Portage, Minnesota 55605
(218) 475-2401
Map Location: #7 (N.E. tip of Minnesota. 300 miles N. of Twin Cities. On Highway 61, five miles from the Canadian border)

Reservation Number: (800) 543-1384
Rooms: 100 Price Range: $44.50-$71.50
Restaurants: 2 Liquor: Yes
Buffets: B-$5.95 D-$7.95
Other Games: Bingo
Casino Marketing: (800) 543-1384
Fun Book: Only given to Lodge guests
Special Features: Located on Lake Superior with lake view rooms. Indoor pool and sauna. Hiking, skiing and snowmobile trails. Gift shop. Marina. RV hook-ups and campground. Free shuttle service to and from Thunder Bay, Ontario.

Jackpot Junction Casino Hotel
P.O. Box 420
Morton, Minnesota 56270
(507) 644-3000
Map Location: #8 (110 miles S.W. of Twin Cities)

Toll-Free Number: (800) WIN-CASH
Rooms: 150 Price Range: $55-$75
Restaurants: 3 (1 open 24 hours) Liquor: Yes

Buffets: B-$4.99 (Fri/Sat 11pm-3am)
       L-$7.99 D-$8.99
Other Games: Bingo
Casino Marketing: (800) WIN-CASH
Special Features: 100-unit campground with full RV hook-up. Live entertainment nightly. Weekly blackjack tournaments. Rooms are at Dakota Inn which is 5 miles from casino.

Lake of the Woods Casino & Bingo
1012 E. Lake Street
Warroad, Minnesota 56763
(218) 386-3381
Map Location: #9 (400 miles N.W. of Twin Cities)

Toll-Free Number: (800) 568-6649
Rooms: 42 Price Range: $30-$150
Restaurants: 2 Liquor: No
Buffets: B-$3.95 L-$5.95 D-$5.95
Casino Hours: 8am-1am/24 hours (Wed-Sun)
Other Games: Bingo (Wed-Sun)
Casino Marketing: (218) 679-2111
Senior Discount: Free soup, sandwich and $5 coupon on Mondays if 55, or older. Also, $5 discount on bingo packages
Fun Book: Ask at casino cage
Special Features: Boat launches, bait shop and tour guides available.

Mystic Lake Casino Hotel
2400 Mystic Lake Boulevard
Prior Lake, Minnesota 55372
(612) 445-9000
Map Location: #10 (25 miles S.W. of Twin Cities. On County Road 83, 3 miles S. of Canterbury Downs)

Toll-Free Number: (800) 262-7799
Reservation Number: (800) 813-7349
Rooms: 200 Price Range: $89-$99
Suites: 16 Price Range: $200-$350
Restaurants: 4 (3 open 24 hours) Liquor: No
Buffets: B-$2.99 (11pm-3am)/$5.95 (Fri/Sat)
       L-$6.95/$8.95 (Sun)
       D-$8.95/$10.95 (Mon)/$13.95 (Wed)
Casino Size: 45,000 Square Feet
Other Games: Bingo
Casino Marketing: (612) 496-1704
Special Features: 1,200-seat bingo hall. Free shuttle bus service from Twin Cities area. Also has a second 45,000-square-foot casino - Dakota Country with 11-store retail arcade.

Northern Lights Casino

HCR73, Box 1003
Walker, Minnesota 56484
(218) 547-2744
Map Location: #11 (175 miles N. of the Twin Cities. Near the S. shore of Lake Leech four miles S. of Walker, MN at the junction of Highways 371 & 200)

Toll-Free Number: (800) 252-PLAY
Restaurants: 1 (Open 24 hours) Liquor: Yes
Casino Marketing: (800) 252-PLAY
Special Features: Weekly blackjack tournaments.

The Palace Bingo & Casino

RR 3, Box 221
Cass Lake, Minnesota 56633
(218) 335-6787
Map Location: #12 (220 miles N.E. of Twin Cities).

Toll-Free Number: (800) 228-6676
Restaurants: 2 (1 open 24 hours) Liquor: No
Other Games: Bingo
Special Features: Blackjack tournament every Tuesday.

Red Lake Casino & Bingo

Highway 1 East
Red Lake, MN 56671
(218) 679-2500
Map Location: #16 (31 miles N. of Bemidji)

Toll-Free Number: (800) 568-6649
Restaurants: 1 Liquor: No
Buffets: B-$3.00 L-$4.00 D-$4.00
Casino Size: 19,800 Square Feet
Casino Hours: 10am-2am Daily
Other Games: Bingo (Wed-Sun)
Senior Discount: Free soup, sandwich and $5 coupon on select day if 55, or older. Also, $5 discount on bingo packages

River Road Casino & Bingo

RR 3, Box 168A
Thief River Falls, Minnesota 56701
(218) 681-4062
Map Location: #15 (275 miles N.W. of Minneapolis)

Toll-Free Number: (800) 568-6649
Restaurants: 1 (open 24 hours) Liquor: No
Buffets: B-$2.00 L-$5.95 D-$5.95
Hours: 8am-1am/24 Hours (Wed-Sun)
Casino Size: 11,818 Square Feet
Other Games: Bingo (Wed-Sun)

Casino Marketing: (800) 568-6649
Senior Discount: Free soup, sandwich and $5 coupon on Tuesdays if 55, or older. Also, $5 discount on bingo packages
Fun Book: Given out by local motels

Shooting Star Casino Hotel

777 Casino Boulevard
Mahnomen, Minnesota 56557
(218) 935-2701
Map Location: #13 (250 miles N.W. of Twin Cities)

Room Reservations: (800) 453-STAR
Rooms: 225 Price Range: $57-$65
Suites: 30 Price Range: $65
Restaurants: 4 (1 open 24 hours) Liquor: Yes
Buffets: L-$5.95 D-$5.95
Casino Marketing: (218) 935-2701 ext.-7231
Fun Book: Lodge guests receive coupons for free continental breakfast and free Fun Book.
Special Features: Nightly live entertainment with country/western bands. Cabaret showroom with big-name acts. Glass-enclosed pool and atrium. Kiddie arcade. RV park with full hook-ups.

Treasure Island Casino

5734 Sturgeon Lake Road
Welch, Minnesota 55089
(612) 388-1171
Map Location: #14 (40 miles S.E. of Twin Cities. Halfway between Hastings and Redwing , off Highway 61 on County Road 18)

Toll-Free Number: (800) 222-7077
Restaurants: 3 (1 open 24 hours) Liquor: Yes
Buffets: B-$6.50 (Sat/Sun) L-$5.95 D-$7.95/ $9.95(Sat)/$11.95 (Mon)
Casino Size: 100,000 Square Feet
Other Games: Bingo, Video Craps
Casino Marketing: (800) 222-7077
Special Features: 250-room hotel expected to open by early 1997. Tropical island theme throughout casino. 2, 4 and 6-deck blackjack offered. RV Park. Marina.

MISSISSIPPI

Mississippi was the third state to legalize riverboat gambling when it was approved by that state's legislature in 1990. The law restricts casinos to coast waters (including the Bay of St. Louis and the Back Bay of Biloxi) along the Mississippi River and in navigable waters of counties that border the river.

Mississippi law also requires that riverboats be permanently moored at the dock and they are not permitted to cruise. This allows the riverboats to offer 24-hour dockside gambling. The Isle of Capri in Biloxi was the first casino to open on August 1, 1992 followed one month later by The President Casino.

Since the law does not require that the floating vessel actually resemble a boat, almost all of the casinos are built on barges. This gives them the appearance of a land-based building, rather than a riverboat. There is no limit to the number of casinos that can be built and as of September 9, 1996 there were 29 riverboat casinos in operation, plus one land-based Indian casino.

Two major projects are in progress and both will be in Biloxi. Mirage Resorts, Inc. is building a $475-million, 1,800-room luxury resort called Beau Rivage. It will feature a 29-story hotel, a retail shopping esplanade, a 1,200-seat showroom and a 38,000-square-foot meeting and convention center. There will also be a 150,000-square-foot barge integrated with the land-based portion of the project that will house an 85,000-square-foot casino. The projected opening date is Spring 1998.

The Imperial Palace is constructing a 30-story hotel which, when completed, will be the tallest building in Mississippi. The 1,050-room hotel will also feature a movie theater complex, an 800-seat showroom, a health and fitness spa, a shopping arcade, a 30th-floor gourmet restaurant and an antique and classic auto collection. There will also be a three-story, 70,000-square-foot casino. The projected opening date is Spring 1997. For updated information on the project you can call the Imperial Palace Resevation number in Las Vegas (800) 634-6441

The Mississippi Gaming Commission does not break down its slot statistics by individual properties. Rather, they are classified by region. The coastal region includes the Biloxi, Gulfport and Bay Saint Louis casinos. The north river region includes Robinsonville and Lula. The south river region includes Vicksburg, Greenville and Natchez.

With that in mind here's information, as supplied by the Mississippi Gaming Commission, showing the slot machine payback percentages for each area's casinos for the one-year period from August 1, 1995 through July 31, 1996:

	Coastal	North	South
5¢ Slots	**89.01%**	87.54%	88.46%
25¢ Slots	91.43%	91.54%	**91.91%**
$1 Slots	94.42%	94.48%	**94.50%**
$5 Slots	**95.87%**	95.59%	95.70%

These numbers reflect the percentage of money returned on each denomination of machine and encompass all electronic machines including video poker and video keno. The best returns for each category are highlighted in bold print and you can see that the coastal casinos offered the best returns on 5¢ machines. In all of the other denominations of machines the differences among the casinos from each region is barely discernible.

Unless otherwise noted, all casinos are open 24 hours and offer: slots, video poker, big six wheel, blackjack, craps, roulette, poker and Caribbean Stud Poker.

Other game listings include: baccarat (B), mini-baccarat (MB), pai gow poker (PGP), Let It Ride (LIR) and keno (K). The minimum gambling age is 21.

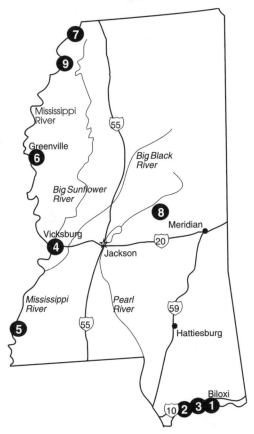

Bay St. Louis

Map Location: #2 (on St. Louis Bay, 40 mil E. of New Orleans)

Casino Magic - Bay St. Louis
711 Casino Magic Drive
Bay St. Louis, Mississippi 39520
(601) 467-9257

Toll-Free Number: (800) 5-MAGIC-5
Rooms: 201 Price Range: $55-$75
Suites: 22 Price Range: $75-$95
Restaurants: 3 (1 open 24 hours)
Buffets: L-$7.50 D-$9.50
Casino Size: 39,500 Square Feet
Other Games: MB, PGP, LIR, K
Casino Marketing: (800) 5-MAGIC-5
Senior Discount: If 55, or older, get discount
on breakfast buffet 6am-9am Mon-Fri.
Fun Book: Bring in postcard from local hotels
or Mississippi Welcome Center

Special Features: 100 hook-up RV Park with picnic tables, laundromat, cable TV, showers and vending machines. 50-slip marina with boat rentals. Golf packages available. On-site golf practice facility.

Biloxi

Map Location: #1 (On the Gulf of Mexico, 80 miles E. of New Orleans)

Boomtown Casino - Biloxi
676 Bayview Avenue
Biloxi, Mississippi 39530
(601) 435-7000

Toll-Free Number: (800) 627-0777
Restaurants: 2 (1 open 24 hours)
Buffets: B-$2.95 L-$5.95 D-$6.95
Casino Size: 33,632 Square Feet
Other Games: PGP, LIR, K
Casino Marketing: (800) 627-0777 ext. 5011

Senior Discount: If 65, or older, get 10% discount in restaurants and gift shop

Fun Book: Given when you join slot club

Special Features: Family entertainment center with motion dynamic theater and arcade. Nightly western entertainment in cabaret. Gift shop with western clothing and collectibles.

Casino Magic - Biloxi
195 E. Beach Boulevard
Biloxi, Mississippi 39530
(601) 467-9257

Toll-Free Number: (800) 5-MAGIC-5
Restaurants: 3 (1 open 24 hours)
Buffets: B-$4.99 L-$6.99 D-$9.99
Casino Size: 47,200 Square Feet
Other Games: MB, PGP, LIR, K
Casino Marketing: (800) 5-MAGIC-5
Senior Discount: If 55, or older, get breakfast buffet discount 6am-9am Mon-Fri.
Fun Book: Bring in postcard from local hotels or Mississippi Welcome Center
Special Features: On-site McDonald's Restaurant. Free Comedy Club Tuesdays at 8:30pm. Continuous laser show nightly from dusk until 2am. Daily entertainment in the Eclipse Showroom. 250-room hotel expected to open by mid-1997.

Grand Casino - Biloxi
265 Beach Boulevard
Biloxi, Mississippi 39530
(601) 436-2946

Toll-Free Number: (800) WIN-2-WIN
Rooms: 491 Price Range: $89-$139
Suites: 17 Price Range: $240-$400
Restaurants: 6 (1 open 24 hours)
Buffets: L-$6.99 D-$9.99
Casino Size: 100,000 Square Feet
Other Games: MB, PGP, LIR, Sic Bo, K
Casino Marketing: (800) 946-2946
Fun Book: Only given to groups
Special Features: Kid's Quest - children's activity center. Video arcade. Free valet parking. Non-smoking gaming areas. Grand Theatre features Las Vegas-style shows and special events. Hotel has pool, full-service spa and Jacuzzi. Specialty shops. 16,500-square-feet of meeting and convention space.

Isle of Capri Casino - Biloxi
151 Beach Boulevard
Biloxi, Mississippi 39530
(601) 435-5400

Toll-Free Number: (800) THE-ISLE
Rooms: 367 Price Range: $109-$119
Restaurants: 3 (open 24 hours)
Buffets: B-$5.95 L-$6.95 D-$10.95
Casino Size: 32,500 Square Feet
Other Games: MB, PGP, LIR
Fun Book: Only given to groups
Special Features: Tropical theme throughout casino.

Lady Luck Casino - Biloxi
307 Beach Boulevard
Biloxi, Mississippi 39530
(601) 435-7639

Toll-Free Number: (800) 539-LUCK
Restaurants: 2 (1 open 24 hours)
Buffets: B-$4.95 L-$6.95 D-$9.95
Casino Size: 22,000 Square Feet
Other Games: LIR, No Poker
Casino Marketing: (800) 539-LUCK
                   ask for ext.-2117
Fun Book: Given when you join the slot club
Special Features: Asian-theme decor throughout casino. Fire-breathing "Dragon of Fortune" shows nightly at 8, 9, 10 and 11pm.

Palace Casino
158 Howard Avenue
Biloxi, Mississippi 39530
(601) 432-8888

Toll-Free Number: (800) PALACE-9
Restaurants: 3 (1 open 24 hours)
Buffets: B-$3.95 L-$5.95 D-$8.95
Casino Size: 32,040 Square Feet
Other Games: No Poker or Caribbean Stud
Casino Marketing: (800) PALACE-9
Senior Discount: If 55, or older, join Senior Circle Club for free slot coins and buffet discounts on Mondays
Special Features: Casino is on a 3-story barge with an all-glass exterior. 500-seat theater features Las Vegas-style entertainment. "Thrifty Gambler" area features $1 blackjack, 25¢ craps and 10¢ roulette from 6pm-7am.

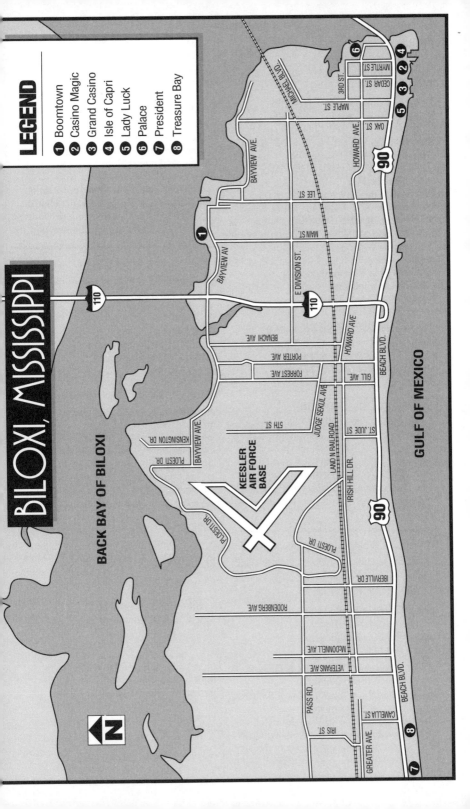

President Casino
2110 Beach Boulevard
Biloxi, Mississippi 39531
(601) 385-3500

Toll-Free Number: (800) THE-PRES
Rooms: 850 Price Range: $65-$95
Restaurants: 2 (1 open 24 hours)
Buffets: B-$6.95 (Sun) L-$5.95 D-$7.95
Casino Size: 38,000 Square Feet
Casino Marketing: (800) THE-PRES
Other Games: PGP, LIR
Fun Book: Only given to hotel guests
Special Features: All rooms are at adjacent
Broadwater Beach Resort. Golf packages (2
courses) also available. Live entertainment
Wed-Sat.

Treasure Bay Casino & Resort
1980 Beach Boulevard
Biloxi, Mississippi 39531
(601) 385-6000

Toll-Free Number: (800) PIRATE-9
Rooms: 262 Price Range: $55-$120
Suites: 8 Price Range: $215-$310
Restaurants: 4 (1 open 24 hours)
Buffets: B-$3.95 L-$6.95 D-$8.95
Size: 56,000 Square Feet
Other Games: MB, PGP, LIR
Casino Marketing: (800) 747-2839
Senior Discount: Room discount to
                 AARP members
Fun Book: Only given to hotel guests
Special Features: Casino is a 400-foot replica
of an 18th century pirate ship and fort that is
built on a barge. Live free entertainment
nightly. Video arcade.

Greenville

Map Location: #6 (On the Mississippi River,
121 miles N.W. of Jackson)

Bayou Caddy's Jubilee Casino
Lake Ferguson Waterfront
Greenville, Mississippi 38701
(601) 335-1111

Toll-Free Number: (800) WIN-MORE
Restaurants: 1 (open 24 hours)
Buffets: L-$4.95 D-$5.95/$6.95 (Fri/Sat)
Casino Size: 34,000 Square Feet
Casino Marketing: (800) WIN-MORE
Special Features: Live entertainment nightly.
Hotel accommodations available in the area
with shuttle service to casino. Daily coin
promotions and nightly cash drawings.

Las Vegas Casino
Lake Ferguson Waterfront
Greenville, Mississippi 38701
(601) 335-5800

Toll-Free Number: (800) VEGAS-21
Restaurants: 1
Buffets: L-$6.95
Casino Size: 18,800 Square Feet
Casino Marketing: (800) VEGAS-21
Other Games: LIR, No Poker
Senior Discount: Wed from 1pm-3pm is
   seniors day. If 50, or older, get choice
   of: $10 in tokens or two free lunch buffets.
Special Features: Live entertainment nightly.

Gulfport

Map Location: #3 (On the Gulf of Mexico, 70
miles E. of New Orleans)

Copa Casino
777 Copa Casino Boulevard
Gulfport, Mississippi 39501
(601) 863-3330

Toll-Free Number: (800) WIN-COPA
Restaurants: 2 (1 open 24 hours)
Buffets: L-$3.99 D-$5.99
Casino Size: 26,000 Square Feet
Other Games: PGP, LIR
Casino Marketing: (601) 867-0147
Senior Discount: If 55, or older, receive a free
   breakfast and $1 roll of nickels on Mon/
   Wed/Fri from 7am to 10am. Look for ad in
   Sun-Herald and bring to Welcome Center.
Fun Book: Present out-of-state ID at
              welcome center
Special Features: Casino is on a 1,500-pas-
senger modern cruise ship with a Rio theme.
Free valet parking. Video arcade.

Grand Casino - Gulfport
3215 W. Beach Boulevard
Gulfport, Mississippi 39501
(601) 870-7777

Toll-Free Number: (800) WIN-7777
Room Reservations: (800) 354-2450
Rooms: 407 Price Range: $89-$139
Suites: 26 Price Range: $240-$400
Restaurants: 7 (1 open 24 hours)
Buffets: L-$6.99 D-$9.99
Casino Size: 105,000 Square Feet
Other Games: MB, PGP, LIR, K
Casino Marketing: (800) WIN-7777

Special Features: Kids Quest - children's activity center. Video arcade. Free valet parking. Non-smoking gaming areas. Entertainment center features 4 nightclubs. 17-story beach front hotel has indoor swimming pool, Jacuzzi, full-service spa and exercise room. 9,000-square-feet of meeting and convention space.

Lula

Map Location #9 (On the Mississippi River, 70 miles S. of Memphis, TN)

Country Casino
777 Lady Luck Parkway
Lula, Mississippi 38644
(601) 363-4600

Toll-Free Number: (800) 789-LUCK
Rooms: 116 Price Range: $39-$69
Restaurants: 4 (1 open 24 hours)
Buffets: B-$4.95 L-$5.95 D-$8.95
Casino Size: 33,000 Square Feet
Other Games: LIR, No Poker
Casino Marketing: (800) 789-LUCK
Fun Book: Given when you sign up for
          Mad Money Slot Club
Special Features: Connected to Lady Luck Rhythm & Blues. $2 continental breakfast.

Lady Luck Rhythm & Blues Casino
777 Lady Luck Parkway
Lula, Mississippi 38644
(601) 363-4600

Toll-Free Number: (800) 789-LUCK
Rooms: 173 Price Range: $39-$89
Suites: 4 Price Range: $79-$99
Restaurants: 4 (1 open 24 hours)
Buffets: B-$4.95 L-$5.95 D-$8.95
Casino Size: 25,000 Square Feet
Other Games: LIR, No Poker
Casino Marketing: (800) 789-LUCK
Fun Book: Given when you sign up for
          Mad Money Slot Club
Special Features: Hotel has outdoor swimming pool, whirlpool and workout spa. All rooms have refrigerators and Jacuzzi tubs. Land based pavilion features 1,000-seat entertainment center with headline acts, two movie theaters and a video arcade.

Natchez

Map Location: #5 (on the Mississippi River, 102 miles S.W. of Jackson)

Lady Luck Casino Hotel- Natchez
53 Silver Street
Natchez, Mississippi 39120
(601) 445-0605

Toll-Free Number: (800) 722-LUCK
Rooms: 144 Price Range: $59-$89
Suites: 2 Price Range: $125-$175
Restaurants: 3
Buffets: L-$5.55 D-$9.99
Size: 14,000 Square Feet
Other Games: LIR
Casino Marketing: (800) 722-LUCK
Fun Book: Given when you join the slot club
Senior Discount: If 55, or older, eligible to
          join Club 55 which offers free brunch
          (first-time members only) on Tue/Thu
          and chance to win monthly drawing for
          trip to Las Vegas
Special Features: Casino resembles an 1860's paddle wheel steamboat, but is actually built on a barge. Live entertainment in Burgundy Room on weekends.

Robinsonville

Map Location: #7 (on the Mississippi River, 28 miles S. of Memphis, TN)

Bally's Saloon/Gambling Hall Hotel
1450 Bally's Boulevard
Robinsonville, Mississippi 38664
(601) 357-1500

Toll-Free Number: (800) 382-2559
Rooms: 200   Price Range: $49-$89
Parlors: 38 Price Range: $99-$119
Restaurants: 2 (1 open 24 hours)
Buffets: B-$3.50 L-$5.95 D-$6.95
Casino Size: 40,000 Square Feet
Other Games: MB, LIR
Special Features: Parlor rooms noted above are slightly larger than standard rooms.

Circus Circus Casino
100 Casino Center Drive
Robinsonville, Mississippi 38664
(601) 357-1111

Toll-Free Number: (800) 9-CIRCUS
Restaurants: 3 (1 open 24 hours)
Buffets: L-$5.95 D-$7.95
Casino Size: 48,000 Square Feet
Other Games: LIR
Casino Marketing: (800) 871-CLUB
Special Features: Free valet parking. Strolling circus entertainment.

Fitzgerald's Casino/Hotel/RV Park
711 Lucky Lane
Robinsonville, Mississippi 38664
(601) 363-5825

Toll-Free Number: (800) 766-LUCK
Rooms: 507 Price Range: $59-$89
Suites: 70 Price Range: $109-$139
Restaurants: 2 (1 open 24 hours)
Buffets: B-$4.95 L-$6.95 D-$7.95
Casino Size: 36,000 Square Feet
Casino Marketing: (800) 766-LUCK
Other Games: LIR, K
Senior Discount: 10% off room rate
                for AARP members
Fun Book: Call marketing department
Special Features: Sports pub. Indoor pool. Ice cream & coffee pub. 100-space RV park with full hook-up for $10 per night.

Grand Casino Tunica
13615 Old Highway 61 N.
Robinsonville, Mississippi 38664
(601) 363-2788

Toll-Free Number: (800) 946-4946
Rooms: 108 Price Range: $89-$109
Suites: 42 Price Range: $150-$400
Restaurants: 7 (1 open 24 hours)
Buffets: B-$4.95 L-$6.95 D-$7.95
Casino Size: 140,000 Square Feet
Other Games: MB, PGP, LIR
Fun Book: Only given to groups
Special Features: World's largest dockside casino. Four themed areas: Western, New Orleans/Mardi Gras, Victorian/San Francisco and Riverpark. By late 1997 complex will include: two more hotels, 18-hole golf course, Kid's Quest - children's activity center, 90-acre lake, convention center, outlet mall and indoor water park.

Harrah's Tunica Casino
1600 Harrah's Drive
Robinsonville, Mississippi 38664
(601) 363-7200

Reservation Number: (800) HARRAHS
Restaurants: 1 (open 24 hours)
Buffets: B-$5.95 L-$6.95 D-$8.95
Casino Size: 27,011 Square Feet
Other Games: B, MB, PGP, LIR, No Poker
Casino Marketing: (888) 789-7900
Senior Discount: 10% off room rate
                for AARP members
Fun Book: Ask at Gold Card desk
Special Features: Two-level casino with large non-smoking area and "Party Island" on 2nd deck. Retail store in land-based pavilion.

Harrah's Tunica Mardi Gras Casino & Hotel
1100 Casino Strip Boulevard
Robinsonville, Mississippi 38664
(601) 363-7777

Reservation Number: (800) HARRAHS
Rooms: 180 Price Range: $69-$99
Suites: 20 Price Range: $89-$109
Restaurants: 3 (open 24 hours)
Buffets: B-$4.99 L-$6.99 D-$8.99
Casino Size: 50,000 Square Feet
Other Games: B, MB, PGP, LIR, K
Casino Marketing: (888) 789-7900
Senior Discount: 10% off room rate
                for AARP members
Fun Book: Ask at Gold Card desk
Special Features: The Planet 4 Kidz - a state-certified child care facility. Teen video arcade. Gift shop. Golf course to open by mid-1997.

Hollywood Casino Hotel & RV Park
1150 Commerce Landing
Robinsonville, Mississippi 38671
(601) 357-7700

Toll-Free Number: (800) 871-0711
Rooms: 509 Price Range:$59-$99
Suites: 23 Price Range:$100-$249
Restaurants: 2 (1 open 24 hours)
Buffets: B-$3.99 L-$6.59 D-$8.83
Size: 54,000 Square Feet
Other Games: LIR
Casino Marketing: (800) 871-0711
Fun Book: Only given to groups
Special Features: Casino features a collection of Hollywood memorabilia. 50-space RV park. Sign up for slot club card and use it for 10% discount in hotel, restaurants and gift shop.

Horseshoe Casino & Hotel
1021 Casino Center Drive
Robinsonville, Mississippi 38664
(601) 357-5500

Toll-Free Number: (800) 303-7463
Rooms: 200 Price Range: $49-$99
Restaurants: 2 (1 open 24 hours)
Buffets: B-$4.95 L-$5.95 D-$7.95
Casino Size: 30,000 Square Feet

Sam's Town Hotel & Gambling Hall
1477 Casino Strip Boulevard
Robinsonville, Mississippi 38664
(601) 363-0711

Toll-Free Number: (800) 456-0711
Rooms: 860 Price Range: $59-$89
Restaurants: 1 (1 open 24 hours)
Buffets: B-$7.95 (Sat/Sun)
          D-$5.95/$9.87 (Fri)
Size: 96,000 Square Feet
Other Games: MB, PGP, LIR, K
Casino Marketing: (800) 946-0711
Fun Book: Look for coupon in
           back of this book
Special Features: 1,600-seat indoor amphi-
theater with headliner-entertainment every
weekend. Video arcade. Hotel has pool, sauna,
Jacuzzi and exercise room.

Sheraton Casino
1107 Casino Center Drive
Robinsonville, Mississippi 38664
(601) 363-4900

Toll-Free Number: (800) 391-3777
Restaurants: 3 (1 open 24 hours)
Buffets: B-$3.97/$6.97(Sun)
          L-$5.97 D-$8.97
Casino Size: 32,000 Square Feet
Other Games: MB, LIR, No Poker
Casino Marketing: (800) 391-3777
Senior Discount: If 55, or older, receive free
    buffet on Mondays from 9am to 4:30pm
Special Features: Three-story casino has an
English Tudor-style appearance. Free live
entertainment nightly in RiverStage lounge.
Non-smoking gaming areas. Free valet park-
ing.

Vicksburg

Map Location: #4 (on the Mississippi River,
44 miles W. of Jackson)

Ameristar Casino - Vicksburg
4146 Washington Street
Vicksburg, Mississippi 39180
(601) 638-1000

Reservation Number: (800) 700-7770
Rooms: 54   Price Range: $49-$65
Suites: 12 Price Range: $65-$70
Restaurants: 3 (1 open 24 hours)
Buffets: L-$7.95 D-$9.95
Casino Size: 44,388 Square Feet
Other Games: LIR
Casino Marketing: (601) 638-1000
Senior Discount: Ask for senior
                 discount book
Special Features: Free cabaret entertainment.
Free valet parking. Free shuttle bus service.

Harrah's Vicksburg Casino Hotel
1310 Mulberry Street
Vicksburg, Mississippi 39180
(601) 636-DICE

Reservation Number: (800) HARRAHS
Rooms: 101 Price Range: $69-$109
Suites: 16 Price Range: $99-$149
Restaurants: 3 (1 open 24 hours)
Buffets: B-$4.95 L-$6.95 D-$8.95
Casino Size: 62,252 Square Feet
Other Games: LIR, No Poker
Casino Marketing: (601) 630-2003
Special Features: Casino is on *Star of
Vicksburg* a 1,200-passenger old-fashioned
paddle wheel riverboat. Non-smoking gam-
ing area.

Isle of Capri Casino - Vicksburg
3990 Washington Street
Vicksburg, Mississippi 39180
(601) 636-5700
Map Location: #5 (on the Mississippi River,
44 miles W. of Jackson)

Toll-Free Number: (800) THE-ISLE
Restaurants: 2 (1 open 24 hours)
Buffets: L-$4.95 D-$6.95
Casino Size: 24,000 Square Feet
Casino Marketing: (800) WIN-ISLE

Senior Discount: If 50, or older, ask for
                free coupon book (Mon-Fri)
Fun Book: Only offered to bus groups
Special Features: Casino features tropical
Caribbean theme. 67-space RV park.

Rainbow Casino
1380 Warrenton Road
Vicksburg, Mississippi 39182
(601) 636-7575

Toll-Free Number: (800) 503-3777
Restaurants: 1
Buffets: B-$3.75 L-$5.25
         D-$7.50/$8.50 (Fri/Sat)
Casino Size: 20,000 Square Feet
Other Games: LIR, No Poker

Indian Casino

Silver Star Hotel & Casino
Highway 16 West
Philadelphia, Mississippi 39350
(601) 656-3400
Map Location: #8 (81 miles N.E. of Jackson)

Toll-Free Number: (800) 557-0711
Rooms: 100 Price Range:$64-$79
Suites: 2   Price Range:$125-$150
Restaurants: 3 (1 open 24 hours)
Buffets: B-$5.95 L-$5.95 D-$7.95
Casino Size: 40,000 Square Feet
Other Games: MB, LIR, K
Casino Marketing: (800) 557-0711

MISSOURI

In November 1992 Missouri voters approved a state-wide referendum to allow riverboat gambling. That made it the fifth state to approve this form of gambling. There is no limit on the number of licenses that may be issued by the state's gaming commission and the law also permits dockside gambling in some locations.

All of the boats on the Missouri River remain dockside. Although originally required to cruise, those boats were later ordered to remain dockside because there were concerns over the safety of passengers on boats that cruised that river.

As of September 1995 there were seven casinos (eight if you count the barge at Casino St. Charles as a separate casino) in operation, four more were in the final stages of licensing and there were 22 more applications on file with the Missouri Gaming Commission.

All riverboats, both cruising and dockside, are limited to two-hour gaming sessions and boarding of the boats must be within 45 minutes of the scheduled starting time. For example, on a 9am cruise you must be on board by 9:45am. The boat would then leave for a trip of about 45 minutes which would bring it back at about 10:30 or approximately 30 minutes before the next scheduled session. The non-cruising boats that remain dockside also follow the same procedures. You still

must be on board within 45 minutes of the scheduled starting time or you won't be allowed to enter.

On all of the boats that charge admission you only have to pay once. After paying your admission fee you are allowed to remain for any of the next sessions at no charge and you are always free to leave a boat at any time.

There is a $500 loss-limit on all sessions/cruises which is enforced by issuing a set of vouchers (usually in increments of $20 and $100) to each passenger as they board the riverboat. In order to get your chips or slot machine tokens you must exchange your cash along with an equal amount of vouchers. For example, if you wanted $100 worth of chips you must give in $100 worth of vouchers along with your $100 cash to receive your chips. If you use all $500 worth of your vouchers you can't gamble anymore during that cruise and you must wait for the next cruise to be issued a new set of vouchers. The sharing of vouchers is prohibited by law - even between spouses. There is no limit on winnings.

For those interested in which casinos provide the best returns on their slot machines we offer the following statistics from the Missouri Gaming Commission for the fiscal year beginning July 1, 1995 and ending June 30, 1996:

CASINO	PAYBACK
Harrah's	94.76%
Sam's Town	93.79%
President	93.74%
St. Charles	93.71%
Argosy	93.67%
St. Jo Frontier	93.09%
Aztar	91.71%

These figures reflect the total percentages returned by each casino for all of their electronic machines including slot machines, video poker, video keno, etc. As you can see, Harrah's returned the most to its slot machine players, while Casino Aztar returned the least.

Unless otherwise noted, all casinos offer: slots, video poker, craps, blackjack, roulette, poker and Caribbean Stud Poker. Optional games include: baccarat (B), mini-baccarat (MB), pai gow poker (PGP) and Let It Ride (LIR). The minimum gambling age is 21.

Argosy Casino
777 N.W. Argosy Parkway
Riverside, Missouri 64150
(816) 746-7711
Map Location: #1 (3 miles W. of Kansas City)

Toll-Free Number: (800) 270-7711
Restaurants: 4 (Deli on boat)
Buffets: B-$4.95 L-$6.95 D-$8.95
Sessions: 8am, 10am, 12pm, 2pm, 4pm,
    6pm, 8pm, 10pm, 12am, 2am
Admission: All sessions are free
Casino Size: 30,000 Square Feet
Other Games: B, MB, PGP, LIR
Casino Marketing: (816) 746-3151
Senior Discount: If 55, or older, receive
    discounts on certain days which vary
Special Features: 1,800-passenger old-fashioned paddle wheeler that remains dockside on the Missouri River. Buffet and fine-dining restaurant are in land-based pavilion.

Casino Aztar
777 East Third
Caruthersville, Missouri 63830
(573) 333-1000
Map Location: #4 (200 miles S. of St. Louis)

Reservation Number: (573) 333-1000
Restaurants: 2
Cruise Schedule (Prices):
8am	($3)
10am	($3)
12pm	($3)
2pm	($3)
4pm	($3)
6pm	($3/$5 Sat)
8pm	($3/$5 Fri/$8 Sat)
10pm	($3/$5 Fri/$8 Sat)
12am	($3/$5 Sat)
2am	($3) Only Fri/Sat

Casino Size: 12,000 Square Feet
Special Features: 800-passenger stern wheeler that cruises the Mississippi River. $1 discount on cruises when you show Casino Aztar slot club card. Restaurant, snack bar, sports bar and gift shop are located in land-based pavilion.

Flamingo Casino Kansas City
1800 E. Front Street
Kansas City, Missouri 64120
(816) 855-7777
Map Location: #1

EXPECTED TO OPEN BY EARLY 1997
Toll-Free Number: (800) 946-8711
Restaurants: 6
Dockside Sessions: 8am, 10am, 12pm, 2pm, 4pm, 6pm, 8pm, 10pm, 12am, 2am, 4am
Admission: All sessions are free
Casino Size: 30,000 Square Feet
Other Games: MB, CSP, LIR
Special Features: 1.700-passenger that remains dockside in a man-made lake fed by the nearby Missouri River. 260-room hotel to open by late 1997.

Harrah's St. Louis
11737 Administration Drive #100
St. Louis, Missouri 63146
(314) 872-7197
Map Location: #2

EXPECTED TO OPEN BY MARCH 1997
Toll-Free Number: (800) HARRAHS

Harrah's North Kansas City
1 Riverboat Drive
Kansas City, Missouri 64116
(816) 472-7777
Map Location: #1

Toll-Free Number: (800) HARRAHS
Restaurants: 4 (Deli on both boats)
Buffets: B-$5.99 L-$6.99
              D-$9.99/$12.99 (Fri/Sat)
Lucky Star Sessions: 8am, 10am, 12pm, 2pm, 4pm, 6pm, 8pm, 10pm, 12am, 2am
North Star Sessions: 9am, 11am, 1pm, 3pm, 5pm, 7pm, 9pm, 11pm, 1am, 3am (Th-Sat)
Sessions: All sessions are free
Casino Size: 33,000 Square Feet (North Star)
Casino Size: 44,000 Square Feet (Lucky Star)
Other Games: MB, LIR
Special Features: Two riverboats that remain dockside on the Missouri River. North Star is 1,600-passenger stern wheeler and Lucky Star is a 1,700-passenger paddle wheeler. $1 discount off buffets when you show Harrah's Gold Card. Restaurants, sports bar and video arcade are located in land-based pavilion.

Players Island Casino - St. Louis
11737 Administration Drive #101
St. Louis, Missouri 63146
(314) 209-0777
Map Location: #2

EXPECTED TO OPEN BY MARCH 1997
Toll-Free Number: (800) 599-6378

President Casino on the Admiral
802 N. First Street
St. Louis, Missouri 63102
(314) 622-3000
Map Location: #2

Toll-Free Number: (800) 544-7881
Restaurants: 2 on boat
Buffets: Sat/Sun Brunch-$9.95 L-$5.95 D-$9.95
Dockside Sessions: 8am, 10am, 12pm, 2pm, 4pm, 6pm, 8pm, 10pm, 12am, 2am
Prices: $2 for all sessions
Parking: Free with casino validation
Special Features: 1940's vintage, 2,500-passenger, art deco riverboat that remains dockside on the Mississippi River at the foot of the Gateway Arch. Free shuttle service to and from all downtown hotels. One block from Metro Link Light Rail Station. Buffet, food court, lounge and gift shop on boat.

Sam's Town - Kansas City
6711 N.E. Birmingham Road
Kansas City, Missouri 64117
(816) 414-7777
Map Location: #1

Toll-Free Number: (800) 988-0711
Restaurants: 2 (snack bar on boat)
Buffets: B-$4.95 L-$6.95
          D-$9.95/$13.95 (Fri/Sat)
Sessions: 8am, 10am, 12pm, 2pm, 4pm,
          6pm, 8pm, 10pm, 12am, 2am
Prices: All sessions are free
Other Games: LIR, No Poker
Casino Size: 28,000 Square Feet
Special Features: 1,550-passenger old-fashioned paddle wheeler that remains dockside on the Missouri River. Land-based pavilion has 2 restaurants/sports bar/ice cream parlor.

Station Casino Kansas City
8201 N.E. Birmingham Road
Kansas City, Missouri 64161
(816) 414-7000
Map Location: #1

EXPECTED TO OPEN BY LATE 1996
Rooms: 200
Restaurants: 5
Special Features: Riverboat casino complex will house two dockside casinos.

Station Casino St. Charles
P.O. Box 720
St. Charles, Missouri 63302
(314) 949-7777
Map Location: #2 (5 miles W. of St. Louis)

Toll-Free Number: (800) 325-7777
Restaurants: 4 (Snack bar on boat)
Buffets: B-$4.95 L-$6.95
          D-$9.95/$11.95 (Fri/Sat)
Boat Sessions: 9am, 11am, 1pm, 3pm,
               5pm, 7pm, 9pm, 11pm, 1am
Prices: $2 (9am/11am are free)
Barge Sessions: 8am, 10am, 12pm, 2pm,
               4pm, 6pm, 8pm, 10pm, 12am, 2am
Prices: $2 (8am/10am/12pm are free)
Casino Size: 55,000 Square Feet
Other Games: M-B, LIR
Casino Marketing: (800) 325-7777
Fun Book: Distributed by local hotels
Special Features: Complex contains two dockside casinos: 2,000-passenger old-fashioned paddle wheeler that remains dockside on the Missouri River and another casino on a barge. Live entertainment daily. Burger King, TCBY Yogurt and pizza shop on barge.

St. Jo Frontier Casino
77 Francis Street
St. Joseph, Missouri 64501
(816) 279-7577
Map Location: #3 (55 miles N. of Kansas City)

Toll-Free Number: (800) 888-2WIN
Restaurants: 2 (1 Deli on boat)
Sessions: 8am, 10am, 12pm, 2pm, 4pm, 6pm,
          8pm, 10pm, 12am, 2am
Prices: $2
Other Games: LIR, No Poker
Casino Size: 9,260 Square Feet
Casino Marketing: (800) WIN-STJO
Fun Book: Only offered to groups
Senior Discount: If 55, or older, receive free admission to all 8am cruises
Special Features: 600-passenger old-fashioned paddle wheeler that remains dockside on the Missouri River. Entertainment barge located next to the casino has a bar and gift shop.

MONTANA

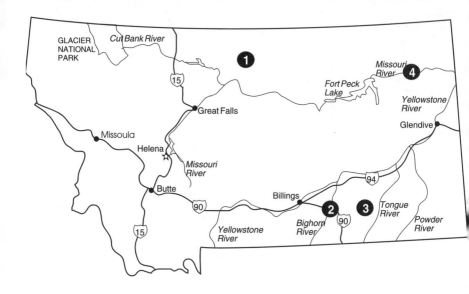

Montana law permits bars and taverns to have up to 20 video gaming devices that play either video poker or video keno. These machines are operated in partnership with the state and are not permitted to pay out in cash; instead, they print out a receipt which must be taken to a cashier.

Additionally, there are four Indian casinos which offer regular video poker and video keno machines which pay out in cash. The minimum gambling age is 18.

4 C's Cafe & Casino
Rocky Boy Route, Box 544
Box Elder, Montana 59521
(406) 395-4850
Map Location: #1 (75 miles N.E. of Great Falls)

Restaurants: 1 Liquor: No
Hours: 8am-2am Daily
Other Games: Bingo (Tue-Thu)

Little Big Horn Casino
P.O. Box 580
Crow Agency, Montana 59022
(406) 638-4444
Map Location: #2 (65 miles S.E. of Billings)

Restaurants: 1 Liquor: No
Hours: 8am-1am/3am (Fri/Sat)
Other Games: Bingo (Thu-Sat)

Northern Cheyenne Casino
P.O. Box 128
Lame Deer, Montana 59043
(406) 477-6677
Map Location: #3 (90 miles S.E. of Billings on Hwy. 212)

Restaurants: 1 Liquor: No
Hours: 9am-2am Daily

Silver Wolf Casino
P.O. Box 726
Wolf Point, Montana 59201
(406) 653-3476
Map Location: #4 (180 miles N.E of Billings on Hwy. 2)

Restaurants: 1 Liquor: No
Hours: 11am-12am Daily
Other Games: Bingo (Thu-Sun)

NEVADA

All Nevada casinos are open 24 hours and, unless otherwise noted, offer: slots, video poker, craps, blackjack, and roulette. The minimum gambling age is 21.

Other games in the casino listings include: sports book (SB), race book (RB), baccarat (B), mini-baccarat (MB), pai gow (PG), poker (P), pai gow poker (PGP), Caribbean Stud Poker (CSP), Let It Ride (LIR), Red Dog (RD), Double Down Stud (DDS), Spanish 21 (S21), casino war (CW), keno (K) and bingo (BG).

Amargosa Valley

Map Location: #8 (91 miles N.W. of Las Vegas on Hwy. 95)

Stateline Saloon
Route 15
Amargosa Valley, Nevada 89020
(702) 372-5238

Other Games: No Craps or Roulette

Battle Mountain

Map Location: #9 (215 mile N.E. of Reno on I-80)

Owl Hotel & Casino
8 E. Front Street
Battle Mountain, Nevada 89820
(702) 635-2453

Rooms: 18 Price Range: $30
Restaurants: 1 (open 24 hours)
Casino Size: 9,450 Square Feet
Other Games: No Craps or Roulette

Beatty

Map Location: #10 (120 miles N.W. of Las Vegas on Hwy. 95)

Burro Inn Motel & Casino
Highway 95 South
Beatty, Nevada 89003
(702) 553-2225

Reservation Number: (800) 843-2078
Rooms: 62 Price Range: $35-$50
Suites: 1 Price Range: $65
Restaurants: 1 (open 24 hours)
Other Games: No Craps or Roulette

Exchange Club Casino & Motel
P.O. Box 97
Beatty, Nevada 89003
(702) 553-2368

Rooms: 43 Price Range: $38-$68
Suites: 1 Price Range: $68
Casino Size: 3,900 Square Feet
Other Games: P, No Craps or Roulette
Fun Book: Ask at motel office

Stagecoach Hotel & Casino
P.O. Box 836
Beatty, Nevada 89003
(702) 553-2419

Reservation Number: (800) 4-BIG-WIN
Rooms: 48 Price Range: $38-48
Restaurants: 2 (1 open 24 hours)
Casino Size: 7,900 Square Feet
Special Features: Swimming pool and Jacuzzi. 7 miles from Rhyolite ghost town.

Boulder City

Map Location: #11 (22 miles S.E. of Las Vegas on Hwy. 93)

Gold Strike Inn & Casino
U.S. Highway 93
Boulder City, Nevada 89005
(702) 293-5000

Reservation Number: (800) 245-6380
Rooms: 380 Price Range: $29-$59
Restaurants: 3 (1 open 24 hours)
Buffets: Brunch (Sat/Sun)-$4.25
          L-$3.95 D-$3.49
Casino Size: 27,440 Square Feet
Other Games: SB, RB, P, CSP, K, BG
Casino Marketing: (800) 245-6380
Fun Book: Given to hotel guests, or show ID at cashier cage

Carson City

Map Location: #7 (32 miles S. of Reno on Hwy. 395)

Carson City Nugget
507 N. Carson Street
Carson City, Nevada 89701
(702) 882-1626

Toll-Free Number: (800) 426-5239
Reservation Number: (800) 338-7760
Rooms: 82 Price Range: $39-$61
Restaurants: 5 (open 24 hours)
Buffets: B-$4.95/$6.95 (Sun)
         L-$4.95 D-$6.95
Casino Size: 65,000 Square Feet
Other Games: SB, LIR, K, BG
Fun Book: Available at local motels
Senior Discount: If 50, or older, receive
               10% discount on room
Special Features: Free supervised children's
lounge. Free valet parking.

Carson Station Hotel/Casino
900 S. Carson Street
Carson City, Nevada 89702
(702) 883-0900

Reservation Number: (800) 528-1234
Rooms: 92   Price Range: $40-$85
Suites: 3   Price Range: $100
Restaurants: 2 (1 open 24 hours)
Casino Size: 13,500 Square Feet
Other Games: SB, RB, P, K
Special Features: Best Western affiliated.

Elko

Map Location: #3 (289 miles N.E. of Reno on I-80)

Commercial Casino
345 4th Street
Elko, Nevada 89801
(702) 738-3181

Restaurants: 2 (1 open 24 hours)
Casino Size: 7,880 Square Feet
Other Games: P, CSP, K, BG, No Craps or Roulette
Fun Book: Show out-of-Elko County ID
         to receive coupon book with gaming,
         drink and cash coupons
Special Features: Oldest casino in Nevada. 10-foot-tall stuffed polar bear in casino. Large gunfighter art collection.

Red Lion Inn & Casino
2065 Idaho Street
Elko, Nevada 89801
(702) 738-2111

Reservation Number: (800) 545-0044
Rooms: 223 Price Range: $69-$89
Suites: 2 Price Range: $250
Restaurants: 2 (1 open 24 hours)
Buffets: B-$4.95 L-$6.50 D-$8.50
Casino Size: 15,356 Square Feet
Other Games: SB, P, CSP, LIR, K
Casino Marketing: (800) 545-0044
Fun Book: Show out-of-state ID at front desk
Special Features: Air junkets offered from 120 cities in the U.S. and Canada - call (800) 258-8800. Video arcade. Sports bar.

Stockmen's Hotel & Casino
340 Commercial Street
Elko, Nevada 89801
(702) 738-5141

Reservation Number: (800) 648-2345
Rooms: 141 Price Range: $32-$60
Suites: 1   Price Range: $100-$120
Restaurants: 2 (1 open 24 hours)
Casino Size: 8,550 Square Feet
Other Games: SB, K, BG
Casino Marketing: (800) 648-2345
Fun Book: Given to hotel guests, show
          out-of-Elko ID at cashier cage
Special Features: Western-themed hotel. 24-hour shuttle service.

Ely

Map Location: #12 (317 miles E. of Reno on Hwy. 50)

Hotel Nevada & Gambling Hall
501 Aultman Street
Ely, Nevada 89301
(702) 289-6665

Reservation Number: (800) 574-8879
Rooms: 63 Price Range: $25-$45
Suites: 2 Price Range: $65-$95
Restaurants: 1 (open 24 hours)
Casino Size: 30,000 Square Feet
Other Games: P, LIR, No Craps
Fun Book: Ask at front desk
Senior Discount: If 60, or older, 10%
               discount on room
Special Features: Built in 1929. Historical display of mining, ranching and railroad artifacts

Fallon

Map Location: #13 (61 miles E. of Reno on Hwy. 50)

Bird Farm
128 E. Williams Avenue
Fallon, Nevada 89406
(702) 423-7877

Other Games: No Roulette

Bonanza Inn & Casino
855 W. Williams Avenue
Fallon, Nevada 89406
(702) 423-6031

Reservation Number: (702) 423-6031
Rooms: 75 Price Range: $49-$65
Suites: 2 Price Range: $80
Restaurants: 2
Casino Size: 3,750 Square Feet
Other Games: K, No Craps or Roulette
Casino Marketing: (702) 423-3111 ext.-228
Fun Book: Only given to hotel guests
Special Features: Only casino with lodging.

Depot Casino & Restaurant
875 W. Williams Avenue
Fallon, Nevada 89406
(702) 423-2411

Restaurants: 1
Casino Size: 2,550 Square Feet
Other Games: BG, No Craps or Roulette

Fallon Nugget
70 S. Maine Street
Fallon, Nevada 89406
(702) 423-3111

Restaurants: 1
Casino Size: 3,600 Square Feet
Other Games: P, No Craps or Roulette

Headquarter's Bar & Casino
134 S. Maine Street
Fallon, Nevada 89406
(702) 423-6355

Other Games: P, No Craps or Roulette

Stockman's Casino
1560 W. Williams Ave.
Fallon, Nevada 89406
(702) 423-2117

Restaurants: 2 (1 open 24 hours)
Other Games: K, No Roulette

Fernley

Map Location: #14 (30 miles E. of Reno on I-80)

Truck Inn - 7 Z's Motel
I-80 Exit 48
Fernley, Nevada 89408
(702) 351-1000

Reservation Number: (702) 351-1000
Rooms: 51 Price Range: $30-$52
Restaurants: 1 (open 24 hours)
Casino Size: 3,700 Square Feet
Other Games: P, No Craps or Roulette

Gardnerville

Map Location: #15 (45 miles S. of Reno on Hwy. 395)

Sharkey's Nugget
P.O. Box 625
Gardnerville, Nevada 89410
(702) 782-3133

Restaurants: 1 (open 24 hours)
Casino Size: 694 Square Feet
Other Games: No Craps or Roulette

Topaz Lodge & Casino
1979 Highway 395 South
Gardnerville, Nevada 89410
(702) 266-3338

Reservation Number: (800) 962-0732
Rooms: 59 Price Range: $39-$53
Restaurants: 1 (open 24 hours)
Buffets: D-$14.95(Fri)/$5.95(Sat)/$4.95(Sun)
Casino Size: 10,700 Square Feet
Other Games: LIR

Hawthorne

Map Location: #16 (138 miles S.E. of Reno on Hwy. 95)

El Capitan Lodge & Casino
540 F Street
Hawthorne, Nevada 89415
(702) 945-3321

Reservation Number: (702) 945-3321
Rooms: 103 Price Range: $36-$45
Restaurants: 1 (open 24 hours)
Casino Size: 10,000 Square Feet
Other Games: CSP, LIR, K, No Roulette
Fun Book: Ask at front desk

Henderson

Map Location: #17 (15 miles S.E. of Las Vegas on Hwy. 93)

Barley's Casino & Brewing Co.
4500 E. Sunset Road #30
Henderson, Nevada 89014
(702) 458-2739

Restaurants: 2 (1 open 24 hours)
Other Games: SB, LIR, No Craps or Roulette
Special Features: Located in a mall. Four varieties of beer are brewed on the premises.

Eldorado Casino
140 Water Street
Henderson, Nevada 89015
(702) 564-1811

Restaurants: 2 (1 open 24 hours)
Casino Size: 16,100 Square Feet
Other Games: SB, CSP, LIR, K, BG

Jokers Wild
920 N. Boulder Highway
Henderson, Nevada 89015
(702) 564-8100

Restaurants: 1 (open 24 hours)
Buffets: B-$7.95 (Sun) L-$3.75 D-$4.95
Casino Size: 25,000 Square Feet
Other Games: SB, LIR, K
Senior Discount: If 55, or older, $1 off dinner buffet Mon/Thu
Special Features: Live entertainment Wed-Sun.

Railroad Pass Hotel & Casino
2800 S. Boulder Highway
Henderson, Nevada 89015
(702) 294-5000

Toll-Free Number: (800) 654-0877
Rooms: 100 Price Range:$29-$39
Suites: 20 Price Range:$29-$39
Restaurants: 3 (1 open 24 hours)
Buffets: B-$4.25 (Sat/Sun) L-$3.49 D-$3.49
Casino Size: 23,698 Square Feet
Other Games: SB, LIR, K, BG
Fun Book: Show out-of-state ID at front desk
Special Features: Swimming pool. Video arcade. Gift shop.

Skyline Restaurant & Casino
1741 N. Boulder Highway
Henderson, Nevada 89015
(702) 565-9116

Restaurants: 1 (open 24 hours)
Buffets: L-$3.25
Casino Size: 8,500 Square Feet
Other Games: P, LIR, No Craps or Roulette
Fun Book: Given at local hotels/motels

Tom's Sunset Casino
444 W. Sunset Road
Henderson, Nevada 89015
(702) 564-5551

Restaurants: 1 (open 24 hours)
Casino Size: 7,340 Square Feet
Other Games: SB, RB, P, No Craps
Fun Book: Given when you join slot club
Special Features: Daily Poker tournament. Weekly blackjack tournament.

Jackpot

Map Location: #18 (Just S. of the Idaho border on Hwy. 93)

Barton's Club 93
Highway 93
Jackpot, Nevada 89825
(702) 755-2341

Toll-Free Number: (800) 258-2937
Rooms: 60 Price Range: $25-$65
Restaurants: 2 (1 open 24 hours)
Buffets: B-$3.93 (Sun)
          D-$2.93/$6.93 (Fri/Sat)/$5.25 (Sun)
Casino Size: 8,025 Square Feet
Other Games: K
Fun Book: Ask at registration desk

Cactus Pete's Resort/Casino
Highway 93
Jackpot, Nevada 89825
(702) 755-2321

Reservation Number: (800) 821-1103
Rooms: 400 Price Range: $55-$85
Suites: 18 Price Range: $150-$175
Restaurants: 4 (1 open 24 hours)
Buffets: B-$5.95 (Sat)/$7.95 (Sun)
          D-$6.95/$8.95 (Fri/Sat)
Casino Size: 25,351 Square Feet
Other Games: SB, P, LIR, K
Special Features: Four-diamond rated by AAA. Every Wednesday from 5pm-11pm all restaurants prices are discounted 50%.

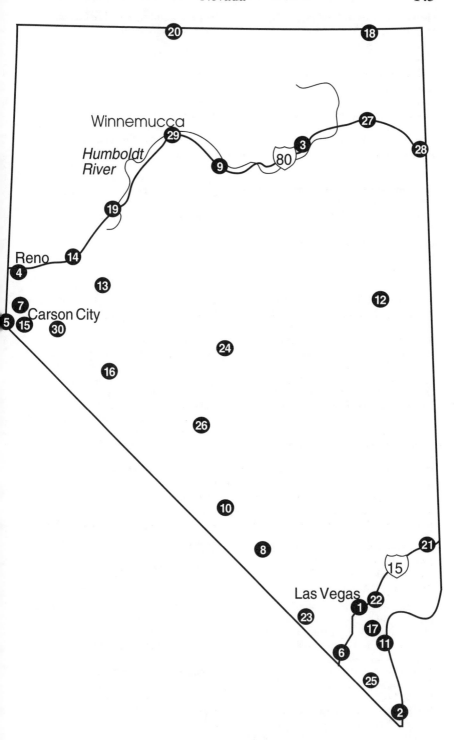

Winnemucca

Humboldt River

80

Reno

Carson City

Las Vegas

15

Horseshu Hotel & Casino
Highway 93
Jackpot, Nevada 89825
(702) 755-7777

Reservation Number: (800) 432-0051
Rooms: 110 Price Range: $40-$65
Suites: 10 Price Range: $60-$85
Restaurants: 1 (open 24 hours)
Casino Size: 3,520 Square Feet
Other Games: K, No Roulette

Jean

Map Location: #6 (22 miles S.W. of Las Vegas on I-15; 12 miles from the California border)

Buffalo Bill's Resort & Casino
I-15 South
Jean, Nevada 89019
(702) 382-1212

Toll-Free Number: (800) FUN-STOP
Rooms: 1,242 Price Range: $29-$80
Suites: 15   Price Range: $195-$250
Restaurants: 5 (1 open 24 hours)
Buffets: B-$4.95 (Sat/Sun)
          L-$4.95 (M-F) D-$5.95
Casino Size: 62,130 Square Feet
Other Games: SB, RB, P, PGP, CSP, LIR, K
Fun Book: Look for brochure in rack at
           tourist welcome centers
Special Features: "Ghost town" replica. The world's tallest and fastest (85 mph) roller coaster. Two motion-simulator theaters. Flume Ride. 3,000-foot rainbow arch. 6,500-seat special events arena. Buffalo-shaped swimming pool. 2 water slides. Movie theater. Video arcade. Western-style train shuttle connects to Whiskey Pete's and Primadonna.

Gold Strike Hotel & Gambling Hall
1 Main Street
Jean, Nevada 89019
(702) 387-5000

Reservation Number: (800) 634-1359
Rooms: 749   Price Range: $21-$39
Mini-Suites: 64 Price Range: $21-$39
Restaurants: 5 (3 open 24 hours)
Buffets: B-$4.79 (Sat/Sun) L-$3.99 D-$4.99
Casino Size: 37,006 Square Feet
Other Games: P, CSP, K
Casino Marketing: (800) 634-1359
Fun Book: Ask at the front desk
Special Features: Video arcade. Free shuttle to Nevada Landing. 95¢ breakfast special.

Nevada Landing Hotel & Casino
2 Goodsprings Road
Jean, Nevada 89019
(702) 387-5000

Reservation Number: (800) 628-6682
Rooms: 273 Price Range: $21-$39
Suites: 30 Price Range: $64
Restaurants: 4 (1 open 24 hours)
Buffets: B-$4.79 (Sat/Sun) L-$3.99 D-$4.99
Casino Size: 37,006 Square Feet
Other Games: SB, CSP, K
Fun Book: Ask at hotel registration desk
Special Features: Video arcade. Free shuttle to Gold Strike Hotel & Gambling Hall.

Primadonna Resort & Casino
I-15 South
Jean, Nevada 89019
(702) 382-1212

Reservation Number: (800) FUN-STOP
Rooms: 661 Price Range: $29-$69
Suites: 4   Price Range: $165-$194
Restaurants: 3 (1 open 24 hours)
Buffets: B-$3.50 L-$3.50 D-$4.50
Casino Size: 23,049 Square Feet
Other Games: SB, RB, P, PGP, CSP, LIR, K
Fun Book: Look for brochure in rack at
           tourist welcome centers
Special Features: RV park with 199 spaces and full hook-ups. Free rides on 100-foot-tall ferris wheel and indoor merry-go-round. 8-lane bowling alley. Video arcade. Free monorail service to Whiskey Pete's Casino Hotel.

Whiskey Pete's Hotel & Casino
I-15 South
Jean, Nevada 89019
(702) 382-1212

Reservation Number: (800) FUN-STOP
Rooms: 777 Price Range: $25-$69
Suites: 4   Price Range: $190
Restaurants: 4 (1 open 24 hours)
Buffets: B-$3.50 L-$3.50 D-$4.50
Casino Size: 36,400 Square Feet
Other Games: SB, RB, P, PGP, CSP, LIR, K
Fun Book: Look for brochure in rack at
           tourist welcome centers
Special Features: Children's entertainment center. Pool with water slide. Fully restored Dutch Schultz gangster car, plus Bonnie and Clyde's "Death Car" are on display. Free monorail service to Primadonna Resort & Casino.

Lake Tahoe

Location: directly on the Nevada/California border; 98 miles northeast of Sacramento and 58 miles southwest of Reno.

The area is best known for its many recreational activities with skiing in the winter and water sports in the summer. Lake Tahoe Airport is located at the south end of the basin. The next closest airport is in Reno with regularly scheduled shuttle service by bus. Incline Village and Crystal Bay are on the north shore of Lake Tahoe, while Stateline is located on the south shore.

Here's information, as supplied by Nevada's State Gaming Control Board, showing the slot machine payback percentages for all of the south shore casinos for the fiscal year beginning July 1, 1995 and ending June 30, 1996:

5¢ Slot Machines	90.47%
25¢ Slot Machines	93.39%
$1 Slot Machines	95.35%
$5 Slot Machines	96.98%
All Slot Machines	94.71%

And here's that same information for the north shore casinos:

5¢ Slot Machines	92.10%
25¢ Slot Machines	93.96%
$1 Slot Machines	95.58%
$5 Slot Machines	95.31%
All Slot Machines	94.48%

These numbers reflect the percentage of money returned to the players on each denomination of machine. All electronic machines including video poker and video keno are included in these numbers.

Optional games in the casino listings include: sports book (SB), race book (RB), baccarat (B), mini-baccarat (MB), poker (P), pai gow poker (PGP), Caribbean Stud Poker (CSP), Let It Ride (LIR), Double Down Stud (DDS), Spanish 21 (S21), keno (K) and bingo (BG).

Caesars Tahoe
55 Highway 50
Stateline, Nevada 89449
(702) 588-3515

Reservation Number: (800) 648-3353
Rooms: 400 Price Range: $95-$215
Suites: 40 Price Range: $300-$950
Restaurants: 5 (1 open 24 hours)
Buffets: B-$4.99/$7.99 (Sat/Sun)
           L-$6.99 D-$8.99
Casino Size: 40,500 Square Feet
Other Games: SB, RB, B, MB, P, PGP,
           CSP, LIR, K
Casino Marketing: (800) 648-3353
Fun Book: Show out-of-state ID at gift shop
Special Features: Located on south shore of Lake Tahoe. Health spa. Indoor pool with waterfalls and islands. Planet Hollywood restaurant. Beauty shop offers massages, facials and body wraps.

**Cal-Neva Lodge Resort Hotel,
Spa & Casino**
P.O. Box 368
Crystal Bay, Nevada 89402
(702) 832-4000

Reservation Number: (800) CAL-NEVA
Rooms: 180 Price Range: $89-$149
Suites: 18 Price Range: $149-$269
Restaurants: 1
Casino Size: 8,000 Square Feet
Other Games: P
Casino Marketing: (800) CAL-NEVA
Special Features: Located on north shore of Lake Tahoe. Lake view rooms. Euro-Spa offers a variety of massages, facials, aromatherapy, hydrotherapy, sauna and body wraps. Outdoor pool. 3 wedding chapels. Honeymoon packages. Florist. Photography studio. Bridal boutique. Gift shop. Airport shuttle.

Crystal Bay Club Casino
14 Highway 28
Crystal Bay, Nevada 89402
(702) 831-0512

Restaurants: 2 (1 open 24 hours)
Casino Size: 10,300 Square Feet
Other Games: K
Fun Book: Look for rack card at local
           hotels and welcome centers
Special Features: Children's arcade. Free lounge entertainment.

Harrah's Lake Tahoe Casino Hotel
P.O. Box 8
Stateline, Nevada 89449
(702) 588-6611

Reservation Number: (800) HARRAHS
Rooms: 454 Price Range: $99-$179
Suites: 80 Price Range: $149-$450
Restaurants: 7 (1 open 24 hours)
Buffets: B-$7.95/$12.95 (Sun) L-$9.95
         D-$11.95/$19.50 (Fri/Sat)
Casino Size: 79,368 Square Feet
Casino Marketing: (800) 346-6569
Other Games: SB, RB, B, P, PGP,
         CSP, LIR, K
Fun Book: Only given to hotel guests
         and bus groups
Special Features: Located on south shore of
Lake Tahoe. Free shuttle service to several
ski areas including Heavenly Valley and Squaw
Valley. Arcade. Indoor pool. Health club. Pet
kennel. Wedding chapel. Warner Brothers
specialty store. 800-seat showroom.

Harveys Resort Hotel/Casino - Lake Tahoe
P.O. Box 128 - Highway 50
Stateline, Nevada 89449
(702) 588-2411

Toll-Free Number: (800) 553-1022
Reservation Number: (800) HARVEYS
Rooms: 740 Price Range: $99-$180
Suites: 36 Price Range: $275-$500
Restaurants: 8 (1 open 24 hours)
Buffets: B-$5.50 L-$7.25
   D-$8.95/$16.95(Fri) /$13.95 (Sat)/
   $12.95 (Sun)
Casino Size: 91,296 Square Feet
Other Games: SB, RB, B, MB, P, PGP,
         CSP, LIR, SP21, K
Casino Marketing: (800) 654-3284
Fun Book: Ask at the Party Card Center
Special Features: Located on south shore of
Lake Tahoe. Rated 4-Diamonds by AAA and
4-Stars by Mobil. Largest hotel and casino in
Lake Tahoe. Complimentary breakfast for
hotel guests. 10% room discount for AAA
members or 15% discount with Harvey's
Party Card. Health Club offers massages,
aromatherapy, plus a year-round outdoor pool
and spa. Children's video arcade. Kids camp
offered for hotel guests. Free shuttle bus
service to/from local motels and ski resorts.

**Hyatt Regency Lake Tahoe
Resort & Casino**
P.O. Box 3239
Incline Village, Nevada 89450
(702) 832-1234

Reservation Number: (800) 233-1234
Rooms: 412 Price Range: $99-$224
Suites: 48 Price Range: $175-$524
Restaurants: 2 (1 open 24 hours)
Buffets: B-$8.95 L-$5.95
         D-$8.75/$15.95 (Fri/Sat)
Casino Size: 18,900 Square Feet
Other Games: SB, P, CSP, LIR
Casino Marketing: (702) 832-1234
Fun Book: Given for package bookings and
         groups, also distributed by local
         motels to their guests
Special Features: Located on north shore of
Lake Tahoe. Two Robert Trent Jones golf
courses.

Jim Kelly's Nugget
P.O. Box 37
Crystal Bay, Nevada 89402
(702) 831-0455

Restaurants: 1 (open 24 hours)
Other Games: No Craps or Roulette

Horizon Casino-Resort
P.O. Box C, Highway 50
Lake Tahoe, Nevada 89449
(702) 588-6211

Toll-Free Number: (800) 322-
Reservation Number: (800) 648-3322
Rooms: 519 Price Range: $69-$150
Suites: 20 Price Range: $89-$500
Restaurants: 3 (1 open 24 hours)
Buffets: B-$5.99 (Sat/Sun)
         D-$8.99/$10.99 (Sat)
Casino Size: 40,000 Square Feet
Other Games: SB, PGP, CSP, LIR, K
Casino Marketing: (800) 322-7723 ext.-3062
Fun Book: Only given to hotel guests
Special Features: Located on south shore of
Lake Tahoe. Outdoor heated pool with 3 hot
tubs. Shopping promenade. Video arcade.

Lakeside Inn & Casino
Highway 50 & Kingsbury Grade
Stateline, Nevada 89449
(702) 588-7777

Toll-Free Number: (800) 523-1291
Reservation Number: (800) 624-7980
Rooms: 123 Price Range: $69-$89
Suites: 2 Price Range: $110-$280
Restaurants: 1 (open 24 hours)
Casino Size: 14,975 Square Feet
Other Games: SB, CSP, LIR, K
Casino Marketing: (800) 523-1291
Special Features: Located on south shore of
Lake Tahoe. Gift shop. Video arcade. $6.99
prime rib special in restaurant (4pm-11pm).
Some rooms with scenic mountain views.

Tahoe Biltmore Lodge & Casino
Highway 28
Crystal Bay, Nevada 89402
(702) 831-0660

Reservation Number: (800) 245-8667
Rooms: 87 Price Range: $49-$89
Restaurants: 1 (open 24 hours)
Casino Size: 10,480 Square Feet
Other Games: Sports Book, Let It Ride, Keno
Casino Marketing: (800) 245-8667
Fun Book: Show out-of-state ID at
               casino cage
Special Features: Located on north shore of
Lake Tahoe. Some lake view rooms. Video
arcade.

Las Vegas

Map Location: #1

Las Vegas is truly the casino capital of the
world! While many years ago the city may
have had a reputation as an "adult play-
ground" run by "shady characters", today's
Las Vegas features many family-oriented facilities run by some of America's most familiar corporate names.

Las Vegas has more hotel rooms - 100,000 -
than any other city in the world and attracts
about 30 million visitors each year. Its popu-
lation base is the fastest growing in the U.S.
and major construction projects are routinely
announced each year.

One of the city's most practical attractions is
a $25-million monorail that opened in June
1995 which links the MGM Grand Hotel,

Casino & Theme Park with Bally's. The 22-
foot high elevated monorail travels north and
south between the two resorts on Audrie
Street which is parallel to the Las Vegas Strip.
The monorail consists of two six-car electric
powered trains on a one-mile, dual lane guide-
way. The air-conditioned monorail has the
capacity to transport 100,000 people per day
at approximately 35 mph. The one-mile ride
takes about three-and-a-half minutes, including loading and unloading, and there is no
charge for the ride. There is one entrance to
the system near MGM Grand's port cochere
entrance and the other entrance is at Bally's
on Audrie Street.

Several new hotel, casino and attraction
projects have been announced for Las Vegas
and here's a rundown on each one:

Bellagio - This one-of-a-kind $1.25 billion
destination resort at Flamingo Road and the
Las Vegas Strip (site of the former Dunes
Hotel, which was imploded in October 1993),
is a project of Mirage Resorts, Inc. Bellagio is
named after a small village that sits on the
shore of Lake Como in Northern Italy and it
will be a 37-story, 3,000-room resort on a
man-made island surrounded by a 15-acre
bay. The property will be entered via foot-
bridges and causeways with all entrances
surrounded by cascading waterfalls. The man-
made lake will offer sailing, water skiing,
wind surfing and other water-related activities. The island's northwest shore will house
an amphitheater with water skier shows and
fireworks. Bellagio is scheduled to open in
early 1998.

Paris Casino Resort - Bally Grand, Inc. is
building this 33-story, 2,500-room gambling
resort on 25 acres adjacent to Bally's Hotel/
Casino on the Las Vegas Strip. The $420
million resort will re-create the city of Paris
with replicas of the Arc de Triomphe, Champs
Elysees, the Paris Opera House, Parc
Monceau, the River Seine and a 50-story
replica of the Eiffel Tower complete with a
Jules Verne restaurant and an observation
lookout. Paris Casino Resort will have a
78,000-square-foot casino, nine theme restaurants, 90,000 square feet of convention space,
a French-theme retail shopping complex and
a 25,000-square-foot health spa. Also on
premise will be a working French winery and
French-style gondola rides. The resort is expected to open by early 1998.

Planet Hollywood - ITT Corp. and Planet Hollywood International are joining forces to build an $830 million, 3,200-room megaresort on 34 acres adjacent to the Sheraton Desert Inn at the intersection of the Las Vegas Strip and Sands Avenue. The project will feature a 100,000-square-foot casino and is expected to open by mid-1998.

Sands - The 44-year old Sands Hotel and Casino closed its doors June 30, 1996 in preparation for the start of construction on the world's largest hotel. The $1.5 billion project will contain 6,000 rooms which will all be 700-square-foot suites. The expected opening date is sometime in 1998.

Masterplan Mile - Circus Circus Enterprises Inc., parent company of Excalibur, Luxor and Circus Circus hotel/casinos on the Las Vegas Strip, purchased the Hacienda Hotel Casino and some 100 surrounding acres in March 1995. It gives the giant gaming company one mile of Las Vegas Strip frontage which the company is calling its "Masterplan Mile."

Officials have outlined a $1.5 billion plan that calls for construction of new resorts and renovation of existing properties over a four-year period. Building plans include construction of twin towers at the Luxor Hotel/Casino. It will cost $240 million and bring the property's room count up to 4,476. There will also be 1,000 rooms added to the Circus Circus Hotel Casino at a cost of $80 million, boosting the room count to 3,800.

New projects include the development of a 4,000-room megaresort on the Hacienda Hotel site and, in partnership with Four Seasons Regent, a 400-room, five star, non-gaming hotel within the Masterplan Mile. Both projects are scheduled to be completed in 1998.

Star Trek: The Experience - Hilton Hotels, Corp. and Paramount Parks are collaborating to create a 40,000-square-foot attraction in the north tower of the Las Vegas Hilton. Each visitor will assume the identity of a Starfleet or alien crew member and participate as that character in the imaginative world of Star Trek. The amusement facility will include a simulated ride using a special viewer perspective image projector; interactive video and virtual reality stations; an upscale 24th Century theme dining experience featuring a Cardassian restaurant with a Starfleet lounge; and a 20,000-square-foot casino that will serve as an entrance and exit to the facility. The expected opening date is early 1997.

Competition among businesses always creates great opportunities for the customer and Las Vegas is no exception to that rule. The abundance of casinos forces them to compete for customers in a variety of ways and thus, there are always great bargains to be had, if you know where to look.

Las Vegas Advisor newsletter publisher, Anthony Curtis is truly the town's resident expert on where to find the best deals. His 238-page book *Bargain City - Booking, Betting and Beating the New Las Vegas* contains more than a decade's worth of powerful, money-saving, profit-making and vacation enhancing tips for the Las Vegas visitor and here's an excerpt with Curtis' tips on the city's best deals:

Best Las Vegas Bargain
NY Steak Dinner, $4, Binion's Horseshoe

A 10-ounce New York steak, big baked potato, salad, vegetable, and roll served 10pm-5:45am 365 days a year. Any way you cut it, this is a great deal! It was the meal that everyone talked about when I first came to Las Vegas in 1979, and it's the one they still talk about today. The original $2 price was raised to $3 in mid-1983, then rolled back to $2 in '85. In '87, it was again raised to $3, rolled back only one year later and raised again to $3 in 1995. In 1996 they raised it another buck to $4. Maybe, by the time you read this it'll be back to $3 again, but don't count on it. Binion's claims to serve nearly a quarter-million late-night steaks every year (almost 700 per day) and loses, as you might imagine, a fair amount of money on every single one. Everyone stays up late in Las Vegas. You will too. Stay up a little later, grab a cab to the Horseshoe, and try one of these steaks - the Las Vegas-value icon.

Best Room Rate
Free, Las Vegas Hotel-Casinos

The only other vacation scenario that includes this possibility involves a tent, sleeping bag, and a lot of wilderness. Why would casinos give rooms away? Competition. Hotels with 3,000, 4,000, and 5,000 rooms open, and the owners of hotels with only 1,000 or 2,000 rooms get nervous. Lulls, city-wide occupancy levels sometimes plummet below 90%, especially in December. Gasp! But mostly, it's the gambling. Gambling winnings subsidize the room department (and the food department, and the alcohol department, and the entertainment department, and...).

Best Loss Leader
Free Money, Four Queens

What a concept. You go to a casino, and they give you money! The Four Queens is famous for dispensing non-negotiable tokens that play like real coins in slot and video poker machines. Not promotional machines with reduced return percentages, but the best-paying machines in the casino. You can get free money by subscribing to certain periodicals (like the *Las Vegas Advisor* or *Casino Player*) and by getting your name on lists at the Four Queens - join the slot club or the great Club 55 for seniors. You want to be known by the casino in case they decide to do a mailing. A free-money infusion is an incredible way to begin a vacation.

Best Breakfast
Old Guard-Binion's Natural, $3.00, Binion's Horseshoe
New Guard-Steak & Eggs, $2.99, Rio

Though scores of others have come and gone, the Natural has held the title of "Las Vegas' best breakfast" the longest. Two eggs, a piece of ham that covers the entire plate, sliced potatoes (not hash browns), toast, and the best coffee and service in town. Quality, quality, quality.

The Rio is the most recent (and most serious) challenger for the title with its T-Bone steak, two eggs and hash browns. Quantity, quantity, quantity.

Best Buffet
The Carnival World, $3.99-$7.99, Rio
Market Street, $3.95-$7.95, Texas Station

These two stand together atop the Las Vegas buffet hierarchy. The Rio's Carnival World is an incredible spectacle, a mini food city with fare ranging from cherry fritters for breakfast to a Mongolian barbecue for dinner. Texas Station's Market Street is the innovative, working-man's buffet. It's built around Texas-style deep-pit barbecue dishes, but it also features Chinese, Italian, Mexican and a special chili bar with eight varieties to choose from.

Best Place to Drink
Nostalgic - Binion's Horseshoe
Classy - Golden Nugget
Friendly - Palace Station
Cheap - Slots-A-Fun

The Horseshoe has been the Las Vegas drinking spot forever. Every visitor should grab at least one beer at one of the Horseshoe's three long wooden bars to get a feeling for the way it was in old Las Vegas. Then walk across the street for the best of the new - the Golden Nugget's drinks at all bars for $1.25. You won't find cocktails or beer for ten bits at any other four-star, four-diamond hotel in the world. Palace Station is the favorite hangout for locals and after shift casino workers, due in no small part to the best 99¢ Margarita special in the city's history. Slots-A-Fun (known as Heineken Headquarters) continues to hold the line on 75¢ imports. Get a bottle of Heineken or Corona with change back for your buck.

Best Meal
T-Bone Steak Dinner, $7.95, Gold Coast

If you eat only one meal in Las Vegas, this should be it. The colossal 16-ounce T-bone harkens back to Las Vegas' bargain steak heyday of a half-decade ago. Charcoal-grilled and cooked perfectly to your specifications, the meat comes with potatoes, onion rings, baked beans, garlic bread, big dinner salad and a glass of draft beer. It's served 24 hours a day, seven days a week in the Gold Coast's Monterey coffee shop. Perhaps, best of all, it's barely advertised, so this steak appears destined to be around for a good long time.

Best Place for Dinner
Pasta Pirate, California Hotel-Casino

Of the 200+ casino restaurants in Las Vegas, this one will satisfy more people than any other. First, the restaurant has three specialties - seafood, steaks and pasta - so most culinary tastes are covered. Second, the room is upscale, but you can dine in casual dress - so most aesthetic and fashion senses are appeased. Third, prices are great - so everyone else will be happy. The Pasta Palace is home to one of Las Vegas' best and most consistent on-going steak dinners, a fantastic filet mignon for only $10.95. The daily specials are also highly recommended. The restaurant accepts reservations. Make them!

Best Story to Tell
59¢ Dinner At Boardwalk

It's a dark and stormy night in the summer of 1993. Two high rollers stroll into a Las Vegas Strip casino for dinner. One orders baked chicken, which comes with a side of spaghetti, two pieces of garlic bread, and a cup of red, white, or rose wine. The other orders roast beef, which comes with mashed potatoes and gravy, mixed vegetables, dinner roll and wine. It's not fancy by any means - the dinners are served on styrofoam plates and the drinks in plastic cups. But the food is as good as home cooking and the plates are so-o-o full that one has a hard time finishing. Then the bill comes: $1.27! They fight like animals for the check. The end.

The boardwalk's 59¢ dinners (25¢ in December 1995) rotate on and off, and may not be available in the future. But don't worry. There'll be some other incredible special to partake of at another Las Vegas casino. It was upon such deals that the Bargain City legend was built. And that's no fairy tale.

Best Freebie
Pirate Show, Treasure Island

This swashbuckling, cannon-firing, powder-keg-exploding free show is a definite must-see, and more than once. It plays six times a night, weather cooperating, every 90 minutes starting at 4:30pm. The best viewing area, at the north end of the veranda at the Battle Bar,

should be staked out as early as 45 minutes prior to show times. Another good viewing locale is the plank bridge between the ships, as close to the frigate-side rope railing as possible. It is necessary to arrive at least 30 minutes prior to show time to secure a good spot. It's a good show for young children, unless they are bothered by crowds, in which case you should watch from the sidewalk across the street.

Best Way to Remember the
Best Vacation on Earth
Free Photo, Binion's Horseshoe

Take your entire group to the Horseshoe between 4pm and midnight and get your picture taken in front of 100 $10,000 bills. That's a million dollars, the coolest mil you'll ever be photographed in front of. You'll join the countless other visitors who've taken home this ultimate Las Vegas souvenir over the 40+ years that the bills have been displayed. Indeed, regulars get their pictures snapped every time they're in Las Vegas, to keep running and accurate memories of each visit.

Bargain City - Booking, Betting and Beating the New Las Vegas may be purchased for $11.95 at your local bookstore, or for $14.95 (including postage) from: Casino Vacations, P.O. Box 703, Dania, Florida, 33004. For credit card orders call (800) 741-1596.

Unlike New Jersey, the Nevada Gaming Control Board does not break down its slot statistics by individual properties. Rather, they are classified by area. The annual gaming revenue report breaks Las Vegas down into two areas: the Strip and downtown. When choosing where to do your slot gambling, you may to keep in mind the following slot payback percentages for Nevada's fiscal year beginning July 1, 1995 and ending June 30, 1996:

5¢ Machines
Downtown - 91.74%
The Strip - 89.42%

25¢ Machines
Downtown - 95.50%
The Strip - 93.73%

$1 Machines
Downtown - 95.46%
The Strip - 95.19%

$5 Machines
Downtown - 96.56%
The Strip - 95.99%

All Machines
Downtown - 95.26%
The Strip - 94.43%

These numbers reflect the percentage of money returned to the players on each denomination of machine. All electronic machines including video poker and video keno are included in these numbers. As you can see, the machines in downtown Las Vegas pay out significantly more than those located on the Strip for the lower denomination 5¢ and 25¢ machines. When you get to the $1 and $5 machines the difference is less noticeable but you can clearly see that the downtown casinos always return more than the Strip area casinos. This information is pretty well known by the locals and that's why most of them do their slot gambling away from the Strip unless they are drawn by a special slot club benefit or promotion.

The Strip casinos do, however, offer an advantage on one of the table games and that is in blackjack. You will find that all downtown casinos will "hit" a soft 17 (a total of 17 with an ace counted as 11 rather than one). This is a slight disadvantage (-0.2%) for the player and the Strip casinos do not hit a soft 17.

As mentioned before, one of the best sources for finding out about the best "deals" on a current basis in the Las Vegas area is the *Las Vegas Advisor*. It is a 12-page monthly newsletter published by gaming expert Anthony Curtis. *Las Vegas Advisor* accepts no advertising and each issue objectively analyzes the best values in lodging, dining, entertainment and gambling to help you get the most for your money when visiting Las Vegas. The newsletter is especially well known for its "Top Ten Values" column which is often quoted by major travel publications. Each subscription also comes with a benefit package valued at more than $150. Ordering information for *Las Vegas Advisor* can be found later in this section.

Besides Anthony Curtis' favorite deals which were mentioned earlier there are also some special vacation programs in Las Vegas that can save you some money. I tried a few out and here are details on two of those programs along with information on how to book them for yourself.

RIVIERA SPREE

A spree is a special gambling package where in return for making a minimum bet, for a minimum amount of time, you are entitled to receive rebates from the casino in the form of cash, chips, rooms, food, drinks, shows, etc. At one time these were fairly popular at Las Vegas casinos, but they are now dying out and are only available at a handful of casinos.

During the past few years the smallest minimum bet I saw for a spree program at a Strip casino was at the Riviera where they required a $5 minimum/$10 average bet during the course of your play. Naturally, there are higher minimum betting levels, such as $25 or $50 and these higher betting levels earn more complimentaries than the lower ones. In all sprees the amount of time required is relative to the length of your hotel stay. On most sprees for two-day stays you must gamble for 8 hours. On three-day stays the minimum is 10 hours and on four-day stays it is 12 hours.

A spree seemed to offer a lot of value if you were willing to put in the required time, so in July, 1992 I decided to try out a four-night program. After reviewing the various sprees available I decided on the Riviera because it had the lowest betting requirements. At that time I was a basic strategy blackjack player (I now count cards) and my bets fluctuated between $5 and $25. Because I was committing myself to 12 hours of play I didn't want to bet more than I felt comfortable with and I felt confident that I would have no problem qualifying even if I hit a major losing streak. The benefits for qualifying in this program were: $100 in cash, $100 in "match play chips" (non-negotiable chips that are only valid for bets that are matched with an equal amount of regular chips), a daily breakfast and lunch buffet, $25 in drinks at the lounge bar and free admission, plus two drinks at four shows: Splash, La Cage, The Improv and Crazy Girls.

We booked our spree through a local Las Vegas travel company for a Thursday through Sunday stay and the cost was $300 for both of us. This amount covered our hotel room and taxes so that even if we didn't qualify for the rebates we knew that our room bill was paid. Sprees are also available in packages with airfare included, but we chose to get ours without it.

At the hotel we had to go to a special check-in area and it took less than five minutes to complete the process. While at the desk, we were each issued a card to keep track of our play in the casino.

On our first visit to the casino we went to the blackjack table and handed our cards over to the pit boss. He made some notations and put the cards aside. When we got up about an hour-and-a-half later, he credited each of us with six units of play and returned the cards to us. You receive one unit for each 15 minutes of play and we both needed a total of 48 units to qualify (48 x 15 minutes = 12 hours).

The pit bosses were very friendly and it wasn't like they were constantly checking up on us to be sure that our bets were averaging $10. They would just come by every once in a while and glance at the bets on the table. Later on in our stay I played almost all of my hands at $5 for about a half-hour to see what would happen. There was no problem. The pit boss gave me my credit and never said a word about not having an average $10 bet. Additionally, they seemed somewhat liberal in writing down the time units. Even if you left at just 40 minutes into a session they still gave you credit for the full 45 minutes.

The program is also flexible because you can put in your time on other table games or slots. On the slot machines you get one point (not unit) for each $5 played and 30 points is equal to one unit. Therefore, for each $150 played ($5 x 30) on the slots, you receive one 15-minute unit. At that rate it would have taken $7,200 in slot play ($150 x 48 units) to complete a 48-unit card, which seemed a little outrageous. We did, however, kill some time playing the slots and we were able to add a unit or two to our cards.

The only other table game we played was pai gow poker which turned out to be a great discovery. Although the paperwork from our travel agency said the minimum bet for spree players was $20 on pai gow poker, it turned out to be just $10. This was great news because the pace on pai gow poker is about three times slower than blackjack. Plus, in pai gow poker you play both a five-card hand and a two-card hand against the dealer's respective hands. To win, both of your hands must beat the dealer's. To lose, both of your hands must lose to the dealer's. If you each have one winning hand the result is a "push" and nobody wins. As you can imagine, most deals result in a tie and that makes this game a great way to kill time without losing too much money! Once we discovered pai gow poker and its low $10 minimum, we completed the rest of our units there. At the end of our stay the only additional charge on the bill was for a local phone call I made from the room.

Summary - my total cost for the spree program was $150. After qualifying, I got back $100 in cash, plus $100 in match play chips (which has a cash equivalent of $50). Those two benefits alone made me even on the deal. Then, I got a breakfast ($4) and lunch ($5) buffet each day for four days which was worth $36 ($9 x 4). The cost to see Splash was $27.50 and admission to the other three shows was $12.50 each for a total of $65 in shows ($27.50 + $37.50). Plus, there was $25 in drinks which brought my total of free benefits to $126 ($36 + $65 + $25).

This program had some great benefits. After all, I was going to Las Vegas to gamble anyway, so what did it matter if most of my gambling was done at the Riviera? The only really bad part is that you are locked in for a set amount of time and if you hit a losing streak you could wind up losing more than you had planned on. Not only that, but if you didn't qualify, then you would have to pay for all of the buffets, drinks and shows which you charged to your room. The really good part though is the $10 minimum at pai gow poker. If I were to go on this spree again I would spend almost all of my time qualifying at pai gow poker. At a $10 minimum it's hard to get hurt and it's too good a deal to pass up.

I checked with the Riviera in September 1996 to see if any changes had been made and, unfortunately, the $10 program was discontinued as of August 1st and the minimum bet is now $25. Other changes to the program include:

1. - Upon qualification you are now given $200 in "action chips," rather than $100 in cash and $100 in "match play chips." These "action chips" are different from "match play chips" because you don't have to match your bet with an equal amount of cash. The non-negotiable "action chips" can be used instead of cash but, win or lose, they are only good for one bet. If you win they will pay you in regular chips an amount equal to your "action chips" bet, but they will also take away your action chips. Generally, you can figure the true value of "action chips" and "match play chips" at 50% of their face value. Therefore, previously the true value of the rebate was $150 ($100 in cash and $100 in chips) and now the true value is $100 ($200 in chips).

2. - The room rate is now $40 Sunday through Thursday and $60 on Friday and Saturday. This is less than the rate we paid three years earlier (probably because the travel agent marked up the price to us). This rate is for up to two people in the room and not per person, however, each person must qualify in order to earn the free benefits. If only one person is on the spree the room rate would be the same, but only that one person would be eligible to qualify for the free benefits.

3. - Only three shows are included. The big production show Splash is no longer part of the program.

4. -Rather than buffets you are given a $75 food credit and a $30 drink credit.

5. - And here's the biggest change: 12 hours of play are now required on the 2 or 3-day spree and 16 hours are required on a 4-day spree.

This used to be a great program for the low-level bettor but with the new $25 minimum that's no longer the case. If you are a $25 player and want to try out this program you can book it directly with the Riviera's casino marketing department at (800) 437-7951. They will only take bookings that do not require airfare. If you need air transportation, you'll have to book through a travel agency. This program is also available through many travel agencies around the country. A good idea is to look in the travel section of your local newspaper on a Sunday for the best air-inclusive prices from your city.

Tropicana Hotel

In early 1993 the Tropicana began offering a special deal to get members in its Island Winners Slot Club. The program allowed you to stay free for two days if - 1.) you were not a current member of their Island Winners Club, and 2.) you gambled on any 25¢ or greater slot (or video poker) machine for a total of four hours or more during your two-day stay. You could also qualify for the free room if you played for four hours or more on craps, roulette or blackjack. This offer sounded pretty good so a friend and I tried it out on a trip to Las Vegas in late May 1993.

Since you are limited to two days and we wanted to stay for four, we both made two-day reservations which allowed us to stay from Friday through Monday. You are re-quired to pre-pay for your first day, which we did over the telephone by credit card. After registering you are given a personalized Is-land Winner's Club card to track your play on the machines or table games.

We each put in our four hours on 25¢ video poker machines by varying our play between the minimum (1 coin) and maximum (5 coins) bets. We had no problem qualifying and we were both given vouchers to present at check out that refunded our pre-payments and gave us the second day at no charge.

Summary - at that time the regular room rate (including tax) was $81 on weekends and $59.40 during the week. Since our room was free, we saved $280.80 on our hotel bill!

Oh yes, and how did we do on our total of eight hours on video poker? We lost. But, by limiting our play to a game with a very low house edge (99.5% return, with perfect play) we kept our losses to about $30. This means we stayed in one of Las Vegas' finer hotels (a great pool!) for only $7.50 per night. Plus, we did get some free drinks while we were play-ing and, if we had only gotten that one card to complete our royal flush, we could have actually won money!

In May 1994 I made a return trip to the Tropicana for this same program and discov-ered that some changes had been made. The biggest change was that the time requirement had been raised to six hours from four. Since

I had already been on the program I was not eligible for the free room offer (although, as a member of the Island Winners Club I was eligible for the room at a reduced rate). My wife was traveling with me and, fortunately, she had not been on the program before so we made the reservation in her name for her maximum two-night stay. Upon arrival the same procedures were followed as in the previous visit, except for one change in how the required play was tracked by the casino. Since we were staying for two nights we had to gamble for a total of six hours and previously you were allowed to do all of your gambling in the first day to fulfill your requirements. That had changed. You now had to gamble for three hours in the first 24-hour period upon receiving your card and then another three hours by the time you were ready to check out. This could be a problem for someone who signed up for the program and then lost most of their bankroll in the first day. Also, even if you had gambled for eight hours on that first day, you still had to gamble for another three hours the next day. It didn't turn out to be a problem for us but it is something that you should be aware of. Once again, 25¢ video poker was the game of choice to put in the required time. We played the maximum five coins on each play and this time we won money! We got a few four-of-a-kinds which helped to put us in the plus column and we ended up winning $92.

Keep in mind that if you want to go and do the same thing we did, be sure to play the 9/6 video poker machines, rather than the 8/5 variety. These numbers refer to the Jacks or better machines with the following pay schedules (per coin on 5-coin play):

Hand	9/6	8/5
Royal Flush	800	800
Straight Flush	50	50
4-of-a-Kind	25	25
Full House	9	8
Flush	6	5
Straight	4	4
3-of-a-Kind	3	3
Two Pair	2	2
Jacks or Better	1	1

As you can see, the 9/6 machines are identical to the 8/5 machines, except for the better payoffs on Full Houses and Flushes. The payback percentage (with perfect play) on a 9/6 machine is 99.5 percent, while the 8/5 machines return 97.3 percent. There is only one bank of 9/6 machines in the 25¢ section and they can be found in the back of the casino near the bar. While you sit there and play you can only wonder why people across the aisle from you are playing an 8/5 machine with its lower payoff. Keep in mind that many Las Vegas casinos offer both 9/6 and 8/5 poker machines, so always look for the better payoffs. For more detailed information be sure to read the video poker story in the front of this book.

In August 1995 the Tropicana made some changes to the program and although it's not quite as good as it used to be it still offers a great value. The free room program is still valid only for new members, but the major changes are that it can't be booked in advance, you are limited to just one free night per person and you can only use the certificate for a future visit.

To participate you have to go to the Island Winners Club redemption center and ask to be issued a temporary card. When you gamble for three hours or more on any 25¢ or greater slot machine (or any of the table games) you will be issued a certificate valid for one free room night on a Sunday through Thursday stay (holidays and conventions excluded). That certificate, however, can only be used for a future stay (within six months) and can't be used immediately. According to Island Winners Club officials it could be used the next day but not if you're staying at the hotel. In order to do that you would have to check out and then check back in. A husband and wife are each eligible for a one night certificate, so they can actually stay free in the hotel for two nights by gambling for a total of six hours.

One thing to keep in mind is that you still must put in your three hours of gambling within a 24-hour period and that period begins when your card is "activated". By "activated" they mean the first time the card is used, *not* when it is issued. For a husband and wife wanting to qualify for a two-day stay this means you may not want to use both cards on the first day (unless you are prepared to gamble for three hours on each card within the same 24 hours). You may prefer to use one card for three hours on the first day and the other card for three hours on the second day. If you have any questions on the program be sure to give the Tropicana marketing department a call at (800) 521-8767.

Of the two vacation programs reviewed, the Tropicana's seems to be the best deal. The property is nicer and with only three hours of gambling required on a 25¢ or greater machine, it's hard to get hurt, even if you hit a bad streak of luck. I highly recommend you try it on your next visit.

There are many free tourist magazines that run coupon offers for casino fun books or special deals. Some sample titles are: *Tourguide of Las Vegas, Showbiz Weekly, What's On In Las Vegas, Las Vegas Today* and *Vegas Visitor*. All of these magazines are usually available in the hotel/motel lobbies or in the rooms themselves. If a fun book listing in this section says to look for an ad in a magazine, then it can probably be found in one of these publications.

Other games in the casino listings include: sports book (SB), race book (RB), baccarat (B), mini-baccarat (MB), pai gow (PG), poker (P), pai gow poker (PGP), Caribbean Stud Poker (CSP), Let It Ride (LIR), Red Dog (RD), Double Down Stud (DDS), Spanish 21 (S21), casino war (CW), keno (K) and bingo (BG).

Aladdin Hotel & Casino
3667 Las Vegas Blvd. South
Las Vegas, Nevada 89109
(702) 736-0111

Reservation Number: (800) 634-3424
Rooms: 1,100 Price Range: $65-$105
Suites: 70 Price Range: $250-$350
Restaurants: 4 (1 open 24 hours)
Buffets: B-$4.95 L-$5.95 D-$6.95
Casino Size: 34,452 Square Feet
Other Games: SB, RB, MB, P, PGP, CSP, LIR, K
Casino Marketing: (800) 367-2850
Fun Book: Ask at cashier cage
Show: "Country Tonite" $17.95/$21.95 with buffet. Children $11.95/$14.95 with buffet, 7:15 and 10:00 nightly, dark Tuesday
Special Features: Two swimming pools. Video arcade for children. Beauty and barber shop. Nightly live lounge entertainment.

Arizona Charlie's Hotel & Casino
740 South Decatur Boulevard
Las Vegas, Nevada 89107
(702) 258-5200

Reservation Number: (800) 342-2695
Rooms: 268 Price Range: $30-$50
Suites: 8   Price Range: $95-$115
Restaurants: 1 (open 24 hours)
Buffets: B-$3.50 L-$3.95 D-$5.50
Casino Size: 56,316 Square Feet
Other Games: SB, RB, MB, P, CSP, LIR, BG
Casino Marketing: (800) 882-5445
Senior Discount: If 65, or older, $5 off weekend room rate
Special Features: 50 championship bowling lanes - open 24 hours.
400-seat bingo parlor - open 24 hours. Video arcade for children.
Swimming pool.

Bally's Las Vegas
3645 Las Vegas Blvd. South
Las Vegas, Nevada 89109
(702) 739-4111

Reservation Number: (800) 634-3434
Rooms: 2,569 Price Range: $99-$190
Suites: 265   Price Range: $273-$2,000
Restaurants: 7 (1 open 24 hours)
Buffets: Brunch-$6.95 D-$11.95
Casino Size: 54,603 Square Feet
Other Games: SB, RB, B, P,
                PGP, CSP, LIR, S21, K
Casino Marketing: (800) 722-5597 ext. 4561
Show: "Jubilee" $46, 8:00 Sun/Mon, 8:00 and 11:00 Tue-Sat, dark Friday
Special Features: Two main showrooms. Men's and women's health spas. Shopping mall with more than 40 stores. 8 tennis courts. Free monorail service to MGM Grand.

Barbary Coast Hotel & Casino
3595 Las Vegas Blvd. South
Las Vegas, Nevada 89109
(702) 737-7111

Reservation Number: (800) 634-6755
Rooms: 188 Price Range: $50-$95
Suites: 10 Price Range: $200-$500
Restaurants: 3 (1 open 24 hours)
Casino Size: 32,000 Square Feet
Other Games: SB, RB, B, PGP, LIR, K
Casino Marketing: (702) 737-7111 ask for
                Slot Club Booth
Fun Book: Only given to hotel guests
Special Features: 24-hour McDonald's restaurant located in basement.

Barcelona Hotel & Casino
5011 E. Craig Road
Las Vegas, Nevada 89115
(702) 644-6300

Toll-Free Number: (800) 223-6330
Rooms: 177 Price Range: $20-$125
Restaurants: 1 (open 24 hours)
Casino Size: 2,200 Square Feet
Other Games: SB, LIR, No Craps or Roulette
Senior Discount: If 62, or older, $5 room discount

Binion's Horseshoe Casino and Hotel
128 E. Fremont Street
Las Vegas, Nevada 89125
(702) 382-1600

Reservation Number: (800) 622-6468
Rooms: 360 Price Range: $40-$60
Restaurants: 4 (1 open 24 hours)
Buffets: D-$9.95/$12.95 (Fri)
Casino Size: 56,929 Square Feet
Other Games: SB, RB, B, MB, P,
                    PGP, CSP, LIR, K, BG
Casino Marketing: (800) 937-6537
Special Features: Offers visitors a free photo in front of one million dollars in cash. Home of the World Series of Poker. Ham & Eggs breakfast for $2.75 from 6am to 2pm. Complete N.Y. steak dinner for $4 from 10pm to 5:45am. Offers very high limits on games.

Boomtown Hotel Casino & RV Resort
3333 Blue Diamond Road
Las Vegas, Nevada 89139
(702) 263-7777

Toll-Free Number: (800) 588-7711
Rooms: 304 Price Range: $45-$85
Suites: 8   Price Range: $150
Restaurants: 5 (1 open 24 hours)
Buffets: B-$3.99 L-$4.99
              D-$6.99/$9.99 (Fri/Sun)
Size: 43,750 Square Feet
Other Games: SB, P, CSP, LIR, CW, K
Casino Marketing: (800) 588-7711
Senior Discount: If 55, or older, join Silver Seekers Club for 10% off room rate and $1 buffet discount
Show: "The Outlaw Women of Boomtown" Free with 2 drink minimum, 5:00 and 7:00 nightly, dark Monday
Special Features: 460-space RV park. Free country/western lounge entertainment. Special area where you can pan for gold ($3 charge). 3 pools with Jacuzzi and water slides. 24-hour grocery store.

Boulder Station Hotel & Casino
4111 Boulder Highway
Las Vegas, Nevada 89121
(702) 432-7777

Toll-Free Number: (800) 981-5577
Reservation Number: (800) 683-7777
Rooms: 300 Price Range:$39-$69
Suites: 6   Price Range:$150-$300
Restaurants: 10 (1 open 24 hours)
Buffets: B-$3.95/$6.95 (Sun) L-$5.95
              D-$7.95
Casino Size: 66,073 Square Feet
Other Games: SB, RB, B, MB, P,
                    CSP, LIR, S21, K, BG
Casino Marketing: (800) 915-3322
Special Features: 99¢ margaritas and $1.25 beer-steamed hot dogs available at all bars. Shuttle service to Palace Station with connecting service to the Strip. Live entertainment nightly. 11-screen movie theater complex. Kid Quest - child care center.

Bourbon Street Hotel & Casino
120 East Flamingo Road
Las Vegas, Nevada 89109
(702) 737-7200

Reservation Number: (800) 634-6956
Rooms: 150 Price Range: $45-$80
Suites: 16 Price Range: $175-$250
Restaurants: 1 (open 24 hours)
Casino Size: 15,376 Square Feet
Other Games: SB, K

Caesars Palace
3570 Las Vegas Blvd. South
Las Vegas, Nevada 89109
(702) 731-7110

Toll-Free Number: (800) 634-6001
Reservation Number: (800) 634-6661
Rooms: 1,324 Price Range: $115-$190
Suites: 194 Price Range: $270-$895
Restaurants: 9 (1 open 24 hours)
Buffets: B-$7.95/$16.00 (Sun) L-$9.95
              D-$14.95
Casino Size: 118,000 Square Feet
Other Games: SB, RB, B, MB, PG,
                    PGP, CSP, LIR, S21, K
Casino Marketing:
              Slots-(800) 262-2502
              Tables-(800) 888-1710
Special Features: Omnimax movie theater, 15,000-seat outdoor arena. Two swimming pools. Health spa. Beauty salon. The Forum Shops at Caesars shopping mall features Planet Hollywood and Warner Brothers Store.

California Hotel Casino & RV Park
12 Ogden Street
Las Vegas, Nevada 89101
(702) 385-1222

Reservation Number: (800) 634-6255
Rooms: 781 Price Range: $40-$60
Suites: 74 Price Range: Private Use
Restaurants: 4 (1 open 24 hours)
Casino Size: 35,848 Square Feet
Other Games: SB, MB, CSP, LIR, K
Casino Marketing: (800) 634-6505
Special Features: 93-space RV park with full hook-up service (800) 634-6505.

Casino Royale & Hotel
3411 Las Vegas Blvd. South
Las Vegas, Nevada 89109
(702) 737-3500

Toll-Free Number: (800) 854-7666
Rooms: 153 Price Range: $45-$125
Restaurants: 2 (both open 24 hours)
Casino Size: 15,000 Square Feet
Other Games: CSP, S21
Casino Marketing: (702) 737-0084

Circus Circus Hotel & Casino
2880 Las Vegas Blvd. South
Las Vegas, Nevada 89109
(702) 734-0410

Reservation Number: (800) 634-3450
Rooms: 2,832 Price Range: $39-$100
Suites: 110 Price Range: $59-$180
Restaurants: 6 (2 open 24 hours)
Buffets: B-$2.99 L-$3.99 D-$4.99
Casino Size: 111,000 Square Feet
Other Games: SB, RB, P, CSP, LIR, K
Special Features: Free circus acts 11 a.m. to midnight. 370-space RV park (800) 634-3450. Wedding chapel. Midway and arcade games. Five-acre indoor water theme park.

Continental Hotel & Casino
4100 Paradise Road
Las Vegas, Nevada 89109
(702) 737-5555

Reservation Number: (800) 634-6641
Rooms: 400 Price Range: $25-$85
Restaurants: 2 (1 open 24 hours)
Buffets: B-$2.95 L-$3.95 D-$5.95
Casino Size: 22,900 Square Feet
Other Games: SB, K, BG
Casino Marketing: (800) 777-4844 ext. 5170
Special Features: Complimentary shuttle to Strip.

Days Inn Town Hall Casino-Hotel
4155 Koval Lane
Las Vegas, Nevada 89109
(702) 731-2111

Reservation Number: (800) 634-6541
Rooms: 357 Price Range: $35-$54
Suites: 3 Price Range: $85-$150
Restaurants: 1 (open 24 hours)
Casino Size: 4,600 Square Feet
Other Games: No Craps or Roulette
Fun Book: Only given to hotel guests

Debbie Reynolds' Hollywood Hotel/Casino/Movie Museum
305 Convention Center Drive
Las Vegas, Nevada 89109
(702) 734-0711

Reservation Number: (800) 633-1777
Rooms: 150 Price Range: $59-$275
Restaurants: 2 (1 open 24 hours)
Casino Size: 4,600 Square Feet
Games Offered: No Craps or Roulette
Show: "Boy-lesque" $24.95, 10:30 Mon-Fri, 9:00 Sat, dark Sunday
Special Features: 6,000-square-foot museum with Hollywood memorabilia ($7.95 admission charge). 500-seat showroom where Debbie Reynolds performs (when she's in town) Mon-Fri evenings at 7:30.

El Cortez Hotel & Casino
600 E. Fremont Street
Las Vegas, Nevada 89101
(702) 385-5200

Reservation Number: (800) 634-6703
Rooms: 308 Price Range: $23-$40
Restaurants: 2 (1 open 24 hours)
Casino Size: 41,300 Square Feet
Other Games: SB, RB, MB, P, K
Special Features: Children's video arcade. Gift shop and ice cream parlor.

Excalibur Hotel/Casino
3850 Las Vegas Blvd. South
Las Vegas, Nevada 89109
(702) 597-7777

Reservation Number: (800) 937-7777
Rooms: 4,032 Price Range: $59-$93
Suites: 46 Price Range: $135-$175
Restaurants: 7 (1 open 24 hours)
Buffets: B-$3.99 L-$4.99 D-$5.99
Casino Size: 123,944 Square Feet
Other Games: SB, RB, MB, P, PGP, CSP, LIR, K

Show: "King Arthur's Tournament" $29.95 dinner show, 6:00 and 8:30 nightly Special Features: Two motion simulator rides. Wedding Chapel. Video arcade and games.

Fiesta Casino Hotel
2400 N. Rancho Drive
Las Vegas, Nevada 89130
(702) 631-7000

Reservation Number: (800) 731-7333
Rooms: 100 Price Range: $29-$79
Suites: 18 Price Range: $66-$118
Restaurants: 6 (1 open 24 hours)
Buffets: B-$3.95 L-$5.95 D-$8.95
Casino Size: 25,160 Square Feet
Casino Marketing: (800) 731-7333
Other Games: SB, RB, CSP, LIR, S21, K, BG
Special Features: Weekly blackjack, slot and video poker tournaments. Festival Buffet offers 12 separate eating stations.

Fitzgeralds Casino/Holiday Inn
301 Fremont Street
Las Vegas, Nevada 89101
(702) 388-2400

Reservation Number: (800) 274-5825
Rooms: 590 Price Range: $30-$60
Suites: 62 Price Range: $50-$90
Restaurants: 5 (1 open 24 hours)
Buffets: B-$4.49/$5.99 (Sat/Sun)
            L-$4.99 D-$7.99
Casino Size: 33,800 Square Feet
Casino Marketing: (800) 274-5825
Fun Book: Given to hotel guests, or
            look for ad in magazines
Other Games: CSP, LIR, S21, K
Special Features: Affiliated with Holiday Inn. Located at the beginning of the Fremont Street Experience. Free valet parking.

Flamingo Hilton Las Vegas
3555 Las Vegas Blvd. South
Las Vegas, Nevada 89109
(702) 733-3111

Toll-Free Number (800) 329-3232
Reservation Number: (800) 732-2111
Rooms: 3,642 Price Range: $69-$145
Suites: 209 Price Range: $250-$580
Restaurants: 8 (1 open 24 hours)
Buffets: B-$4.95 D-$6.95
Casino Size: 80,334 Square Feet
Other Games: RB, SB, MB, P, CSP, LIR, K
Casino Marketing: (800) 225-4882
Fun Book: Given to hotel guests,
            or look for ad in magazines

Show: "The Great Radio City Rockettes Spectacular" $45.50 for dinner show at 7:45, $38.20 for cocktail show at 10:30, dark Friday Special Features: Health Spa. Five outdoor swimming pools. Shopping arcade. Tennis Club and Pro Shop. Six floors of rooms for non-smokers.

Four Queens Hotel/Casino
202 Fremont Street
Las Vegas, Nevada 89101
(702) 385-4011

Reservation Number: (800) 634-6045
Rooms: 700 Price Range: $47-$57
Suites: 40 Price Range: $85-$95
Restaurants: 4 (1 open 24 hours)
Casino Size: 32,296 Square Feet
Casino Marketing: (800) 634-6045
Other Games: SB, CSP, LIR, K
Special Features: "Queens Machine" - world's largest slot machine. Prime Rib special for $4.95 from 6pm to 2am. 99¢ shrimp cocktail.

Fremont Hotel & Casino
200 E. Fremont Street
Las Vegas, Nevada 89101
(702) 385-3232

Reservation Number: (800) 634-6460
Rooms: 428 Price Range: $30-$60
Restaurants: 4 (1 open 24 hours)
Buffets: B-$4.95/$7.95 (Sun) L-$5.95 D-$8.95/$13.95 (Sun/Tue/Fri)
Casino Size: 27,618 Square Feet
Other Games: SB, RB, PGP, CSP, LIR, K
Casino Marketing: (800) 874-0711
Fun Book: Given to hotel guests,
            or look for ad in magazines
Special Features: 99¢ shrimp cocktail at the snack bar next to the Lanai Cafe.

Frontier Hotel & Gambling Hall
3120 Las Vegas Blvd. South
Las Vegas, Nevada 89109
(702) 794-8200

Reservation Number: (800) 634-6966
Rooms: 550 Price Range: $35-$55
Suites: 434 Price Range: $55-$85
Restaurants: 3 (1 open 24 hours)
Buffets: L-$4.95
            D-$7.95/$10.95 (Fri)/$8.95 (Sat/Sun)
Casino Size: 41,325 Square Feet
Other Games: SB, RB, CSP, LIR, S21, K
Casino Marketing: (800) 421-7806
Special Features: Casino has $1 minimum blackjack and also offers single-deck play.

Gold Coast Hotel & Casino
4000 W. Flamingo Road
Las Vegas, Nevada 89103
(702) 367-7111

Reservation Number: (800) 331-5334
Rooms: 750 Price Range: $35-$50
Suites: 26 Price Range: $100-$165
Restaurants: 5 (1 open 24 hours)
Buffets: B-$4.95/$6.95 (Sun)
         L-$5.95 D-$6.95
Casino Size: 71,000 Square Feet
Other Games: SB, RB, P, PGP,
            MB, CSP, LIR, K, BG
Casino Marketing: (800) 331-5334
            ask for Slot Club Booth
Special Features: 72-lane bowling center. 2 movie theaters. 700-seat bingo parlor. 2 entertainment lounges with no cover/no minimum. Dance hall. Free child-care.

Gold Spike Hotel & Casino
400 E. Ogden Avenue
Las Vegas, Nevada 89101
(702) 384-8444

Reservation Number: (800) 634-6703
Rooms: 102 Price Range: $20
Suites: 7 Price Range: $30
Restaurants: 1 (open 24 hours)
Casino Size: 5,820 Square Feet
Other Games: P, K, No Craps

Golden Gate Hotel & Casino
One Fremont Street
Las Vegas, Nevada 89101
(702) 385-1906

Reservation Number: (800) 426-1906
Rooms: 106 Price Range: $35-$50
Restaurants: 2 (2 open 24 hours)
Casino Size: 9,090 Square Feet
Other Games: K, CSP, LIR
Special Features: Shrimp cocktail for 99¢ (24 hours) at the San Francisco Shrimp Bar & Deli. Live piano music daily from noon to midnight. Las Vegas' oldest hotel - established 1906.

The Golden Nugget
129 E. Fremont Street
Las Vegas, Nevada 89101
(702) 385-7111

Toll-Free Number: (800) 634-3403
Reservation Number: (800) 634-3454
Rooms: 1,805 Price Range: $69-$150
Suites: 102 Price Range: $275-$375
Restaurants: 5 (1 open 24 hours)
Buffets: B-$5.75/$10.95 (Sun)
         L-$7.50 D-$10.95
Casino Size: 34,680 Square Feet
Other Games: SB, RB, B, MB,
            PGP, CSP, LIR, K
Casino Marketing: (800) 289-4269
Show: "Country Fever" $22.50, 7:15 and 10:15 nightly, dark Friday
Special Features: Mobil "Four Star" and AAA "Four Diamond" rating. Spa, beauty salon, fitness center and his and hers spas. World's largest gold nugget (61 pounds) on display.

Hacienda Resort Hotel & Casino
3950 Las Vegas Blvd. South
Las Vegas, Nevada 89109
(702) 739-8911

Reservation Number: (800) 634-6713
Rooms: 1,140 Price Range: $48-$135
Suites: 25 Price Range: $125-$500
Restaurants: 4 (1 open 24 hours)
Buffets: B-$2.99 L-$3.99 D-$5.99
Casino Size: 27,400 Square Feet
Other Games: SB, P, PGP, CSP, LIR, S21, K
Casino Marketing: (800) 843-2637

Hard Rock Hotel & Casino
4455 Paradise Road
Las Vegas, Nevada 89109
(702) 693-5000

Toll-Free Number: (800) HRD-ROCK
Rooms: 311 Price Range:$75-$150
Suites: 28 Price Range:$250-$500
Restaurants: 2 (1 open 24 hours)
Casino Size: 28,000 Square Feet
Other Games: SB, B, PGP, CSP, LIR
Casino Marketing: (800) 693-ROCK
Special Features: Rock and Roll memorabilia located throughout hotel and casino. Piano-shaped roulette tables. Slot machines with guitar handles. The Joint - 1,400-seat showroom. Beach Club with whirlpools, spas, cabanas and sandy beaches. Lagoon with underwater music. Athletic club. Hard Rock retail store.

Flying to Las Vegas?
Make This Your First Stop!

A great "guaranteed winner" promotion being run by one of the smaller Las Vegas casino hotels is at Vacation Village which will give you the chance to win back the cost of your airline ticket (up to a maximum of $400), or a free suite for two nights, or cash. To participate you must go to the More For Four Club Booth in the casino and present your airline ticket within 12 hours of your arrival in Las Vegas. The booth is open from 8am until 11pm daily.

On my last trip to Vegas in February 1996 our plane arrived late in the evening and when we got to the casino the booth was closed. One of the pit bosses then issued us a raincheck so we could get a 12-hour extension and come back the next day. On our return visit we presented our raincheck along with our airline tickets and they took us over to a big-6 wheel that had been slightly altered so that it had one space to represent "airfare," another for "suite" and the rest of the spaces were the standard numbers (mostly ones and twos) that represented cash prizes. My spin landed a few spaces from the airfare spot and I won $1. My friend was a bit luckier when his spin landed on $2. Okay, so we didn't win a fortune, but it was fun and it was free! Just make believe you're on *The Price Is Right* and you're spinning the big wheel trying to make it into the final showcase showdown. Who knows, maybe you'll win the airfare prize and actually, the odds aren't all that bad. According to *Las Vegas Advisor* publisher Anthony Curtis the average spin is worth more than $13.

Keep in mind that the property isn't exactly in the class of the glitzier Strip casinos, but for a few minutes of your time it's definitely worth the trip and if you like to play video poker you'll especially enjoy the visit. In the 1996 "Best of Las Vegas" poll conducted by the *Las Vegas Review-Journal*, Vacation Village won the award for best video poker because of its generous pay tables and bonus award promotions. The casino also conducts daily drawings for cash prizes and while you're there you can go to the front bar and get a free hot dog & beer with a $10 change buy-in (nickels or quarters).

Vacation Village is about three miles south of the airport at 6711 Las Vegas Boulevard South. From McCarran Airport take the I-215 Airport Beltway to exit 9. For more information call (702) 897-1700 or (800) 658-5000. Remember to get there within 12 hours of your arrival and if the booth is closed when you arrive just ask for a raincheck for a 12-hour extension.

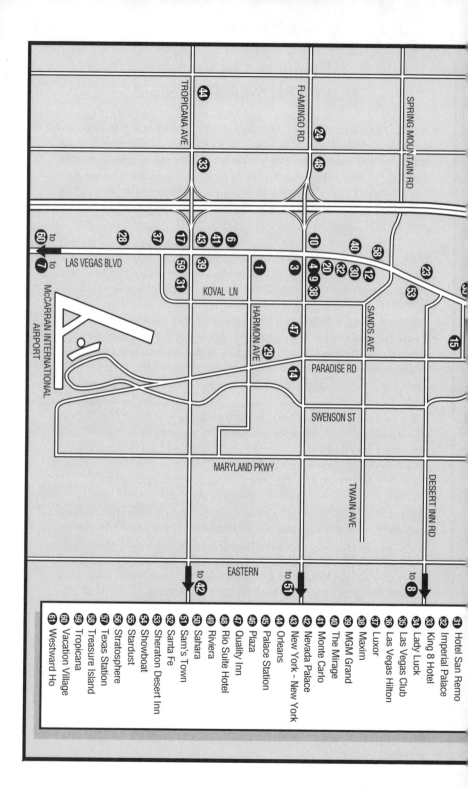

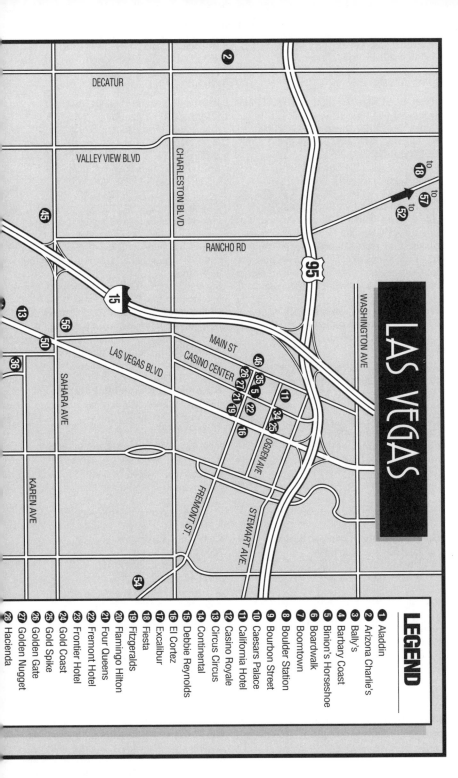

LAS VEGAS

LEGEND

1. Aladdin
2. Arizona Charlie's
3. Bally's
4. Barbary Coast
5. Binion's Horseshoe
6. Boardwalk
7. Boomtown
8. Boulder Station
9. Bourbon Street
10. Caesars Palace
11. California Hotel
12. Casino Royale
13. Circus Circus
14. Continental
15. Debbie Reynolds
16. El Cortez
17. Excalibur
18. Fiesta
19. Fitzgeralds
20. Flamingo Hilton
21. Four Queens
22. Fremont Hotel
23. Frontier Hotel
24. Gold Coast
25. Gold Spike
26. Golden Gate
27. Golden Nugget
28. Hacienda

DECATUR

VALLEY VIEW BLVD

CHARLESTON BLVD

RANCHO RD

95

WASHINGTON AVE

MAIN ST

CASINO CENTER

LAS VEGAS BLVD

SAHARA AVE

KAREN AVE

FREMONT ST.

OGDEN AVE

STEWART AVE.

15

to 18
to 57
to 52

Harrah's Las Vegas
3475 Las Vegas Blvd. South
Las Vegas, Nevada 89109
(702) 369-5000

Reservation Number: (800) HARRAHS
Rooms: 1,675 Price Range: $99-$149
Suites: 36   Price Range: $195-$250
Restaurants: 5 (1 open 24 hours)
Buffets: B-$4.99 L-$5.99 D-$7.99
Casino Size: 73,754 Square Feet
Other Games: SB, RB, B, MB, P, PGP,
            CSP, LIR, RD, S21, CW, K
Casino Marketing: (800) 392-9002
Show: "Spellbound" $29.95, 7:30 and 10:00
nightly, dark Sunday
Special Features: $150-million expansion with
675 new rooms expected to be complete by
mid-1997. Mardi Gras and Carnaval themed
casino. Health club and Olympic-size pool.

Holiday Inn Casino-Boardwalk
3750 Las Vegas Blvd. South
Las Vegas, Nevada 89109
(702) 735-2400

Reservation Number: (800) 635-4581
Rooms: 203 Price Range: $65-$150
Restaurants: 2 (1 open 24 hours)
Buffets: B-$3.99
Casino Size: 66,000 Square Feet
Other Games: SB, RB, LIR
Casino Marketing: (800) 635-4581
Show: "Teeze" $19.95, 7:15 and 10:30 nightly,
dark Tuesday
Special Features: Prime Rib dinner for $5.95
($3.95 Wed) from 5pm to 10pm. 24-hour
coffee shop offers $1.29 breakfast specials.

Hotel San Remo Casino & Resort
115 East Tropicana Avenue
Las Vegas, Nevada 89109
(702) 739-9000

Reservation Number: (800) 522-REMO
Rooms: 680 Price Range: $59-$130
Suites: 31 Price Range: $159-$400
Restaurants: 5 (1 open 24 hours)
Buffets: B-$5.75/$6.75 (Sun)
          L-$6.75 D-$7.75
Other Games: SB, PGP, CSP, LIR, K
Casino Size: 22,500 Square Feet
Casino Marketing: (800) 235-5987
Show: "Showgirls of Magic" $19.95, 8:00
and 10:30 (adults only) nightly, dark Monday

Imperial Palace Hotel & Casino
3535 Las Vegas Blvd. South
Las Vegas, Nevada 89109
(702) 731-3311

Reservation Number: (800) 634-6441
Rooms: 2,700 Price Range: $49-$99
Suites: 225 Price Range: $79-$325
Restaurants: 9 (1 open 24 hours)
Buffets: B-$4.99 L-$5.99 D-$6.99
Casino Size: 75,000 Square Feet
Other Games: SB, RB, MB, PGP,
            CSP, LIR, K
Casino Marketing: (800) 351-7400 ext.-1
Fun Book: Need card found in brochure
            racks around town
Show: "Legends In Concert" $29.50/$14.75
children under 12, 7:30 and 10:30 nightly,
dark Sunday
Special Features: Oriental theme throughout
hotel and casino. Rare and antique Auto Col-
lection on display (admission charge). Mini
shopping mall. Video arcade for children. 24-
hour wedding chapel. Independent 24-hour
medical facility with no appointment necessary and most travel insurance accepted.

King 8 Hotel & Gambling Hall
3330 West Tropicana Avenue
Las Vegas, Nevada 89103
(702) 736-8988

Reservation Number: (800) 634-3488
Rooms: 305 Price Range: $40-$55
Restaurants: 1 (open 24 hours)
Casino Size: 4,516 Square Feet
Other Games: SB, RB, P, LIR, K
Casino Marketing: (800) 634-3488

Lady Luck Casino Hotel
206 N. Third Street
Las Vegas, Nevada 89101
(702) 477-3000

Toll-Free Number: (800) 634-6580
Reservation Number: (800) LADY-LUCK
Rooms: 621 Price Range: $39-$75
Suites: 171 Price Range: $75-$95
Restaurants: 4 (1 open 24 hours)
Buffets: B-$3.49/$5.49 (Sat/Sun) L-$4.49
          D-$6.99/$8.99 (Tue/Wed)
Casino Size: 18,350 Square Feet
Other Games: SB, MB, S21, K
Casino Marketing: (800) LADY-LUCK
Fun Book: Given to all hotel guests. Also
given to non-Nevada residents with valid
photo ID, or with flyer/coupon from maga-
zines. Go to Mad Money booth to redeem.

Special Features: Voted #1 Fun Book in Las Vegas. Non-smoking casino area and rooms. Free airport shuttle bus service. Daily and weekly gaming tournaments.

Las Vegas Auto/Truck Plaza
8050 S. Industrial Rd.
Las Vegas, Nevada 89118
(702) 361-1176

Restaurants: 1 (Open 24 hours)
Casino Size: 644 Square Feet
Other Games: LIR, No Craps or Roulette
Special Features: Players club for table players for comps and discounts

Las Vegas Club Hotel & Casino
18 E. Fremont Street
Las Vegas, Nevada 89101
(702) 385-1664

Reservation Number: (800) 634-6532
Rooms: 220 Price Range: $40-$115
Suites: 2   Price Range: $125
Restaurants: 2 (1 open 24 hours)
Casino Size: 22,300 Square Feet
Other Games: SB, RB, CSP, LIR, K
Casino Marketing: (800) 634-6532
Special Features: Sports theme throughout hotel and casino. Sports Hall of Fame contains one of the world's largest collection of baseball memorabilia and sports artifacts. Casino offers very liberal blackjack rules.

Las Vegas Hilton
3000 Paradise Road
Las Vegas, Nevada 89109
(702) 732-5111

Reservation Number: (800) 732-7117
Rooms: 2,900 Price Range: $85-$259
Suites: 305   Price Range: $310-$995
Restaurants: 12 (1 open 24 hours)
Buffets: B-$5.99/$9.99 (Sat/Sun)
         L-$7.99 D-$12.99
Casino Size: 76,500 Square Feet
Other Games: SB, RB, B, MB, P,
          PGP, CSP, LIR, K
Casino Marketing: (800) 547-2600
Show: "Starlight Express" $19.50-$45.00, 7:30 and 10:30 nightly (only 7:30 on Mon/Wed), dark Friday
Special Features: "Star Trek: The Experience," an interactive adventure, expected to open by Spring 1997. Largest race and sports book in Las Vegas. State-of-the-art health club. Outdoor heated Olympic pool and 24-seat spa. Putting green. 6 tennis courts.

Longhorn Casino
5288 Boulder Highway
Las Vegas, Nevada 89122
(702) 435-9170

Restaurants: 1 (open 24 hours)
Casino Size: 1,175 Square Feet
Other Games: No Craps or Roulette
Special Features: $1 blackjack games. Monthly tournaments.

Luxor Las Vegas
3900 Las Vegas Blvd. South
Las Vegas, Nevada 89119
(702) 262-4000

Reservation Number (800) 288-1000
Rooms: 4,300 Price Range: $59-$139
Suites 464   Price Range: $150-$350
Restaurants: 9 (1 open 24 hours)
Buffets: B-$4.49 L-$5.49 D-$7.49
Casino Size: 100,000 Square Feet
Other Games: SB, RB, MB, P,
          PGP, CSP, LIR, K
Casino Marketing: (702) 262-4331
Special Features: 30-story pyramid-shaped hotel with elevators that move at a 39-degree angle. 3 adventure rides. Sega USA high-tech video arcade - "VirtuaLand." Full-size replica of King Tut's tomb. Wedding chapel.

Maxim Hotel/Casino
160 East Flamingo Road
Las Vegas, Nevada 89109
(702) 731-4300

Reservation Number: (800) 634-6987
Rooms: 757 Price Range: $39-$175
Suites: 38 Price Range: $175-$300
Restaurants: 4 (1 open 24 hours)
Buffets: B-$5.95/$7.95 (Sat/Sun) D-$7.49
Casino Size: 21,084 Square Feet
Other Games: SB, CSP, LIR, K
Casino Marketing: (800) 634-6987
Fun Book: Ask in the gift shop
Show: "Comedy Max" $13.90/$18.25 with buffet, 7:00, and 9:00 nightly; "Comedy Magic" $9.95/$12.95 with buffet, 1:00 and 3:00 daily, dark Sunday
Special Features: A short walk to the Strip and other major casino/hotels. Free covered parking.

MGM Grand Hotel Casino & Theme Park
3799 Las Vegas Blvd. South
Las Vegas, Nevada 89109
(702) 891-1111

Reservation Number: (800) 929-1111
Rooms: 4,265 Price Range: $89-$189
Suites: 744   Price Range: $169-$650
Restaurants: 8 (1 open 24 hours)
Buffets: B-$7.22 L-$8.29 D-$10.97
Casino Size: 171,500 Square Feet
Other Games: SB, RB, B, MB, P, PGP,
                        CSP, LIR, CW, K
Casino Marketing: (702) 891-3651
Show: "EFX! with Michael Crawford" $70,
7:30 and 10:30 nightly (no 10:30 show on
Sun), dark Thursday
Special Features: The world's largest hotel
and casino. 2 showrooms. 5 lounges/bars.
Comedy Club. "Youth hotel" with supervised
activities for children of hotel guests. 30,000-
square-foot midway and arcade. 144,000-
square-foot swimming complex with beach-
entry pool and cabanas. 33-acre "MGM Grand
Adventures" theme park includes 7 rides, 5
shows, 2 wedding chapels and strolling characters. Free entrance to theme park. Price for
all-day passes for park's rides and attractions
is adjusted seasonally.

The Mirage
3400 Las Vegas Blvd. South
Las Vegas, Nevada 89109
(702) 791-7111

Reservation Number: (800) 627-6667
Rooms: 3,049 Price Range: $89-$299
Suites: 279   Price Range: $300-$750
Restaurants: 10 (1 open 24 hours)
Buffets: B-$7.50/$13.95 (Sun)
             L-$8.95 D-$12.95
Casino Size: 95,300 Square Feet
Other Games: SB, RB, B, MB, P,
                        PGP, CSP, LIR, K
Casino Marketing: (800) 627-6667
Show: "Siegfried & Roy" $83.85, 7:30 and
11:00 nightly, dark Wednesday/Thursday
Special Features: Dolphin Habitat with 1.5
million-gallon pool (admission charge).
20,000-gallon saltwater aquarium at recep-
tion area. Royal White Tiger Habitat. "Live"
volcano at entrance that erupts periodically.

Monte Carlo Resort & Casino
3770 Las Vegas Blvd. South
Las Vegas, Nevada 89109
(702) 730-7777

Reservation Number: (800) 311-8999
Rooms: 3,759 Price Range: $89-$149
Suites: 255   Price Range: $159-$400
Restaurants: 6 (1 open 24 hours)
Buffets: B-$5.49 L-$6.49 D-$8.49
Casino Size: 90,000 Square Feet
Other Games: SB, RB, B, MB, P, PGP,
                        CSP, LIR, K, BG
Casino Marketing: (800) 822-8656
Show: "Lance Burton, Master Magician"
$34.95, 7:30 and 10:30 nightly, dark Sun/
Mon
Special Features: Casino has single-zero rou-
lette. Food court with McDonald's, Nathan's,
Sbarro's, Haagen Daz and Bagel Shop. On
premises brewery serves six varieties of beer.
3 swimming pools and "lazy river" ride.
Health spa. Tennis courts. 12 retail shops.

Nevada Palace Hotel & Casino
5255 Boulder Highway
Las Vegas, Nevada 89122
(702) 458-8810

Reservation Number: (800) 634-6283
Rooms: 214 Price Range: $35-$100
Restaurants: 2 (1 open 24 hours)
Buffets: B-$3.99 D-$5.99
Casino Size: 13,425 Square Feet
Other Games: SB, CSP, LIR, K
Senior Discount: If 55, or older, join slot club
                        to get 10% discount on meals
Fun Book: Only given to hotel guests
Casino Marketing: (702) 458-8810 ext. 7175

New York-New York Hotel & Casino
3790 Las Vegas Blvd. South
Las Vegas, Nevada 89109
(702) 740-6969

EXPECTED TO OPEN BY EARLY 1997
Reservation Number: (800) NY-FOR-ME
Rooms: 1,938 Price Range: $79-$139
Suites: 255   Price Range: $129-$1,000
Restaurants: 6 (1 open 24 hours)
Casino Size: 84,000 Square Feet
Other Games: SB, RB, MB, PGP,
                        CSP, LIR, K
Special Features: Design recreates the New
York skyline and includes a replica of the
Statue of Liberty and the Empire State Build-
ing. Features Manhattan Express - a Coney
Island-style roller coaster.

1995 Las Vegas Coupon Run Results

If you've read Anthony Curtis' *Couponomy* story in the front of this book then you're already familiar with the term "coupon run." If you haven't read it yet please turn to it now and the rest of us will wait for you right here. All set? Good, let's begin.

In March, 1995 my friend and I made our own coupon run to see how well we could do. First, we scanned all of the tourist magazines for free fun book ads. Next, we went to one of the brochure racks to see if there were any other offers available. The racks are usually located at the car rental agencies, or non-casino hotels/motels throughout the city and are serviced by a company called Fun City Distributing (702) 456-9660. You can give them a call to ask the location of the rack closest to where you're staying. We went to Payless Car Rental on Paradise Road near the Hard Rock Cafe. After collecting all of our offers we consulted our map and planned our itinerary. We began on the south end of the strip at the Hacienda and headed north toward downtown. Here's how we did:

Hacienda - We got two free luggage identification tags. We won four 7-5 bets and lost four 7-5 bets. Up $8.

Maxim - Some good bonus coupons for the machines, but no table game coupons in their fun book. They had a coupon for a free soft drink at the snack bar, so we each got a free Coke. However, we also had a coupon that appeared in last year's edition of this book for two free entries in the Maxim's daily slot tournament (which was later discontinued). My friend wins third place and earns $25. Now up $33.

Flamingo Hilton - They have a thick coupon book that's heavily advertised in the local magazines. A lot of offers for food, but there are no table game coupons. No bets made; still up $33.

O'Shea's - Two free drinks at the bar. Lost four 2-1 bets and won two 2-1's which made us even for our visit. Still up $33.

Imperial Palace - Our free scratch-off Slotto cards got us one key chain and two free drinks. Also, we each had a coupon for $2 extra in coins when you bought $10 in coins. We exchanged our coupons, got our $10 rolls of quarters and made a $4 profit! Now up $37.

Harrah's - They happened to be running a special to get people in their slot club. We both joined and each got a coupon for a 2-for-1 lunch buffet. These were worth $4.99 each. Also, after playing $10 in coins on any machine we were entitled to come back the next day and get a $10 cash rebate. We found some 9/6 video poker machines in the rear of the casino and we each played about $15. We ended up losing $2 between us, but then we came back the next day and we each got our $10 rebate. That made us $18 ahead for our visit. Now up $55

Sands - We each got a free souvenir coffee mug with the Sands logo. We lost three 7-5's and won one 7-5. On the 2-1's we won one and lost one. The net loss was $8 and we were now up $47.

Riviera - Lost three 3-2's and two 7-5's. Won four 7-5's and two 3-2's for a total net win of $18. Now up $65.

Circus Circus - We each got a free hip pack. Lost one $1 match play bet and won one. Still up $65.

Slots-A-Fun - Free popcorn and two free hats. One winning and one losing $1 match play bets. Still up $65.

Silver City - More free popcorn. Two losing $1 match play bets. Now up $63.

Stardust - Won two 7-5 bets and lost three 7-5 bets resulting in a $1 loss. Note: This coupon is not available in magazines or coupon racks. We got ours by using the coupon in the back of the 1995 edition of this book. Now up $62.

Sahara - Lots of action here! Won eight 3-2's and lost ten 3-2's, but we still ended up $4 ahead. Now up $66.

Fitzgerald's - Won four 3-2's and lost four 3-2's for a net gain of $4. Now up $70.

Fremont - We each got a free deck of playing cards. On our bets we won three 7-5's and two 3-2's. We lost one 7-5 and two 3-2's for a net win of $18. Now up $88.

Four Queens - Because we both subscribed to *Casino Player Magazine* we both received coupons for $20 in slot play at this casino. Also, since we both subscribed to *Las Vegas Advisor* newsletter we each received another coupon valid for another $15 in slot play. That was a combined total of $70 in free slot machine play between us. We chose to play our credits on 9/6 video poker machines and we ended up winning $71 in real cash. Now up $159.

The end result? Well, although we wound up $159 ahead, you need to make some adjustments to come up with a true figure of how our bets did. After deducting the $25 winnings from the slot tournament at the Maxim, the $18 bonus for joining the slot club at Harrah's, the $4 coin bonus at the Imperial Palace and the $71 in slot play winnings at the Four Queens, you are left with $41 as the amount we won on bets using our fun book coupons. Now, keep in mind that we made a total of 76 bets and we had more losing bets (41) than winning bets (35), yet we still came out ahead! Plus, we also got some cute souvenirs, free food, sodas and cocktails. We never played any of the keno, poker or race book coupons. On the blackjack coupons we used basic strategy and on the roulette coupons we played red or black. For craps we bet the pass line.

Was it worth it? Well, it was a lot of work (you may want do your coupon run spread out over a few days) and we were very tired after it was finished, but sure, it was worth it. We got to visit a variety of casinos and we ended up winning money. Isn't that what you go to Las Vegas for? The important thing to remember from this experience is that without the coupons we would have lost money. Even though we were betting small amounts, the power of the gambling coupons gave us an edge over the casinos and we came out winners. You can do the same. Have fun!

1996 Las Vegas Trip

On my trip to Las Vegas in February 1996 I didn't make a full coupon run but, as always, I still found some good deals:

Sam's Town - By subscribing to *Las Vegas Advisor* I got a coupon for a free night's stay. We used it on the first night and saved $40. A great deal!

Vacation Village - We each took a spin on a promotional Big-6 wheel trying to win our airfare reimbursement (up to $400). I won $1, my friend won $2. We also both used a special coupon from *Las Vegas Advisor* for a bonus payoff on the video poker machines. I won an extra $8.75 and he won an extra $12.50.

Palace Station - This was a strange one. My friend called the marketing department in advance and asked about getting the casino rate of $39 weekdays/ $49 weekends for our 4-night stay. He gave them his name and they said he was already in their computer and qualified for that rate. He didn't remember ever being rated there. I then called and asked about the casino rate but they wouldn't give it to me. He booked the room at his casino rate and we saved about $100. Using the coupons from the fun books they gave us at the front desk we each got a free drink from the bar, plus I won $10 and he won $5. We also used coupons from that same book to each buy a $12.95 t-shirt for $4.95 in the gift shop.

Sands - We each got a free souvenir coffee mug with the Sands logo. We won four 7-5's and lost two 7-5's resulting in a net win of $14.

Tropicana - I used my slot club membership to get a $39 rate for a 2-night stay, saving $80 off the regular rate. They also had a coupon sheet for a free souvenir key chain (with a $20 change buy-in) and a special $5 souvenir t-shirt.

Fiesta - By joining the slot club we each got a free Margarita, plus a free deck of playing cards. We also got a fun book with coupons for a free buffet, a free hot dog and a free ice cream cone. Using the fun book coupons for betting we won two 5-3's and lost two 5-3's and two 2-1's for a net win of $2.

Circus Circus - We each got a collapsible water bottle with the Circus Circus logo. Lost two $1 match plays. Went next door to **Slots-A-Fun** for free popcorn, hats and cards, one winning and one losing $1 match play bets. Net $1 loss.

Riviera - A free deck of playing cards for each of us. Lost three 7-5's and three 3-2's. Won one 3-2 and three 7-5's for a net win of $5.

Hard Rock - We each got a free souvenir shot glass, a free cocktail and a coupon for a free breakfast. Won two 7-5's and lost two 7-5's for a net win of $4.

Downtown - The **Lady Luck** had a fun book with a coupon for a free foot-long hot dog and a free souvenir photo. Over to **Binion's Horseshoe** for another free souvenir photo, this time standing in front of $1 million in cash! The Binion's photo was processed in a few minutes and also came with an attractive folder. Because we both subscribed to *Casino Player Magazine* we both received coupons for $20 in slot play at the **Four Queens**. Also, since we both subscribed to *Las Vegas Advisor* we each received coupons valid for another $30 in Four Queens slot play ($10 per day for 3 days). That was a combined total of $100 in free slot play between us. We played our credits on 9/6 video poker machines and we ended up winning $83.75 in real cash. Another great deal!

HIT THE JACKPOT!

...with a subscription to Casino Player Magazine

and receive $800 in casino vouchers as a special gift!

Casino Player, the nation's largest circulation gaming magazine, features gambling strategies and tips from the world's most respected professional gamblers. In every issue you will find inside information on tables game odds and slot percentages, features from casinos around the world and in-depth articles on Atlantic City, Nevada, Riverboat and Caribbean casino hotels. Reading **Casino Player** will increase your knowledge of casino gaming giving you more of the information you need to be a winner at the casinos! Subscribe today!

The Orleans Hotel & Casino
4500 W. Tropicana Avenue
Las Vegas, Nevada 89103
(702) 365-7111

EXPECTED TO OPEN BY EARLY 1997
Reservation Number: (800) 331-5354
Rooms: 810 Price Range: $69-$89
Suites: 30 Price Range: $175-$225
Restaurants: 6 (1 open 24 hours)
Casino Size: 92,000 Square Feet
Other Games: SB, RB, B, P, PGP, LIR, K
Special Features: New Orleans theme throughout hotel and casino. All rooms are "petite suites" with separate sitting areas. Wedding chapel. 70-lane bowling center.

Palace Station Hotel & Casino
2411 West Sahara Avenue
Las Vegas, Nevada 89102
(702) 367-2411

Reservation Number: (800) 634-3101
Rooms: 948 Price Range: $59-$119
Suites: 82 Price Range: $99-$750
Restaurants: 5 (1 open 24 hours)
Buffets: B-$4.49 L-$5.99 D-$8.99
Casino Size: 76,490 Square Feet
Other Games: SB, RB, MB, P, PGP,
                 CSP, LIR, S21, K, BG
Casino Marketing: (800) 367-2717
Fun Book: Only given to hotel guests or
              through tour operator packages
Special Features: 99¢ Margaritas at the Guadalajara bar (24 hours). Non-smoking slot area and hotel floors.

Plaza Hotel & Casino
1 Main Street
Las Vegas, Nevada 89101
(702) 386-2110

Reservation Number: (800) 634-6575
Rooms: 1,037 Price Range: $30-$75
Suites: 40 Price Range: $60-$150
Restaurants: 3 (1 open 24 hours)
Casino Size: 57,120 Square Feet
Other Games: SB, RB, MB, P, K
Casino Marketing: (800) 634-6575
Show: "Xposed" $19.95, 8:00 and 10:00 nightly, dark Friday
Special Features: High-rise restaurant has excellent view of Fremont Street Experience.

Quality Inn & Casino
377 East Flamingo Road
Las Vegas, Nevada 89109
(702) 733-7777

Reservation Number: (800) 634-6617
Rooms: 325 Price Range: $49-$250
Restaurants: 1
Casino Size: 7,500 Square Feet
Other Games: No Craps or Roulette
Casino Marketing: (702) 733-7777 ext. 2031
Senior Discount: If 55, or older,
                    10% off room rate
Special Features: All rooms are mini-suites with wet bars/refrigerators. Swimming pool with whirlpool spa. Coin-operated laundry facilities. Gift shop.

Rio Suite Hotel & Casino
3700 W. Flamingo Road
Las Vegas, Nevada 89103
(702) 252-7777

Reservation Number: (800) PLAY RIO
Suites: 1,410 Price Range: $85-$279
Restaurants: 12 (1 open 24 hours)
Buffets: B-$4.99 L-$6.99 D-$8.99
Casino Size: 82,837 Square Feet
Other Games: SB, RB, B, MB, P,
                 PGP, CSP, LIR, K
Casino Marketing: (800) 777-1711
Show: "Copacabana Show" $39.95 includes dinner, 6:00 and 8:30 nightly, dark Sunday and Monday
Special Features: All rooms are suites. Pool area has waterfall and sand beach.

Riviera Hotel & Casino
2901 Las Vegas Blvd. South
Las Vegas, Nevada 89109
(702) 734-5110

Reservation Number: (800) 634-6753
Rooms: 2,100 Price Range: $75-$145
Suites: 154 Price Range: $185-$500
Restaurants: 6 (1 open 24 hours)
Buffets: B-$4.95 L-$5.95 D-$7.95
Casino Size: 102,300 Square Feet
Other Games: SB, RB, B, MB, P,
                 PGP, CSP, LIR, K
Casino Marketing: Slots (800) 637-5687
Casino Marketing: Tables (800) 634-3420
Fun Book: Look for ad in magazines
Shows: "Splash II" $39.50/$49.50 VIP seating, 7:30 (family show) and 10:30 (adult show) nightly
"An Evening at La Cage" $18.95/$23.95 VIP seating, 7:30 and 9:30 nightly, 11:15 (Wed/Sat), dark Tuesday

"Crazy Girls" $16.95/$21.95 VIP seating, 8:30 and 10:30 nightly, midnight (Sat), dark Monday
"Bottoms Up" $9.95, 2:00 and 4:00 daily, dark Thursday
"Riviera Comedy Club" $14.95, 8:00 and 10:00 nightly, 11:45 (Fri/Sat)
Special Features: Four showrooms. Men's and women's health facilities. Many specialty shops. 2 lighted tennis courts.

Royal Hotel/Casino
99 Convention Center Drive
Las Vegas, Nevada 89109
(702) 735-6117

Reservation Number: (800) 634-6118
Rooms: 236 Price Range: $45-$125
Restaurants: 1
Casino Size: 6,500 Square Feet
Other Games: No Craps

Sahara Hotel & Casino
2535 Las Vegas Blvd. South
Las Vegas, Nevada 89109
(702) 737-2111

Reservation Number: (800) 634-6666
Rooms: 1,949 Price Range: $45-$95
Suites: 100   Price Range: $200-$285
Restaurants: 5 (1 open 24 hours)
Buffets: B-$2.50 L-$3.50 D-$5.50
Casino Size: 26,956 Square Feet
Other Games: SB, RB, B, P, PGP,
                CSP, LIR, S21, K
Casino Marketing: (800) 634-6645
Fun Book: Go to cashier cage

Sam's Town Hotel & Gambling Hall
5111 Boulder Highway
Las Vegas, Nevada 89122
(702) 456-7777

Reservation Number: (800) 634-6371
Rooms: 620 Price Range: $40-$70
Suites: 30 Price Range: $150-$250
Restaurants: 10 (1 open 24 hours)
Buffets: B-$3.99 L-$5.99 D-$7.99
Casino Size: 118,000 Square Feet
Other Games: SB, RB, P, PGP,
                CSP, LIR, K, BG
Casino Marketing: (702) 454-8126
Fun Book: Only given to hotel guests
Special Features: An indoor park with trees, flowers, flowing streams, life-like birds and animals, dancing waters and a mountain. Indoor park is home to a free laser-light show called "sunset stampede" which is shown four times daily. 56-lane bowling center (open 24 hours). Two R.V. parks with 500 spaces and full hook-up. Western Emporium: a 25,000-square-foot western wear retail store. Sports bar with indoor basketball court and other games.

Santa Fe Hotel & Casino
4949 North Rancho Drive
Las Vegas, Nevada 89130
(702) 658-4900

Reservation Number: (800) 872-6823
Rooms: 200 Price Range: $36-$50
Restaurants: 5 (1 open 24 hours)
Buffets: B-$3.95/$6.95 (Sun) L-$4.95
          D-$6.95/$8.95 (Thu)
Casino Size: 77,882 Square Feet
Other Games: SB, RB, P, PGP, CSP,
                LIR, S21, K, BG
Casino Marketing: (702) 658-4950
Special Features: 17,000-square-foot ice arena. 60-lane bowling center. 2 lounges with live entertainment. On-property nursery for children 6 months to 8 years open 9am-11pm.

Sheraton Desert Inn
3145 Las Vegas Blvd. South
Las Vegas, Nevada 89109
(702) 733-4444

Reservation Number: (800) 634-6906
Rooms: 726 Price Range: $129-$175
Suites: 95 Price Range: $205-$2,500
Restaurants: 5 (1 open 24 hours)
Buffets: B-$9.75 L-$11.75
Casino Size: 18,900 Square Feet
Other Games: SB, RB, B, MB, PG, P,
                PGP, CSP, LIR, K
Casino Marketing: (800) 634-6909
Special Features: 18-hole championship golf course and pro shop. World-class European-style health spa offers hydrotherapy, thermography, massage, fitness, toning and skin-care programs. Four Diamond-rated by AAA. 5 tournament-class lighted tennis courts.

Showboat Hotel & Casino
2800 Fremont Street
Las Vegas, Nevada 89104
(702) 385-9123

Reservation Number: (800) 826-2800
Rooms: 480 Price Range: $45-$105
Suites: 5 Price Range: $90-$195
Restaurants: 5 (1 open 24 hours)
Buffets: B-$5.95 (Sat/Sun) L-$4.95
          D-$6.95/$7.95 (Wed-Fri)

Casino Size: 49,351 Square Feet
Other Games: SB, RB, P, PGP, CSP, LIR, K, BG
Casino Marketing: (800) 826-2800
Special Features: Casino has single-deck blackjack. 106-lane bowling center. 1,100-seat bingo hall. Mardi Gras Room has live entertainment daily.

Silver City Casino
3001 Las Vegas Blvd. South
Las Vegas, Nevada 89109
(702) 732-4152

Restaurants: 1 (open 24 hours)
Casino Size: 15,258 Square Feet
Other Games: P, PGP, LIR
Fun Book: By mail or given out at the south and front exits of Circus Circus
Special Features: Free popcorn available from 9am to 1am.

Slots-A-Fun
2890 Las Vegas Blvd. South
Las Vegas, Nevada 89109
(702) 794-3814

Restaurants: 1 Snack Bar
Casino Size: 16,733 Square Feet
Other Games: PGP, CSP, LIR, RD
Casino Marketing: (702) 794-3842
Special Features: 75¢ for domestic and foreign brands of bottled beer.

Stardust Resort & Casino
3000 Las Vegas Blvd. South
Las Vegas, Nevada 89109
(702) 732-6111

Toll-Free Number: (800) 824-6033
Reservation Number: (800) 634-6757
Rooms: 2,340 Price Range: $36-$100
Suites: 161 Price Range: $175-$300
Restaurants: 6 (1 open 24 hours)
Buffets: B-$4.95/$6.95 (Sun)
          L-$5.95 D-$7.95
Casino Size: 65,538 Square Feet
Other Games: SB, RB, B, MB, P, PGP, CSP, LIR, K
Casino Marketing: (800) 824-6033
Fun Book: Only through tour operator packages
Show: "Enter The Night" $26.95, 7:30 and 10:30 (Wed/Thu/Sat), 8:00 (Sun/Mon), dark Friday

Stratosphere Hotel & Casino
2000 Las Vegas Blvd. South
Las Vegas, Nevada 89104
(702) 380-7777

Reservation Number: (800) 99-TOWER
Rooms: 1,350 Price Range: $59-$119
Suites: 150 Price Range: $69-$149
Restaurants: 5 (1 open 24 hours)
Buffets: B-$4.99 L-$5.99 D-$7.99
Casino Size: 97,000 Square Feet
Other Games: SB, P, CSP, LIR, K
Show: "Danny Gans - The Man of Many Voices" $29.50, 9:00 nightly Thu-Mon, dark Tue/Wed
Special Features: 1,149-foot observation tower. Observation decks. 2 thrill rides. 4 wedding chapels. Revolving restaurant. Kid's Quest child care center. Video arcade.

Texas Station
2100 North Rancho Drive
Las Vegas, Nevada 89102
(702) 631-1000

Reservation Number: (800) 654-8888
Rooms: 200 Price Range: $39-$69
Restaurants: 7 (1 open 24 hours)
Buffets: B-$3.95/$6.95 (Sun) L-$5.95 D-$8.95/$10.95 (Wed)
Casino Size: 60,000 Square Feet
Other Games: SB, RB, B, P, PGP, CSP, LIR, S21, K
Special Features: 12 movie theaters. Western dance hall and lounge.

Treasure Island
3300 Las Vegas Blvd. South
Las Vegas, Nevada 89109
(702) 894-7444

Reservation Number: (800) 944-7444
Rooms: 2,688 Price Range: $79-$229
Suites: 212 Price Range: $119-$300
Restaurants: 7 (1 open 24 hours)
Buffets: B-$6.25/$11.25 (Sun)
          L-$8.75 D-$11.25
Casino Size: 75,294 Square Feet
Other Games: SB, RB, MB, P, PGP, CSP, LIR, K
Casino Marketing: (800) 944-7444
Show: "Cirque du Soleil's Mystere" $64.90/ $32.45 children under 12, 7:30 and 10:30 nightly, dark Mon/Tue
Special Features: Live-action sea battle between pirates and British sailors takes place every 90 minutes from 4pm until 10pm (4:30 to midnight in summer). Arcade and games. Two wedding chapels.

Tropicana Resort & Casino
3801 Las Vegas Blvd. South
Las Vegas, Nevada 89109
(702) 739-2222

Reservation Number: (800) 634-4000
Rooms: 1,908 Price Range: $65-$169
Suites: 120 Price Range: $250-$500
Restaurants: 8 (1 open 24 hours)
Buffets: B-$6.95 L-$6.95 D-$9.95
Casino Size: 45,194 Square Feet
Other Games: SB, B, P, PGP, CSP, LIR, K
Casino Marketing: (800) 521-8767
Show: "Folies Bergere" $30.95 for 7:30 dinner show/$23.95 for 10:30 cocktail show, dark Saturday
Special Features: Five-acre tropical gardens and pool. Wedding chapel. Swim-up blackjack table (seasonal).

Vacation Village Hotel/Casino
6711 Las Vegas Blvd. South
Las Vegas, Nevada 89120
(702) 897-1700

Reservation Number: (800) 658-5000
Rooms: 313 Price Range: $25-$65
Suites: 8 Price Range: $80-$200
Restaurants: 3 (2 open 24 hours)
Buffets: L-$4.99 D-$6.99
Casino Size: 17,640 Square Feet
Other Games: LIR
Fun Book: Ask at promotion booth
Casino Marketing: (800) 658-5000
Special Features: Room-front parking. 2 pools.

Western Hotel & Casino
899 East Fremont Street
Las Vegas, Nevada 89101
(702) 384-4620

Reservation Number: (800) 634-6703
Rooms: 116 Price Range: $16-$20
Restaurants: 1 (open 24 hours)
Casino Size: 13,050
Other Games: K, BG, No Craps

Westward-Ho Hotel & Casino
2900 Las Vegas Blvd. South
Las Vegas, Nevada 89109
(702) 731-2900

Reservation Number: (800) 634-6803
Rooms: 777 Price Range: $37-$75
Suites: 60 Price Range: $71-$111
Restaurants: 2 (both open 24 hours)
Buffets: B-$4.95 D-$6.95
Casino Size: 34,427 Square Feet
Other Games: CSP, LIR, K

Show: "Hurray America" $12.95, 7:00 (Sun-Tue/Thu/Fri), 9:00 Wed, dark Saturday
Special Features: Free airport shuttle. Roomfront parking. 7 pools and Jacuzzi.

Laughlin

Map location: #2 (on the Colorado River, 100 miles south of Las Vegas and directly across the river from Bullhead City, Arizona)

Laughlin is named after Don Laughlin, who owns the Riverside Hotel & Casino and originally settled there in 1966. The area offers many water sport activities on the Colorado River as well as at nearby Lake Mojave. If you are planning an overnight visit it is strongly recommended that you make advance reservations because many hotels are frequently fully booked and there are no other rooms available in Laughlin.

Here's information, as supplied by Nevada's State Gaming Control Board, showing the slot machine payback percentages for all of Laughlin's casinos for the fiscal year beginning July 1, 1995 and ending June 30, 1996:

5¢ Slot Machines	88.28%
25¢ Slot Machines	94.59%
$1 Slot Machines	95.80%
$5 Slot Machines	96.73%
All Slot Machines	94.76%

These numbers reflect the percentage of money returned to the players on each denomination of machine. All electronic machines including video poker and video keno are included in these numbers. As you can see, the numbers are quite comparable to Las Vegas' downtown casinos and slightly better than the Las Vegas Strip area casinos.

Optional games in the casino listings include: sports book (SB), race book (RB), baccarat (B), mini-baccarat (MB), poker (P), pai gow poker (PGP), Caribbean Stud Poker (CSP), Let It Ride (LIR), Double Down Stud (DDS), Spanish 21 (S21), keno (K) and bingo (BG).

Colorado Belle Hotel & Casino
2100 S. Casino Drive
Laughlin, Nevada 89029
(702) 298-4000

Reservation Number: (800) 458-9500
Rooms: 1,225 Price Range: $18-$64
Suites: 13   Price Range: $75-$120
Restaurants: 6 (1 open 24 hours)
Buffets: B-$2.99 L-$3.49 D-$4.59
Casino Size: 44,536 Square Feet
Other Games: SB, P, PGP, CSP, LIR, K

Don Laughlin's Riverside Resort Hotel & Casino
1650 S. Casino Drive
Laughlin, Nevada 89029
(702) 298-2535

Reservation Number: (800) 227-3849
Rooms: 1,336 Price Range: $17-$75
Suites: 68 Price Range: $59-$91
Restaurants: 6 (2 open 24 hours)
Buffets: B-$2.99 L-$3.99
            D-$4.99/$7.99 (Fri-Seafood)
Casino Size: 77,763 Square Feet
Other Games: SB, RB, P, CSP, LIR, K, BG
Casino Marketing; (800) 227-3849
Senior Discount: If AARP member,
            10% off room rate
Fun Book: Only for hotel guests or groups
Special Features: 900-space RV park with full hook-ups. Six-plex cinema. Classic car exhibition hall. Boating and river cruises.

Edgewater Hotel/Casino
2020 S. Casino Drive
Laughlin, Nevada 89029
(702) 298-2453

Reservation Number: (800) 67-RIVER
Rooms: 1,44 Price Range: $17-$60
Suites: 5   Price Range: $75-$120
Restaurants: 4 (1 open 24 hours)
Buffets: B-$2.99 L-$3.49 D-$4.59
Casino Size: 60,000 Square Feet
Other Games: SB, RB, P, PGP, CSP, LIR K
Casino Marketing: (800) 289-8777
Senior Discount: If 65, or older,
            room rate discount
Fun Book: Look in brochure racks at
            tourist information centers.
Special Features: River view rooms. Pool and spa. Children's video arcade. Cruises aboard Little Belle Paddle wheel Riverboat. Free airport shuttle. Non-smoking and handicapped rooms. Lounge with live music nightly except Mon.

Flamingo Hilton Laughlin
1900 S. Casino Drive
Laughlin, Nevada 89029
(702) 298-5111

Reservation Number: (800) FLAMINGO
Rooms: 1,970 Price Range: $19-$85
Suites: 30 Price Range: $200-$275
Restaurants: 5 (1 open 24 hours)
Buffets: B-$3.99 L-$4.49 D-$5.99
Casino Size: 60,000 Square Feet
Other Games: SB, RB, B, MB, P, PGP,
            CSP, LIR, DDS, S21, K
Casino Marketing: (800) 662-6050
Fun Book: Inquire at front desk
Special Features: Casino has 2 "Colossus" slot machines - the world's largest. All rooms have a river view. 2,100-seat outdoor amphitheater. 3 lighted tennis courts Non-smoking area in casino. Laughlin's only Burger King and Dairy Queen.

Gold River Resort & Casino
2700 S. Casino Drive
Laughlin, Nevada 89029
(702) 298-2242

Reservation Number: (800) 835-7903
Rooms: 973   Price Range: $17-$60
Suites: 30 Price Range: $80-$200
Restaurants: 7 (1 open 24 hours)
Buffets: B-$2.99 L-$3.49 D-$5.99
Casino Size: 71,300 Square Feet
Other Games: SB, RB, P, PGP, CSP, K, BG
Casino Marketing: (800) 835-7904 ext.-2206
Fun Book: Only given to hotel guests

Golden Nugget Laughlin
2300 S. Casino Drive
Laughlin, Nevada 89029
(702) 298-7222

Reservation Number: (800) 950-7700
Rooms: 296 Price Range: $25-$65
Suites: 4 Price Range: $150-$190
Restaurants: 4 (1 open 24 hours)
Buffets: B-$2.99 L-$3.99 D-$4.99
Casino Size: 32,600 Square Feet
Other Games: SB, RB, PGP, CSP, LIR, K
Casino Marketing: (800) 955-SLOT
Fun Book: Only offered to groups
Special Features: Atrium entrance with 2 water falls and 300 flora from around the world. Tarzan's lounge with nightly entertainment. Gift shop.

Harrah's Laughlin Casino & Hotel
2900 S. Casino Drive
Laughlin, Nevada 89029
(702) 298-4600

Reservation Number: (800) 447-8700
Rooms: 1,619 Price Range: $20-$85
Suites: 39   Price Range: $140-$220
Restaurants: 7 (1 open 24 hours)
Buffets: B-$5.49 L-$5.49 D-$6.49
Casino Size: 47,000 Square Feet
Other Games: SB, RB, P, CSP, LIR, K
Casino Marketing: (800) 447-8700
Fun Book: Only given to groups
Special Features: Separate non-smoking casino. Only beach and health club in Laughlin. 2 pools. 2 covered parking garages. R/V plaza and convenience store.

Pioneer Hotel & Gambling Hall
2200 S. Casino Drive
Laughlin, Nevada 89029
(702) 298-2442

Reservation Number: (800) 634-3469
Rooms: 375 Price Range: $28-$55
Suites: 29 Price Range: $55-$75
Restaurants: 3 (1 open 24 hours)
Buffets: B-$2.95 L-$4.95 D-$5.95
Casino Size: 19,500 Square Feet
Other Games: CSP, LIR, K
Casino Marketing: (800) 634-3469 ext. 4135

Ramada Express Hotel & Casino
2121 S. Casino Drive
Laughlin, Nevada 89029
(702) 298-4200

Reservation Number: (800) 2RAMADA
Rooms: 1,449 Price Range: $19-$69
Suites: 52   Price Range: $69-$200
Restaurants: 5 (1 open 24 hours)
Buffets: B-$3.49 L-$4.49 D-$5.95
Casino Size: 53,000 Square Feet
Other Games: SB, PGP, LIR, K
Casino Marketing: (800) 343-4533 and
                     ask for slot club booth
Fun Book: Ask at slot club booth
Special Features: Victorian railroad station themed-hotel/casino with more than $1 million worth of railroad antiques and memorabilia. Free train rides on a replica 19th century steam train. Train-shaped swimming pool. Free airport shuttle. Non-smoking rooms. 3 gift shops. Video arcade.

Regency Casino
1950 Casino Way
Laughlin, Nevada 89029
(702) 298-2439

Restaurants: 1 Snack Bar (open 24 hours)
Other Games: No Craps or Roulette

Lovelock

Map Location: #19 (92 miles N.E. of Reno on I-80)

Sturgeon's
1420 Cornell Avenue
Lovelock, Nevada 89419
(702) 273-2971

Reservation Number: (800) 528-1234
Rooms: 74 Price Range: $47-$65
Restaurants: 2 (1 open 24 hours)
Casino Size: 3,000 Square Feet
Other Games: No Craps or Roulette
Fun Book: Only given to hotel guests
Special Features: Affiliated with Best Western.

McDermitt

Map Location: #20 (Just S. of the Oregon border on Hwy. 95)

Say When
P.O. Box 375
McDermitt, Nevada 89421
(702) 532-8515

Restaurants: 1 (open 24 hours)
Other Games: No Craps or Roulette

Mesquite

Map Location: #21 (77 miles N.E. of Las Vegas on I-15 at the Arizona border)

Oasis Resort Hotel & Casino
P.O. Box 360
Mesquite, Nevada 89024
(702) 346-5232

Reservation Number: (800) 621-0187
Rooms: 708   Price Range: $39-$59
Suites: 30   Price Range: $99-$119
Restaurants: 7 (1 open 24 hours)
Buffets: B-$4.50 L-$5.50 D-$7.50

Casino Size: 32,080 Square Feet
Other Games: SB, B, P, LIR, K
Fun Book: Only given to hotel guests
Special Features: Two 18-hole golf courses. 6 swimming pools. Wagon trail rides. Petting zoo. Video arcade. Shotgun sports club. RV park. Health club and spa.

Players Island Resort
P.O. Box 2737
Mesquite, Nevada 89024
(702) 346-PLAY

Reservation Number: (800) 896-4567
Rooms: 482 Price Range: $59-$79
Suites: 18 Price Range: $75-$435
Restaurants: 4 (1 open 24 hours)
Buffets: B-$5.50 L-$6.50 D-$9.50
Casino Size: 40,000 Square Feet
Other Games: SB, MB, P, PGP, CSP, LIR, K
Senior Discount: If 50, or older, register with
    Players Preferred Desk and get 20% room
    discount, plus restaurant and spa discounts
Fun Book: Only given to groups
Special Features: 18-hole golf course. 3 lighted tennis courts. Lagoon swimming pool with waterfall and slide. Full-service health spa offering massages, body care, facials and mud treatments.

Stateline Casino
490 Mesquite Blvd.
Mesquite, Nevada 89024
(702) 346-5752

Rooms: 12 Price Range: $21-$26
Restaurants: 1 (open 24 hours)
Casino Size: 4,500 Square Feet
Other Games: No Craps or Roulette

Virgin River Hotel & Casino
915 Mesquite Boulevard
Mesquite, Nevada 89024
(702) 346-7777

Reservation Number: (800) 346-7721
Rooms: 720 Price Range: $20-$45
Suites: 2 Price Range: $100-$125
Restaurants: 3 (1 open 24 hours)
Buffets: B-$3.79 L-$4.79 D-$6.99
Casino Size: 27,900 Square Feet
Other Games: SB, RB, BG

Minden

Map Location: #15 (42 miles S. of Reno on Hwy. 395)

Carson Valley Inn
1627 Highway 395
Minden, Nevada 89423
(702) 782-9711

Reservation Number: (800) 321-6983
Rooms: 145 Price Range: $55-$79
Suites: 9 Price Range: $69-$159
Restaurants: 3 (1 open 24 hours)
Casino Size: 11,500 Square Feet
Other Games: SB, P, LIR, K, No Roulette
Casino Marketing: (800) 321-6983
Senior Discount: If 50, or older, ask for
    Senior Savers Club card for discounts.
Fun Book: Given to all lodging guests
Special Features: 60-space RV park with full hook-ups and laundry. 24-hour convenience store. Live entertainment. Wedding chapel. Golf, hunting and ski packages offered. Supervised children's recreation center.

N. Las Vegas

Map Location: #22 (5 miles N.E. of the Las Vegas Strip on Las Vegas Blvd. N.)

Jerry's Nugget
1821 Las Vegas Blvd. North
N. Las Vegas, Nevada 89030
(702) 399-3000

Restaurants: 1 (open 24 hours)
Casino Size: 25,144 Square Feet
Other Games: SB, RB, K, B

Joe's Longhorn Casino
3016 E. Lake Mead Blvd.
N. Las Vegas, Nevada 89030
(702) 642-1940

Restaurants: 1 (open 24 hours)
Casino Size: 3,300 Square Feet
Other Games: No Craps or Roulette

Mahoney's Silver Nugget
2140 Las Vegas Blvd. North
N. Las Vegas, Nevada 89030
(702) 399-1111

Restaurants: 1 (open 24 hours)
Other Games: SB, P, LIR, K, BG, No Roulette

Opera House Saloon & Casino
2542 Las Vegas Blvd. N.
N. Las Vegas, Nevada 89030
(702) 649-8801

Restaurants: 1 (open 24 hours)
Other Games: No Craps or Roulette

The Poker Palace
2757 Las Vegas Blvd. N.
N. Las Vegas, Nevada 89030
(702) 649-3799

Restaurants: 1 (open 24 hours)
Casino Size: 14,350 Square Feet
Other Games: SB, RB, P, LIR, S21

Pahrump

Map Location: #23 (59 miles W. of Las Vegas on Hwy. 160)

Saddle West Hotel/Casino
P.O. Box 234
Pahrump, Nevada 89041
(702) 727-5953

Reservation Number: (800) GEDDY-UP
Rooms: 110 Price Range: $30-$45
Suites: 10 Price Range: $50-$120
Restaurants: 1 (open 24 hours)
Buffets: B-$2.99/$4.99 (Sat/Sun)
　　　　　 L-$3.99 D-$5.99
Casino Size: 15,523 Square Feet
Other Games: P, K, BG

Reno

Map Location: #4 (near the California border, 58 miles N.E. of Lake Tahoe and 32 miles N. of Carson City)

Reno may be best known for its neon arch on Virginia Street that welcomes visitors to "The Biggest Little City in the World." The current arch is actually the fourth one since the original arch was built in 1927. The area also houses the nation's largest car collection at the National Automobile Museum.

Here's information, as supplied by Nevada's State Gaming Control Board, showing the slot machine payback percentages for all of the Reno area casinos for the fiscal year beginning July 1, 1995 and ending June 30, 1996:

5¢ Slot Machines	92.33%
25¢ Slot Machines	94.11%
$1 Slot Machines	95.82%
$5 Slot Machines	96.90%
All Slot Machines	95.05%

These numbers reflect the percentage of money returned on each denomination of machine and encompass all electronic machines including video poker and video keno. For a 5¢ slot player Reno's casinos offer much better returns than the Las Vegas area casinos both on and off the Strip. Overall, the slot returns for Reno's casinos are among the highest in the state and are actually only beaten in one category (25¢ machines) by the downtown Las Vegas casinos.

Optional games in the casino listings include: sports book (SB), race book (RB), baccarat (B), mini-baccarat (MB), pai gow (PG), poker (P), pai gow poker (PGP), Caribbean Stud Poker (CSP), Let It Ride (LIR), Red Dog (RD), Double Down Stud (DDS), Spanish 21 (S21), keno (K) and bingo (BG).

Atlantis Casino Resort
3800 S. Virginia Street
Reno, Nevada 89502
(702) 825-4700

Reservation Number: (800) 723-6500
Rooms: 590 Price Range: $39-$295
Suites: 26 Price Range: $95-$395
Restaurants: 5 (1 open 24 hours)
Buffets: B-$4.99/$6.99 (Sat)/$10.99 (Sun)
　　　　　 L-$6.99/$7.99 (Sat)
　　　　　 D-$8.99/$15.99 (Fri)/$14.99 (Sat)
Casino Size: 32,000 Square Feet
Other Games: SB, PGP, CSP, K
Casino Marketing: (702) 824-4400
Fun Book: Show out-of-town ID at gift shop
Senior Discount: If 55, or older, receive 10% discount in restaurant and on room rate (15% if member of casino's Club Paradise slot club)
Special Features: Exotic island theme casino with waterfalls, thatched huts and tropical gardens. All blackjack games are single deck. Free 24-hour valet parking. Outdoor heated pool and spa. Free cabaret entertainment nightly.

Bonanza Casino
4720 N. Virginia St.
Reno, Nevada 89503
(702) 323-2724

Restaurants: 1 (open 24 hours)
Casino Size: 8,083 Square Feet
Other Games: SB, K, No Roulette

Bordertown
19575 Hwy. 395
N. Reno, Nevada 89506
(702) 972-1309

Restaurants: 1
Casino Size: 4,650 Square Feet
Other Games: No Craps or Roulette

Circus Circus Hotel/Casino - Reno
500 N. Sierra Street
Reno, Nevada 89503
(702) 329-0711

Reservation Number: (800) 648-5010
Rooms: 1,548 Price Range: $19-$119
Suites: 72   Price Range: $39-$139
Restaurants: 3 (1 open 24 hours)
Buffets: B-$2.99/$4.99 (Sun) L-$3.99
           D-$4.99/$6.99 (Fri/Sat)
Casino Size: 40,150 Square Feet
Other Games: SB, RB, MB, P,
             PGP, CSP, LIR, K
Casino Marketing: (800) 262-8705
Fun Book: Only given to hotel guests
Special Features: Free live circus acts. Midway with carnival games. Video arcade. 24-hour gift shop/liquor store.

Club Cal-Neva
38 N. Virginia Street
Reno, Nevada 89505
(702) 323-1046

Restaurants: 3 (1 open 24 hours)
Casino Size: 30,601 Square Feet
Other Games: SB, RB, P, PGP, CSP, LIR, K
Casino Marketing: (702) 323-1046 ext.-3266
Fun Book: Write or call for information
Special Features: Only deals single-deck 21.

Colonial Casino
250 N. Arlington Ave.
Reno, Nevada 89501
(702) 323-2039

Restaurants: 1
Casino Size: 5,040 Square Feet
Other Games: No Craps or Roulette

Comstock Hotel Casino
200 W. Second Street
Reno, Nevada 89501
(702) 329-1880

Reservation Number: (800) COM-STOC
Rooms: 304 Price Range: $35-$125
Suites: 6   Price Range: $99-$350
Restaurants: 3 (1 open 24 hours)
Casino Size: 15,900 Square Feet
Casino Marketing: (800) COM-STOC
Fun Book: Only given to hotel guests
Other Games: SB, PGP, LIR, K
Special Features: 1800's atmosphere with rooms in Victorian decor. Pool, Jacuzzi, sauna and exercise facilities. Video arcade. Gift shop.

Diamond's Casino at Holiday Inn
1010 E. 6th Street
Reno, Nevada 89512
(702) 323-4183

Reservation Number: (800) 648-4877
Rooms: 280 Price Range: $69-$120
Suites: 6   Price Range: $85-$175
Restaurants: 2 (1 open 24 hours)
Casino Size: 10,000 Square Feet
Other Games: SB, LIR, K,
             No Craps or Roulette
Fun Book: Only given to hotel guests
Special Features: Located in the Holiday Inn.

Eldorado Hotel/Casino
345 N. Virginia Street
Reno, Nevada 89501
(702) 786-5700

Reservation Number: (800) 648-5966
Rooms: 817 Price Range: $49-$110
Suites:127 Price Range: $110-$750
Restaurants: 8 (1 open 24 hours)
Buffets: B-$4.99/$6.99 (Sat)/$7.99 (Sun)
           L-$5.99 D-$7.99/$10.99 (Sat)
Casino Size: 74,000 Square Feet
Other Games: SB, RB, B, MB,
             PGP, CSP, LIR, K
Casino Marketing: (800) 777-5325
Special Features: In-house coffee roasting. Pasta shop. Micro brewery featuring 7 made-on-premises micro brews. Bakery. Butcher shop. Gelato factory. Video arcade. Pool and Jacuzzi.

Fitzgeralds Casino/Hotel
255 N. Virginia Street
Reno, Nevada 89504
(702) 785-3300

Reservation Number: (800) 648-5022
Rooms: 351 Price Range: $48-$150
Suites: 8   Price Range: $78-$240
Restaurants: 3 (1 open 24 hours)
Buffets: B-$3.49 L-$4.49 D-$5.99
Casino Size: 26,260 Square Feet
Other Games: CSP, LIR, RD, K, BG

Flamingo Hilton Reno
255 N. Sierra Street
Reno, Nevada 89501
(702) 322-1111

Reservation Number: (800) 648-4882
Rooms: 604 Price Range: $59-$219
Suites: 64 Price Range: $150-$245
Restaurants: 5 (1 open 24 hours)
Buffets: B-$3.95 L-$3.95
          D-$6.95/$9.95 (Sat)
Casino Size: 53,000 Square Feet
Other Games: SB, RB, B, PG, P,
          PGP, CSP, LIR, K
Casino Marketing: (800) 950-2WIN
Fun Book: Go to Casino Services desk
Special Features: Top of the Hilton - Reno's only rooftop restaurant. Non-smoking rooms in hotel. Funland arcade. Benihana Steak House. Baskin Robbins Ice Cream shop.

Harrah's Reno Casino Hotel
219 N. Center Street
Reno, Nevada 89501
(702) 786-3232

Reservation Number: (800) HARRAHS
Rooms: 559 Price Range: $79-$135
Suites: 7 Price Range: $210-$375
Restaurants: 7 (1 open 24 hours)
Buffets: B-$6.50/$8.95 (Sat/Sun) L-$6.95
          D-$8.95/$15.95 (Fri/Sat)
Casino Size: 56,700 Square Feet
Other Games: SB, RB, B, PGP, CSP, LIR, K
Casino Marketing: (800) 423-1121
Special Features: Fully equipped health club. Complimentary airport shuttle and cable TV movies. Planet Hollywood restaurant. World's largest Hampton Inn is connected to Harrah's.

Holiday Hotel/Casino
111 Mill Street
Reno, Nevada 89501
(702) 329-0411

Reservation Number: (800) 648-5431
Rooms: 192 Price Range: $42-$68
Suites: 2 Price Range: $100-$260
Restaurants: 1 (open 24 hours)
Casino Size: 9,926 Square Feet
Other Games: K, B, No Craps
Casino Marketing: (800) 648-5431
Fun Book: Only given to groups

Nevada Club
224 N. Virginia St.
Reno, Nevada 89501
(702) 329-1721

Restaurants: 1 (open 24 hours)
Casino Size: 10,730 Square Feet
Other Games: K

Peppermill Hotel Casino
2707 S. Virginia Street
Reno, Nevada 89502
(702) 826-2121

Reservation Number: (800) 282-2444
Rooms: 1,070 Price Range: $49-$99
Suites: 175 Price Range: $129-$400
Restaurants: 5 (1 open 24 hours)
Buffets: B-$5.99/$10.99 (Sun) L-$6.99
          D-$8.95/$15.95 (Fri/Sat)
Casino Size: 30,785 Square Feet
Other Games: SB, MB, P, PGP, CSP,
          K, Single-Zero Roulette
Casino Marketing: (800) 648-6992 ext. 7100
Fun Book: Only given to hotel guests
Special Features: Free valet parking. Complimentary airport shuttle. 24-hour gift shop. Health club.

Pioneer Inn Hotel/Casino
221 S. Virginia Street
Reno, Nevada 89501
(702) 324-7777

Reservation Number: (800) 879-8879
Rooms: 242 Price Range: $38-$100
Suites: 10 Price Range: $125-$200
Restaurants: 4 (1 open 24 hours)
Casino Size: 5,195 Square Feet
Other Games: K
Fun Book: Only given to hotel guests

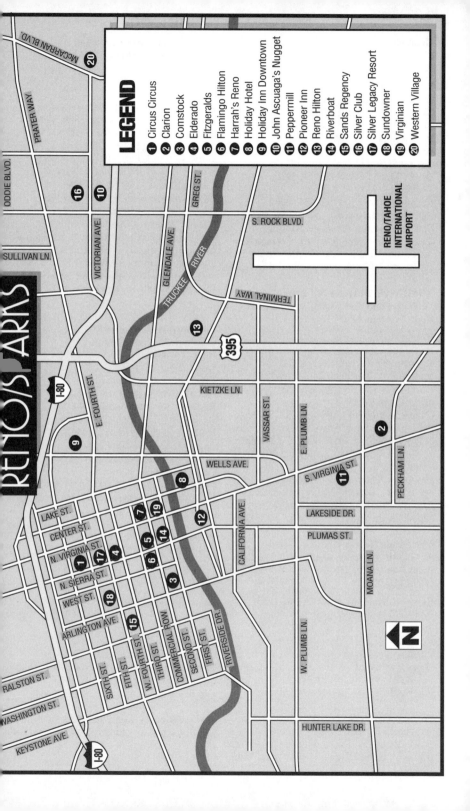

Reno Hilton
2500 E. Second Street
Reno, Nevada 89595
(702) 789-2000

Reservation Number: (800) 648-5080
Rooms: 1,847 Price Range: $69-$119
Suites: 154 Price Range: $130-$630
Restaurants: 6 (1 open 24 hours)
Buffets: B-$4.99 L-$5.99 D-$7.99
Casino Size: 114,600 Square Feet
Other Games: SB, RB, B, P, PGP,
　　　　　　CSP, LIR, K
Casino Marketing: (702) 789-2362
Fun Book: Only given to hotel guests
Special Features: Free valet parking. 2 movie theaters. 265-space RV park. 50-lane bowling center. Health club. 40 retail stores. Tennis courts. Video arcade. Golf driving range.

The Riverboat Hotel & Casino
34 W. Second Street
Reno, Nevada 89501
(702) 323-8877

Reservation Number: (800) 888-5525
Rooms: 297 Price Range: $30-$75
Restaurants: 2 (1 open 24 hours)
Casino Size: 13,380 Square Feet
Other Games: LIR, K
Casino Marketing: (702) 323-8877
Senior Discount: If 55, or older, go to Slots Ahoy booth on Fridays for 2-for-1 dinner coupon, double slot points and prize drawing entries
Fun Book: Only given to hotel guests
Special Features: Free valet parking and validated self-parking at the Parking Gallery, just across Sierra Street.

The Sands Regency Hotel Casino
345 North Arlington Avenue
Reno, Nevada 89501
(702) 348-2200

Reservation Number: (800) 648-3553
Rooms: 911 Price Range: $29-$65
Suites: 27 Price Range: $95-$375
Restaurants: 10 (1 open 24 hours)
Casino Size: 27,000 Square Feet
Other Games: SB, K
Casino Marketing: (702) 348-2200
Fun Book: Show out-of-town ID at
　　　　　　Guest Services Booth
Special Features: Health Club and Spa. Winchell's Donuts, Baskin-Robbins, Arby's, Tony Roma's, Pizza Hut Express and Blimpie's Subs. Discount liquor store. Video arcade.

Silver Legacy Resort Casino
407 N. Virginia Street
Reno, Nevada 89501
(702) 329-4777

Reservation Number: (800) 687-8733
Rooms: 1,600 Price Range: $49-$109
Suites: 120 Price Range: $100-$175
Restaurants: 5 (1 open 24 hours)
Buffets: B-$4.99/$8.49 (Sun) L-$5.99
　　　　　D-$7.99/$8.99 (Fri/Sat)
Casino Size: 85,000 Square Feet
Other Games: B, PGP, CSP, LIR, K
Casino Marketing: (800) 215-7721
Special Features: Connected by skyways to both Circus Circus and Eldorado Hotels. Tallest hotel in Nevada - 37 stories. Working, automated mining machine 120 feet above casino floor. Health spa and beauty salon. Shopping mall with 8 stores.

Sundowner Hotel Casino
450 N. Arlington Avenue
Reno, Nevada 89503
(702) 786-7050

Reservation Number: (800) 648-5490
Rooms: 593 Price Range: $24-$60
Restaurants: 3 (1 open 24 hours)
Buffets: B-$3.95 (Sat)/$4.95 (Sun)
　　　　　D-$4.95/$8.95 (Fri)
Casino Size: 19,040 Square Feet
Other Games: K
Casino Marketing: (800) 648-5490
Fun Book: Only given to hotel guests

Virginian Hotel & Casino
140 N. Virginia Street
Reno, Nevada 89501
(702) 329-4664

Reservation Number: (800) 874-5558
Rooms: 118 Price Range: $28-$120
Suites: 6 Price Range: $90-$400
Restaurants: 2 (1 open 24 hours)
Casino Size: 13,669 Square Feet
Other Games: LIR, K, No Roulette
Casino Marketing: (702) 329-4664
Fun Book: Only given to hotel guests
　　　　　　or groups
Special Features: Complimentary valet parking. Some non-smoking rooms.

Searchlight

Map Location: #25 (58 miles S. of Las Vegas on Hwy. 95)

Searchlight Nugget Casino
100 N. Highway 95
Searchlight, Nevada 89046
(702) 297-1201

Reservation Number: (702) 297-1201
Rooms: 20 Price Range: $35-$50
Casino Size: 3,260 Square Feet
Other Games: No Craps or Roulette

Sparks

Map Location: #4 (Sparks is a suburb of Reno and is located one mile east of Reno on I-80)

Here's information, as supplied by Nevada's State Gaming Control Board, showing the slot machine payback percentages for all of the Sparks area casinos for the fiscal year beginning July 1, 1995 and ending June 30, 1996:

5¢ Slot Machines	95.22%
25¢ Slot Machines	95.50%
$1 Slot Machines	96.44%
$5 Slot Machines	96.90%
All Slot Machines	95.91%

These numbers reflect the percentage of money returned on each denomination of machine and encompass all electronic machines including video poker and video keno. For a 5¢ slot player Sparks' casinos offer incredibly high returns and overall, the Sparks area casinos offer not only the best returns in Nevada, but also the entire United States.

Baldini's Casino
865 South Rock Boulevard
Sparks, Nevada 89431
(702) 358-0116

Restaurants: 3 (1 open 24 hours)
Buffets: B-$3.99 L-$4.99 D-$6.99
Casino Size: 19,840 Square Feet
Other Games: SB, RB, LIR, K, BG
Casino Marketing: (702) 358-0116
Senior Discount: If 55, or older, receive
            25% restaurant discount
Fun Book: Show out-of-state picture ID and
            room key at Club Bonus Counter

Special Features: Country/western entertainment and dance floor. Periodic autograph signings by celebrity athletes. Convenience store with propane and RV dump. Gas station.

Giudici's Victorian Gambling Hall
1324 Victorian Avenue
Sparks, Nevada 89431
(702) 359-8868

Restaurants: 1 (open 24 hours)
Casino Size: 4,500 Square Feet
Other Games: No Craps or Roulette

John Ascuaga's Nugget
1100 Nugget Avenue
Sparks, Nevada 89431
(702) 356-3300

Reservation Number: (800) 648-1177
Rooms: 1,400 Price Range: $28-$105
Suites: 150 Price Range: $195-$290
Restaurants: 8 (1 open 24 hours)
Buffets: B-$8.95 (Sun) L-$6.95
            D-$8.95/$15.95(Fri/Sat)
Casino Size: 78,000 Square Feet
Other Games: SB, RB, P, PGP, CSP,
            LIR, K, BG
Casino Marketing: (800) 648-1177
Fun Book: Only issued through hotel packages, however, if you go to the information booth (next to the oyster bar) and show your airline ticket, they will give you a coupon for a free show with 2 free drinks at the Celebrity Showroom
Special Features: Free valet parking. Wedding chapel. Video game arcade. Year-round pool and health club.

Plantation Station Gambling Hall
2121 Victorian Avenue
Sparks, Nevada 89431
(702) 359-9440

Restaurants: 1 (open 24 hours)
Casino Size: 16,620 Square Feet
Other Games: SB, RB, K

Sierra Sid's
200 North McCarran Blvd.
Sparks, Nevada 89434
(702) 359-0550

Restaurants: 1 (open 24 hours)
Buffets: B-$4.95 L-$5.95 D-$6.95
Casino Size: 2,862 Square Feet
Other Games: No Craps or Roulette
Senior Discount: If 65, or older, 10% restaurant discount

Fun Book: Only given to groups
Special Feature: 24-hour travelmart. Laundry facility. Western Union office. Commemorative gun collection including the guns of Elvis and jewelry from the Presley estate.

Silver Club Hotel/Casino
1040 Victorian Avenue
Sparks, Nevada 89432
(702) 358-4771

Reservation Number: (800) 648-1137
Rooms: 207 Price Range: $45-$59
Suites: 8   Price Range: $65-$85
Restaurants: 4 (1 open 24 hours)
Buffets: L-$4.99 D-$6.99
Casino Size: 17,502 Square Feet
Other Games: SB, CSP, LIR, K
Casino Marketing: (800) 648-1137
Fun Book: Only given to hotel guests or groups

Western Village Inn & Casino
815 Nichols Boulevard
Sparks, Nevada 89432
(702) 331-1069

Reservation Number: (800) 648-1170
Rooms: 280 Price Range: $32-$68
Suites: 5 Price Range: $100-$150
Restaurants: 3 (1 open 24 hours)
Casino Size: 27,000 Square Feet
Other Games: SB, K
Casino Marketing: (800) 648-1170
Fun Book: Only given to hotel guests
Special Features: Free nightly lounge entertainment.

Tonopah

Map Location:#26 (200 miles N.W. of Las Vegas on Hwy. 95 where it meets Hwy. 6)

The Station House
P.O. Box 1351
Tonopah, Nevada 89049
(702) 482-9777

Reservation Number: (702) 482-9777
Rooms: 75 Price Range: $35-$42
Suites: 3 Price Range: $60-$82
Restaurants: 1 (open 24 hours)
Casino Size: 2,900 Square Feet
Other Games: No Roulette
Special Features: 20-space RV camp with full hook-ups.

Verdi

Map Location: #4 (4 miles W. of Reno on I-80 at the California border)

Boomtown Hotel & Casino
P.O. Box 399
Verdi, Nevada 89439
(702) 345-6000

Reservation Number: (800) 648-3790
Rooms: 122 Price Range: $39-$49
Suites: 2 Price Range: $65-$70
Restaurants: 4 (2 open 24 hours)
Buffets: B-$6.95 (Sat/Sun) L-$4.95
              D-$6.95/$7.95 (Sat)
Casino Size: 38,841 Square Feet
Other Games: P, PGP, LIR, K
Casino Marketing: (702) 345-8640
Fun Book: Only given to hotel guests
               and groups
Special Features: 203-space RV park. 24-hour mini-mart. Family fun center with indoor ferris wheel, 18-hole miniature golf course, dynamic motion theater, antique carousel and more than 100 video and arcade games.

Gold Ranch
P.O. Box 160
Verdi, Nevada 89439
(702) 345-6789

Restaurants: 1 (open 24 hours)
Casino Size: 3,100 Square Feet
Other Games: No Craps or Roulette

Wells

Map Location: #27 (338 miles N.E. of Reno on I-80)

Four Way Bar/Cafe & Casino
U.S. 93 & Interstate 80
Wells, Nevada 89835
(702) 752-3344

Restaurants: 1 (open 24 hours)
Casino Size: 4,500 Square Feet
Other Games: No Craps or Roulette
Fun Book: Given at local motels, or to bus groups

Wendover

Map Location: #28 (Just W. of the Utah border on I-80)

Peppermill Inn & Casino
P.O. Box 100
Wendover, Utah 84083
(702) 664-2255

Reservation Number: (800) 648-9660
Rooms: 90 Price Range: $44-$66
Restaurants: 1 (1 open 24 hours)
Buffets: B-$4.95 L-$6.95
D-$8.95/$11.95 (Fri)
Casino Size: 22,862 Square Feet
Other Games: SB, LIR, K
Fun Book: Only given to hotel guests
Special Features: Single-zero roulette

Rainbow Casino
1045 Wendover Boulevard
W. Wendover, Nevada 89883
(702) 664-4000

Toll-Free Number: (800) 217-0049
Restaurants: 1 (open 24 hours)
Buffets: B-$6.91 L-$6.91 D-$9.53
Casino Size: 6,452 Square Feet
Casino Marketing: (800) 217-0049
Other Games: SB, LIR, K

Red Garter Hotel & Casino
P.O. Box 2399
W. Wendover, Nevada 89883
(702) 664-3315

Toll-Free Number: (800) 982-2111
Rooms: 46 Price Range: $29-$59
Restaurants: 1 (open 24 hours)
Casino Size: 12,500 Square Feet
Casino Marketing: (800) 982-2111
Fun Book: Ask at welcome center
Special Features: Show out-of-state ID for
$11 in cash and coupons. $1.99 ham & eggs
special offered 24-hours.

State Line/Silver Smith Casinos
100 Wendover Blvd.
W. Wendover, Nevada 89883
(702) 664-2221

Reservation Number: (800) 848-7300
Rooms: 498 Price Range: $39-$76

Suites: 50 Price Range: $58-$155
Restaurants: 8 (2 open 24 hours)
Buffets: B-$4.95/$6.95 (Sat/Sun)
D-$8.95/$9.95 (Fri)
Casino Size: 17,287 Square Feet (Silver Smith)
Casino Size: 22,671 Square Feet (State Line)
Other Games: SB, P, CSP, LIR, K
Casino Marketing: (800) 848-7300
Fun Book: Only given to hotel guests
or groups
Special Features: 2 casinos connected by sky
bridge. Non-smoking rooms. 2 pools. Tennis
courts and gym. Gift shop. Live entertain-
ment nightly.

Winnemucca

Map Location: #29 (164 miles N.E. of Reno
on I-80)

Model T Hotel/Casino/RV Park
1130 W. Winnemucca Blvd.
Winnemucca, Nevada 89446
(702) 623-2588

Reservation Number: (800) 645-5658
Rooms: 73 Price Range: $50-$70
Restaurants: 1 (open 24 hours)
Other Games: SB, LIR, K,
No Craps or Roulette
Casino Marketing: (702) 625-1111
Fun Book: Only given to hotel/RV guests,
or groups
Senior Discount: Room discounted for
AARP members
Special Features: Free cooked-to-order break-
fast for each adult room guest. 60-space RV
park. Gift shop. Food court with Baskin-
Robbins, KFC Express and Coffee Counter.
Seasonal pool facilities.

Red Lion Inn & Casino
741 W. Winnemucca Blvd.
Winnemucca, Nevada 89445
(702) 623-2565

Reservation Number: (800) 633-6435
Rooms: 100 Price Range: $65-$79
Suites: 7 Price Range: $99-$150
Restaurants: 1 (open 24 hours)
Casino Size: 3,675 Square Feet
Other Games: No Craps or Roulette
Fun Book: Given to all hotel guests and also
distributed by local motels

Winners Hotel/Casino
185 W. Winnemucca Blvd.
Winnemucca, Nevada 89445
(702) 623-2511

Reservation Number: (800) 648-4770
Rooms: 83   Price Range: $37-$50
Suites: 2   Price Range: $74
Restaurants: 2 (1 open 24 hours)
Buffets: L-$5.49 D-$7.49/$8.99 (Fri)
Casino Size: 11,340 Square Feet
Other Games: LIR, B
Casino Marketing: (800) 648-4770
Fun Book: Given to all hotel guests and tour
    groups. Also available to guests of local
    motels and RV parks.
Special Features: Courtesy car service to other
motels, local businesses and airport/transportation facilities. Lounge with live entertainment. Gift shop. Children's video arcade.

Yerington

Map Location: #30 (60 miles S.E. of Reno on
Hwy. Alt. 95)

Casino West
11 N. Main Street
Yerington, Nevada 89447
(702) 463-2481

Reservation Number: (800) 227-4661
Rooms: 56 Price Range: $38-$52
Restaurants: 1
Buffets: B-$3.95 (Sun) D-$4.95/$11.95 (Fri)

Casino Size: 5,700 Square Feet
Other Games: B, K, No Craps or Roulette
Special Features: Movie theater. 12-lane bowling alley.

Lucky Club
45 N. Main Street
Yerington, Nevada 89447
(702) 463-2868

Restaurants: 1
Casino Size: 3,400 Square Feet
Other Games: No Craps or Roulette

Indian Casino

Avi Hotel & Casino
10000 Aha Macao Parkway
Laughlin, Nevada 89029
(702) 535-5555
Map Location: #2

Toll-Free Number: (800) AVI-2-WIN
Rooms: 302 Price Range: $15-$45
Suites: 29 Price Range: $50-$99
Restaurants: 3 (1 open 24 hours)
Buffets: B-$3.49 L-$3.99 D-$4.99
Casino Size: 30,000 Square Feet
Other Games: SB, CSP, LIR, K
Fun Book: Only to hotel guests
Special Features: 500-space RV park. Located on the Colorado River and has a boat dock and launch. Video arcade. Baskin-Robbins and Subway shops.

NEW JERSEY

Map Location: #1 (on the Atlantic Ocean in southeast New Jersey, 130 miles south of New York City and 60 miles southeast of Philadelphia).

Once a major tourist destination that was world-famous for its steel pier and boardwalk attractions, Atlantic City gradually fell into decline and casino gambling was seen as its salvation when voters approved it there in 1976.

The first casino (Resorts International) opened to "standing-room-only crowds" in 1978. Since then 11 more casinos have opened and all but two are located along the boardwalk. The other two (Harrah's and Trump's Castle)

are located in the marina section. A 13th casino, Trump's World's Fair Casino, is an extension of Trump Plaza and opened in early 1996. Atlantic City was the northeast's only area for casino gambling until the Foxwoods Casino opened in Ledyard, Connecticut in February, 1992.

There has been a resurgence of interest among casino operators in Atlantic City and it is estimated that the number of casino hotel rooms will triple from 9,000 to more than 27,000 rooms by the end of 1999. Also, six new casino projects have been announced. The first involves a 150-acre tract of land in the marina area that will be the site for at least three different casinos with a value of almost

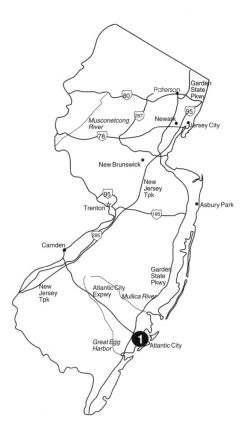

$2 billion. Mirage Resorts will be building a $750-million, 2,000-room resort called Beau Rivage and it will also be developing a joint project with Boyd Gaming Corp. in another $500-million, 1,000-room resort called Stardust - Atlantic City. Circus Circus will also be building a $600-million, 2,000-room resort adjoining the Beau Rivage. The three properties are expected to open by late 1998.

In the boardwalk section of Atlantic City MGM Grand announced plans to build a $700-million, 2,500-room "majestic destination resort." The property will be built next to the Showboat and will feature a 335,000-square-foot mall and entertainment complex.

ITT Corp. the parent company of Caesars World, Inc. and Planet Hollywood are teaming up to build a $490-million, 1,000-room Planet Hollywood casino resort on a 7.5 acre site at Indiana Avenue and the Boardwalk, adjacent to the Sands Casino Hotel.

Sun International Hotels, Ltd. owner of Sun City in South Africa and the Atlantis Casino Resort in Paradise Island, Bahamas announced plans to build a $700 million, 2,000-room casino resort next to the new MGM complex.

In early 1993 the New Jersey Casino Control Commission authorized simulcasting of pari-mutuel events, plus the addition of poker. On May 30, 1993 the Showboat became the first Atlantic City casino to offer betting on races that were simulcast to its facility. Poker made its Atlantic City debut the next month. Later that year the commission gave the okay for keno and the first casinos began offering it on June 15, 1994.

For those interested in which casinos offer the best return on their slot machines, we offer the following information from the New Jersey Casino Control Commission regarding average slot payout percentages for the three-month period from May through July 1996:

CASINO	PAYBACK
Harrah's	92.8%
Tropicana	92.6%
Sands	91.8%
Trump's Castle	91.8%
The Grand	91.7%
Bally's Park Place	91.6%
Showboat	91.6%
Trump Taj Mahal	91.6%
Caesars	91.4%
Trump Plaza	91.4%
Resorts	91.0%
Claridge	90.6%

These figures reflect the total percentages returned by each casino for all of their electronic machines which includes slot machines, video poker, etc. As you can see, Harrah's returned the most to their slot machine players, while the Claridge returned the least. Although these numbers are only for a three month period, they pretty much remain the same from month-to-month with Harrah's and Tropicana at the top, the Claridge always at the bottom and the others somewhere in between.

All casinos are open 24 hours and unless otherwise noted, the games offered are: slots, video poker, big six, craps, blackjack, roulette, baccarat, mini-baccarat, Caribbean Stud Poker, Let It Ride, Pai Gow Poker and keno. The minimum gambling age is 21.

Bally's Park Place Casino Resort
Park Place and the Boardwalk
Atlantic City, New Jersey 08401
(609) 340-2000

Reservation Number: (800) BALLYS-7
Rooms: 1,265 Price Range: $79-$215
Suites: 99 Price Range: $250-$580
Restaurants: 10 (1 open 24 hours)
Buffets: B-$9.95/$11.25 (Sat/Sun)
          L/D-$13.95/$16.95 (Sat/Sun)
Casino Size: 80,000 Square Feet
Other Games: Poker, Red Dog, Sic Bo,
          Simulcasting
Casino Marketing: (800) 772-7777 ext. 2700
Special Features: 40,000 square-foot world-class spa offers package plans and body treatments.

Caesars Atlantic City
2100 Pacific Avenue
Atlantic City, New Jersey 08401
(609) 348-4411

Reservation Number: (800) 443-0104
Rooms: 447 Price Range: $110-$150
Suites: 194 Price Range: $225-$500
Restaurants: 11 (1 open 24 hours)
Buffets: B-$9.95 L-$10.50 D-$13.95/$16.95
Casino Size: 67,600 Square Feet
Casino Marketing: (800) 257-5219
Other Games: Poker, Simulcasting
Special Features: Planet Hollywood restaurant. Two blocks from convention center. Health spa. Shopping arcade. Outdoor pool. Rooftop tennis. Miniature golf. Unisex beauty salon. Amusement arcade. New tower with 620 rooms will be completed in early 1998.

Claridge Casino Hotel
Boardwalk & Park Place
Atlantic City, New Jersey 08401
(609) 340-3400

Reservation Number: (800) 257-8585
Rooms: 449 Price Range: $80-$165
Suites: 58 Price Range: $180-$495
Restaurants: 5 (1 open 24 hours)
Buffets: B- $4.72 L/D-$6.60
Casino Size: 59,000 Square Feet
Other Games: Sic Bo
Casino Marketing: (800) 847-LUCK
Special Features: Blackjack games offer surrender. Indoor pool and health spa. Unisex salon. Gift shop.

The Grand Casino Resort
Boston at Pacific Avenues
Atlantic City, New Jersey 08404
(609) 347-7111

Reservation Number: (800) 257-8677
Rooms: 368 Price Range: $100-$225
Suites: 132 Price Range: $175-$1,500
Restaurants: 5 (1 open 24 hours)
Buffets: L/D-$14.95
Casino Size: 60,000 Square Feet
Other Games: Poker, Sic Bo, Simulcasting
Casino Marketing: (800) THE-GRAND
Special Features: Blackjack games offer surrender and double exposure. Spa facilities with indoor pool. The Grand Theater - entertainment complex. Unisex salon. 300-room addition to be completed by summer of 1997.

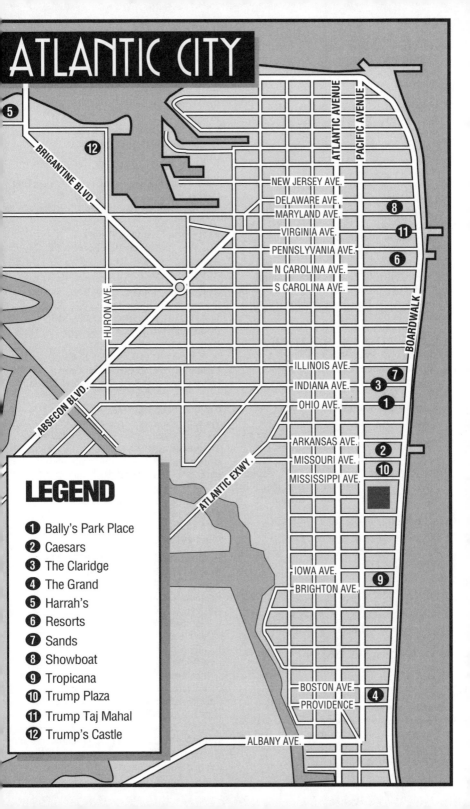

Harrah's Atlantic City
777 Harrah's Boulevard
Atlantic City, New Jersey 08401
(609) 441-5000

Reservation Number: (800) HARRAHS
Rooms: 506   Price Range: $65-$125
Suites: 254 Price Range: $90-$165
Restaurants: 8 (1 open 24 hours)
Buffets: B-$7.77/$15.99 (Sun)
          L-$11.99 D-$15.99
Casino Size: 79,293 Square Feet
Other Games: Poker, Mini-Craps
Casino Marketing: (800) 2-HARRAH
Special Features: 75-slip marina. Health spa
with indoor swimming pool. 5 retail shops.
Teen center with game room.

Merv Griffin's Resorts Casino Hotel
North Carolina Avenue and the Boardwalk
Atlantic City, New Jersey 08401
(609) 344-6000

Reservation Number: (800) 336-MERV
Rooms: 662 Price Range: $70-$225
Suites: 30 Price Range: $250-$500
Restaurants: 7 (1 open 24 hours)
Buffets: B-$7.11 L/D-$9.99
Casino Size: 60,000 Square Feet
Other Games: Poker, Sic Bo, Pai Gow,
          Mini-Craps, Simulcasting
Casino Marketing: (800) 336-MERV
Special Features: Health Spa with state-of-
the-art Nautilus equipment. Indoor/outdoor
pool with saunas and Jacuzzis. Racquet ball
club. Game room. Shopping arcade.

Sands Hotel & Casino
Indiana Avenue & Brighton Park
Atlantic City, New Jersey 08401
(609) 441-4000

Reservation Number: (800) 257-8580
Rooms: 476 Price Range: $99-$179
Suites: 58 Price Range: $300-$425
Restaurants: 5 (1 open 24 hours)
Buffets: B-$6.95/$22.95 (Sun)
          L-$11.95 D-$15.95
Casino Size: 54,464 Square Feet
Other Games: Poker, Pai Gow, Sic Bo,
          Simulcasting
Casino Marketing: (800) AC-SANDS
Special Features: Indoor pool and Jacuzzi.
Nautilus fitness center with sauna and tan-
ning booth. Food court with six restaurants
and fast food outlets.

Showboat Casino-Hotel
801 Boardwalk
Atlantic City, New Jersey 08401
(609) 343-4000

Reservation Number: (800) 247-8370
Rooms: 741 Price Range: $122-$182
Suites: 59 Price Range: Private Use
Restaurants: 8 (1 open 24 hours)
Buffets: B-$8.49 L-$9.99 D-$9.99
Casino Size: 79,963 Square Feet
Other Games: Poker, Pai Gow, Simulcasting
Casino Marketing: (800) 621-0200
Special Features: 60-lane Bowling Center.

Tropicana Casino & Resort
Brighton Avenue and the Boardwalk
Atlantic City, New Jersey 08401
(609) 340-4000

Reservation Number: (800) THE-TROP
Rooms: 1,370 Price Range: $75-$195
Suites: 254   Price Range: $115-$175
Restaurants: 8 (1 open 24 hours)
Buffets: B-$7.95 L-$10.95
          D-$11.95 ($13.95 Sat/Sun)
Casino Size: 110,000 Square Feet
Other Games: Poker, Single-Zero Roulette,
          Pai Gow
Casino Marketing: (800) 338-5553
Special Features: Largest hotel in New Jer-
sey. Suites are only available Monday through
Thursday nights. Shopping arcade with retail
stores. Indoor health spa with indoor and
outdoor swimming pools. Tennis courts.

Trump Plaza Hotel and Casino
The Boardwalk at Mississippi Avenue
Atlantic City, New Jersey 08401
(609) 441-6000

Reservation Number: (800) 677-7378
Rooms: 831 Price Range: $120-$230
Suites: 73 Price Range: $220-$400
Restaurants: 9 (1 open 24 hours)
Buffets: L-$10.95 D-$13.95/$15.95
Casino Size: 90,281 Square Feet
Other Games: Pai Gow, Sic Bo
Casino Marketing: (800) 677-0711
Fun Book: Look for vouchers at area hotels
   (not Trump Plaza) and motels that can be
   redeemed at promotions booth
Special Features: Trump's World's Fair Ca-
sino is across the street and accessible by a
walkway between the properties. Mobil Travel
Guide 4-star and AAA Four Diamond rating.
Health spa with massage, herbal wraps, and
salt-glo loofah cleansing. Indoor pool.

Trump Taj Mahal Casino Resort
1000 Boardwalk at Virginia Avenue
Atlantic City, New Jersey 08401
(609) 449-1000

Reservation Number: (800) TAJ-TRUMP
Rooms: 1,013 Price Range: $125-$225
Suites: 237 Price Range: $275 and up
Restaurants: 9 (1 open 24 hours)
Buffets: B-$6.95 L-$7.95 D-$12.95
Casino Size: 120,000 Square Feet
Casino Marketing: (800) 825-8888
Other Games: Poker, Red Dog, Sic Bo,
            Pai Gow, Mini-Baccarat,
            Chemin de Fer
Special Features: Mobil Travel Guide 4-star rating. Health spa and indoor Olympic-size pool.

Trump's Castle Casino Resort
One Castle Boulevard
Atlantic City, New Jersey 08401
(609) 441-2000

Reservation Number: (800) 365-8786
Rooms: 568 Price Range: $90-$150
Suites: 157 Price Range: $110-$500
Restaurants: 7 (1 open 24 hours)
Buffets: B-$5.99 L-$13.50 D-$13.50
Casino Size: 71,031 Square Feet
Other Games: Poker, Sic Bo, Pai Gow
Casino Marketing: (800) 777-8477
Special Features: Lunch and dinner buffet prices are $8.96 with Castle Card membership. Adjacent to state marina with 640 slips. 3-acre recreation deck with pools, jogging track, tennis courts, miniature golf course and health club.

NEW MEXICO

There are 11 Indian casinos in New Mexico that signed compacts with Governor Gary Johnson in February 1995. Later that year, however, New Mexico's supreme court overturned the compact agreements because they weren't first approved by the state legislature. Ever since that ruling the state's attorney general has been trying to shut down all Indian casinos but as of September 1996 the issue remained unresolved and the casinos were still operating.

Unless otherwise noted, all New Mexico casinos are open 24 hours and offer: blackjack, craps, roulette, video slots and video poker. Some casinos also offer: mini-baccarat (MB), poker (P), Caribbean Stud Poker (CSP), keno (K), video keno (VK), Big 6 Wheel (B6) and bingo (BG). The minimum gambling age is 18 (21 if liquor is served).

Apache Nugget
P.O. Box 650
Dulce, New Mexico 87528
(505) 759-3777
Map Location: #7 (150 miles N. of Santa Fe)

Restaurants: 1
Liquor: Yes
Other Games: P
Special Features: Rooms are available at nearby Best Western Jicarilla Inn (800) 742-1398.

Camel Rock Casino
Route 11, Box 3A
Santa Fe, New Mexico 87501
(505) 984-8414
Map Location: #2

Toll-Free Number: (800) GO-CAMEL
Restaurants: 4 (2 open 24 hours)
Buffets: B-$1.99 L-$4.95 D-$5.95
Liquor: No
Casino Size: 60,000 Square feet
Other Games: P, CSP, K, BG

Casino Apache
P.O. Box 269
Mescalero, New Mexico 88340
(505) 257-5141
Map Location: #4 (90 miles N.E. of Las Cruces)

Reservation Number: (800) 545-9011
Rooms: 250 Price Range: $90-$120
Restaurants: 2 (1 open 24 hours)
Liquor: Yes
Buffets: Sun Brunch-$15.95
Other Games: P, VK, No Roulette
Special Features: 2 casinos are located in Inn of the Mountain Gods hotel. One casino is slots only and is open 24 hours. The other is table games only and open 11am-1am/2am (Fri/Sat).

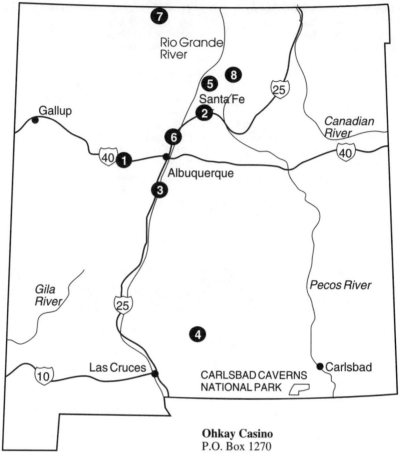

Cities of Gold Casino
Route 11, Box 21-B
Santa Fe, New Mexico 87501
(505) 455-3313
Map Location: #2

Toll-Free Number: (800) 455-3313
Restaurants: 2   Liquor: No
Buffets: B-$1.95 L-$4.95 D-$5.95
Casino Size: 40,000 Square Feet
Other Games: P, CSP, VK, BG
Fun Book: Given at local hotels/motels

Isleta Gaming Palace
11000 Broadway S.E.
Albuquerque, New Mexico 87022
(505) 869-2614
Map Location: #3

Toll-Free Number: (800) 460-5686
Restaurants: 1 Snack Bar Liquor: No
Other Games: P, CSP, BG

Ohkay Casino
P.O. Box 1270
San Juan Pueblo, New Mexico 87566
(505) 747-1668
Map Location: #5 (24 miles N. of Santa Fe)

Restaurants: 1 (open 24 hours) Liquor: No
Buffets: B-$1.50 L-$4.00 D-$5.00
Other Games: P
Senior Discount: $1 off every meal, plus 10th
meal is free, if 55 or older

Sandia Casino
P.O. Box 10188
Albuquerque, New Mexico 87184
(505) 897-2173
Map Location: #3

Toll-Free Number: (800) 526-9366
Restaurants: 2 (1 open 24 hours)
Buffets: B-$2.50 L-$4.00 D-$5.00
Liquor: No
Other Games: C, R, P, CSP, K, BG
Special Features: Has Subway sub shop and
snack bar.

San Felipe Casino Hollywood
25 Hagan Road
Algodones, New Mexico 87001
(505) 867-6700
Map Location: #6 (17 miles N. of Albuquerque)

Restaurants: 1
Liquor: No
Buffets: B-$1.49 L-$2.49 D-$2.49

Santa Ana Star Casino
54 Jemez Dam Canyon Road
Bernalillo, New Mexico 87004
(505) 867-0000
Map Location: #6 (17 miles N. of Albuquerque)

Restaurants: 1 Snack Bar Liquor: No
Casino Size: 19,000 Square Feet
Other Games: MB, P, CSP

Sky City Casino
P.O. Box 519
San Fidel, New Mexico 87049
(505) 552-6017
Map Location: #1 (50 miles W. of Albuquerque)

Toll-Free Number: (888) SKY-CITY
Restaurants: 1 Snack Bar Liquor: No
Other Games: P, B6, BG
Special Features: Gift shop. Convenience store and gas station across the street.

Taos Slot Room
P.O. Box 1477
Taos, New Mexico 87571
(505) 758-4460
Map Location: #8 (65 milesN.E. of Santa Fe)

Restaurants: 1 Snack Bar Liquor: No
Other Games: Only Slots and Video Poker

NEW YORK

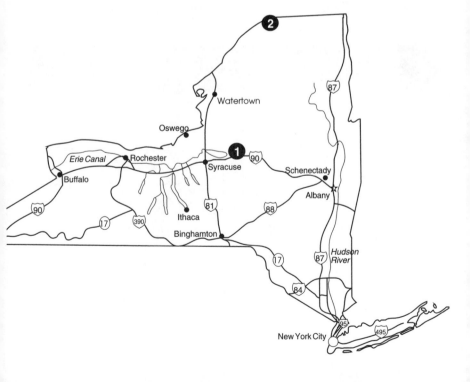

Governor Cuomo signed a compact with the Oneida tribe in April 1993 that allows the tribe to offer virtually any form of table games. Slot machines, video games, off-track betting, poker and lottery games are not permitted. Later that same year the governor also signed a compact with the St. Regis Mohawk tribe to offer virtually the same games. The Oneida tribe's casino opened July 20, 1993 and the Mohawk's is expected to open on their reservation in Hogansburg (map location #2) sometime in early 1997. For more current information on the St. Regis Mohawk casino you can contact the tribe at its bingo operation.

The Oneida's casino is open 24 hours and offers the following games: blackjack, craps, roulette, pai gow poker, red dog, chuck-a-luck, baccarat, mini-baccarat, Caribbean Stud Poker, Let It Ride, keno, instant multi-game machines (similar to slots), a money (big six) wheel and high-stakes bingo. The minimum gambling age is 18.

Mohawk Bingo Palace
St. Regis Indian Reservation, Route 35
Hogansburg, New York 13655
(518) 358-2246
Map Location: #2 (180 miles N.E. of Syracuse)

CASINO TO OPEN BY EARLY 1997

Turning Stone Casino
Patrick Road
Verona, New York 13478
(315) 361-7711
Map Location: #1 (adjacent to NY State Thruway exit 33 at Verona, off Route 365, 35 miles E. of Syracuse).

Toll-Free Number: (800) 771-7711
Rooms: 277 Price Range: $50-$130
Suites: 30 Price Range: $75-$200
HOTEL TO OPEN BY EARLY 1997
Restaurants: 3 (1 open 24 hours)
Buffets: D-$9.75/$11.75 (Fri-Sun)
Liquor: No
Casino Size: 90,000 Square Feet
Casino Marketing: (800) 771-7711
Fun Book: Only given to groups
Special Features: Juice/soda/coffee bar in casino. Gift shop. Smoke shop. Offers single-deck blackjack.

NORTH CAROLINA

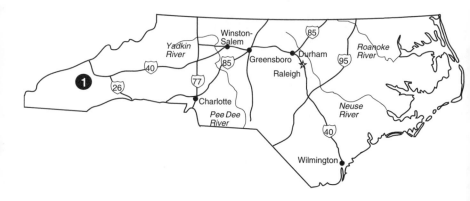

In August, 1994 the state's Eastern Band of Cherokee Indians signed a compact with the governor to allow some form of video gambling with jackpots of up to $25,000.

The tribe's casino opened in early 1995 in their old bingo hall but they have signed a management agreement with Harrah's to develop their gaming operations and a new $95 million, 60,000-square-foot casino is expected to open by late 1997.

The only games available are video poker, video craps and video blackjack. The casino is open 24 hours and the minimum gambling age is 18.

Tribal Casino
P.O. Box 455
Cherokee, North Carolina 28719
(704) 497-6835
Map Location: #1 (55 miles S.W. of Asheville)

Restaurants: 2 Snack Bars
Liquor: No

NORTH DAKOTA

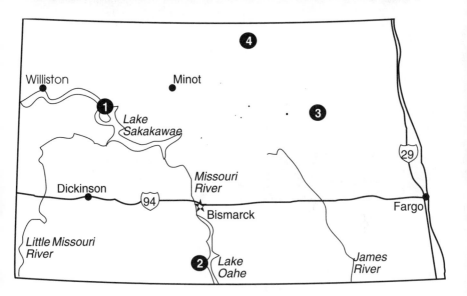

North Dakota has more than 800 sites throughout the state that offer blackjack, with a $5 maximum bet, for the benefit of charities.

There are also four Indian casinos which, although not restricted to that same $5 amount, are limited by law to the following maximum bets: blackjack-$50, craps-$25, slots-$5, video poker-$5 and poker-$10 per bet, per round with a maximum of three rounds.

Unless otherwise noted, all Indian casinos are open 24 hours and offer: blackjack, craps, poker, slots and video poker. The minimum gambling age is 18 (21 if liquor is served).

Four Bears Casino & Lodge
P.O. Box 579
New Town, North Dakota 58763
(701) 627-4018
Map Location: #4 (150 miles N.W. of Bismarck)

Toll-Free Number: (800) 294-5454
Rooms: 40   Price Range:$55
Restaurants: 2 Liquor: Yes
Hours: 8am-2am/4am (Fri/Sat)
Other Games: Bingo, Big Six Wheel
Senior Discount: If 55, or older, eligible for $49.50 room rate. Also, receive $5 in players cash on designated days until 5pm
Special Features: 80-space RV park with laundry and shower facilities.

Prairie Knights Casino & Lodge
HC 1, Box 26-A
Fort Yates, North Dakota 58538
(701) 854-7777
Map Location: #5 (60 miles S. of Bismarck)

Toll-Free Number: (800) 425-8277
Rooms: 68 Price Range: $45-$77
Suites: 2 Price Range: $120
Restaurants: 2 Liquor: Yes
Buffets: L-$7.95 D-$7.95
Casino Size: 40,000 Square Feet
Other Games: No Craps, Video Keno
Casino Marketing: (800) 425-8277
Fun Book: Only given to bus or limo groups
Special Features: Live entertainment on weekends. 2 bars. RV Parking.

Spirit Lake Casino
Highway 57
Spirit Lake, North Dakota 58370
(701) 766-4747
Map Location: #3 (6 miles S. of Devil's Lake)

Toll-Free Number: (800) WIN-U-BET
Restaurants: 2 Liquor: No
Buffets: B-$3.00 (Sat/Sun) L-$5.50 D-$6.00

Hours: 9am-3am/24 hours (Fri/Sat)
Other Games: Keno, Bingo, Simulcasting
Special Features: Free shuttle service from Devil's Lake. Gift shop. Discount smoke shop. New hotel expected to open by late 1997.

Wild Rose Casino
P.O. Box 1449, Highway 5 West
Belcourt, North Dakota 58316
(701) 477-3281
Map Location: #2 (120 miles N.E. of Minot)

Toll-Free Number: (800) 477-3497
Restaurants: 1 Liquor: Yes
Buffets: L-$4.95 D-$4.95
Casino Size: 25,000 Square Feet
Other Games: Bingo (Fri-Wed),
                      Simulcasting
Fun Book: Look for ads in newspaper
Special Features: Free RV parking.

OREGON

Oregon law permits bars and taverns to have up to five video lottery terminals that offer up to five different versions of video poker. These machines are the same as regular video gaming devices but are called lottery terminals because they are regulated by the state's lottery commission which receives a share of each machine's revenue. The machines accept cash but do not pay out in cash; instead, they print out a receipt which must be taken to a cashier.

Oregon law permits VLT's to return a maximum of 90.5% over time. During the 1996 fiscal year the VLT's had slightly less than $3.3 billion played and returned slightly more than $2.9 billion which worked out to an actual return of 89.17%.

There are eight Indian tribes that have signed compacts with the state. Six of the tribes have casinos in operation. Of the remaining two tribes one is expected to open a casino by mid-

1997 and the other (Confederated Tribes of Coos, Lower Umpqua and Siuslaw Casino) had no plans to open a casino before the end of 1997.

All Indian casinos offer blackjack, poker, video slots, video poker, video keno, video blackjack and pull tabs. The minimum gambling age is 18 (21 if liquor is served).

Chinook Winds Gaming Center
1777 N.W. 44th Street
Lincoln City, Oregon 97367
(541) 996-5825
Map Location: #4 (45 miles W. of Salem)

Toll-Free Number: (888) 244-6665
Restaurants: 2 Liquor: Yes
Buffets: B-$3.99 (Sat/Sun) L-$4.99 D-$7.99
Other Games: Keno, Bingo, Simulcasting,
                      Pai Gow Poker

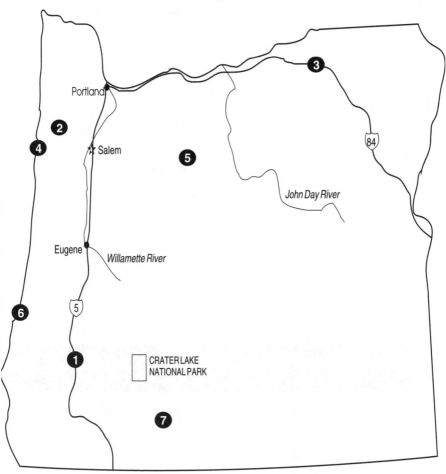

Indian Head Gaming Center
P.O. Box 720
Warm Springs, Oregon 97761
(541) 553-6123
Map Location: #5 (100 miles E. of Portland)

Toll-Free Number: (800) BET-N-WIN
Reservation Number: (800) 554-4786
Rooms: 139 Price Range: $95-$140
Suites: 3   Price Range: $115-$190
Restaurants: 3 (1 open 24 hours) Liquor: Yes
Hours: 10am-2am Daily
Fun Book: Only given to resort guests
Other Games: Keno, Caribbean Stud Poker,
            Let It Ride
Special Features: Casino is located inside the
Kahneeta Resort which contains a restaurant
and bar facilities. Resort features 18-hole
golf course, tennis, horseback riding, hot
springs spa and water slide.

Klamath Tribe Casino
P.O. Box 436
Chiloquin, Oregon 97624
(541) 783-2219
Map Location: #7 (20 miles N. of Klamath
Falls)

EXPECTED TO OPEN BY MID-1997

The Mill Casino
3201 Tremont Street
North Bend, Oregon 97459
(541) 756-8800
Map Location: #6 (75 miles S.W. of Eugene)

Toll-Free Number: (800) 953-4800
Restaurants: 2 (1 open 24 hours)
Buffets: B-$4.95 (Sun) L-$4.95 (Mon-Fri)
          D-$6.95 (Tue)

Liquor: Yes
Other Games: Bingo
Special Features: Free valet parking. Free shuttle bus from local motels. Children's video arcade. Hotel expected to open by late 1997.

Seven Feathers Hotel & Resort
146 Chief Miwaleta Lane
Canyonville, Oregon 97417
(541) 839-1111
Map Location: #1 (80 miles S. of Eugene)

Toll-Free Number: (800) 548-8461
Rooms: 156 Price Range: $89-$109
Restaurants: 1 Liquor: No
Casino Size: 29,000 Square Feet
Other Games: Keno, Bingo

Spirit Mountain Casino
P.O. Box 39
Grand Ronde, Oregon 97347
(503) 879-2350
Map Location: #2 (85 miles S.W. of Portland)
Toll-Free Number: (800) 760-7977
Restaurants: 4 (2 open 24 hours) Liquor: No
Buffets: L-$5.50 D-$8.75
Fun Book: Ask at Player Services Desk
Other Games: Keno, Bingo

Wild Horse Gaming Resort
72777 Highway 331
Pendleton, Oregon 97801
(541) 278-2274
Map Location: #3 (211 miles E. of Portland)

Toll-Free Number: (800) 654-9453
Rooms: 90 Price Range: $45-$60
Suites: 10 Price Range: $115-$135
Restaurants: 2 (1 open 24 hours) Liquor: No
Buffets: Brunch-$8.95 (Sun)
Casino Size: 40,000 Square Feet
Other Games: Keno, Bingo, Simulcasting

RHODE ISLAND

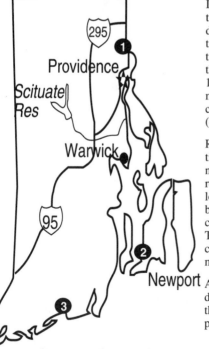

In mid-1994 an agreement was reached between the governor and the Narragansett Indians to allow a casino to be built on the tribe's property in Charlestown (map location #3). There have been numerous delays on the project and it will probably be at least late 1997 before the casino begins operating. For more current information on the status of the casino you can contact the tribe directly at (401) 364-1100.

Rhode Island also has two pari-mutuel facilities which both feature video lottery terminals (VLT's). These machines are the same as regular video gaming devices but are called lottery terminals because they are regulated by the state's lottery commission which receives a share of each machine's revenue. The machines accept cash but don't pay out in cash; instead, they print out a receipt which must be taken to a cashier.

All VLT's are programmed to play at least six different games: blackjack, keno, slots and three versions of poker (jacks or better, joker poker and deuces wild). The Rhode Island

Lottery does not provide figures to determine the actual paybacks on its VLT's, however, according to William DiMuccio, gaming manager for the Rhode Island Lottery, the VLT's are programmed to pay back the following amounts over time: Blackjack - 99.1%, Video Poker - 95%, 25¢ Keno - 92%, 50¢ Keno - 94%, $1 Keno - 96%. The minimum gambling age in Rhode Island is 18.

Lincoln Park Greyhound Track

1600 Louisquisset Pike
Lincoln, Rhode Island 02865
(401) 723-3200
Map Location: #1 (10 miles N. of Providence)

Toll-Free Number: (800) 720-7275
Restaurants: 2
Hours: 10am-1am Daily
Special Features: Live dog racing (Mon/Wed/Thu-Sat) throughout the year. Daily simulcasting of horse and dog racing.

Newport Jai-Alai

150 Admiral Kalbfus Road
Newport, Rhode Island 02840
(401) 849-5000
Map Location: #2

Toll-Free Number: (800) 451-2500
Restaurants: 1
Hours: 10am-1am Daily
Special Features: Live jai-alai games (Mon/Wed-Sun) during the season which runs from early April through early September. Daily simulcasting of horse and dog racing.

SOUTH DAKOTA

South Dakota's bars and taverns are allowed to have up to 10 video lottery terminals (VLT's) that offer the following games: poker, keno, blackjack and bingo. These machines are the same as regular video gaming devices but are called lottery terminals because they are regulated by the state's lottery commission which receives a share of each machine's revenue. The machines accept cash but don't pay out in cash; instead, they print out a receipt which must be taken to a cashier. Slot machines, as well as blackjack and poker are only permitted at Indian casinos and in Deadwood.

Deadwood was once most famous for being the home of Wild Bill Hickok who was shot to death while playing cards in the No. 10 Saloon. The hand he held at the time was two pairs: black aces and eights, which ever since is usually referred to as a "dead man's hand." Wild Bill is buried in the local cemetery along with another local celebrity: Calamity Jane.

Today the town is still well known for those colorful characters, but it's also known as the home of slot machines, poker and blackjack ever since voters approved those forms of

gambling more than seven years ago. When the first casinos opened on November 1, 1989 the promoters expected betting of $4 million a year. The estimate was a little low because in the first two years alone the betting totaled more than $500 million!

All of the buildings in the downtown area are required to conform with the city's authentic 1880's architecture and many of the casinos are located in historic structures. As a matter of fact, the No. 10 Saloon is still there and you can actually gamble in the same spot where old Wild Bill bit the dust! One of the casinos - Midnight Star, is owned by movie actor Kevin Costner and his brother, Dan. They are also working together on the Dunbar Resort and Conference Center which is a 320-room, 635-acre project scheduled to open by Spring of 1998.

South Dakota law limits each licensee to a maximum of 30 slot machines in a building and no business is allowed to hold more than three licenses. The law also limits blackjack (and poker) bets to a maximum of $5, but you are permitted to play more than one hand at a time. In addition to the Deadwood casinos, there are eight Indian casinos in South Dakota which are also subject to the same $5 maximum bet law.

For those interested in the slot machine payback percentages, we offer the following statistics from the South Dakota Commission on Gaming for all of Deadwood's slot machines for the 1995 calendar year from January 1, 1995 through December 31, 1995:

AMOUNT	PAYBACK %
5¢	89.36%
10¢	90.89%
25¢	90.77%
50¢	91.78%
$1.00	91.37%
$5.00	94.92%

Most casinos are open from 8am until 12am Sunday through Thursday and 8am until 2am on the weekends. Unless otherwise noted, all casinos offer slot machines and video poker. The minimum gambling age is 21 (18 at Indian casinos that don't serve alcohol).

Deadwood

Map Location: #1 (in the Black Hills, 41 miles N.W. of Rapid City. Take I-90 W. Get off at the second Sturgis exit and take Hwy. 14-A into Deadwood)

B. B. Cody's
681 Main Street
(605) 578-3430

Other Games: Blackjack

Bella Union
645 Main Street
(605) 578-1591

Restaurants: 1
Casino Size: 5,000 Square Feet
Other Games: Blackjack

Best Western Hickok House
137 Charles Street
(605) 578-1611

Reservation Number: 800-528-1234
Rooms: 38   Price Range: $49-$99
Restaurants: 1
Special Features: Hot tub and sauna. AAA rated. Trolley service.

Big Jake's Cardroom
639 Main Street
(605) 578-3631

Bodega Bar
662 Main Street
(605) 578-1996

Restaurants: 1
Other Games: Blackjack

Buffalo Saloon
658 Main Street
(605) 578-9993

Bullock Hotel
633 Main Street
(605) 578-1745

Reservation Number: 800-336-1876
Rooms: 29   Price Range: $65-$95
Suites: 7   Price Range: $135-$155
Restaurants: 1
Hours: 24 hours daily
Other Games: Blackjack
Fun Book: Only given to hotel guests
Special Features: Deadwood's oldest hotel. Victorian-styled rooms. Gift shop. Exercise facility. 3-Diamond AAA rated.

Carnival Queen
606 Main Street
(605) 578-1574

Dakota Territory Saloon
652 Main Street
(605) 578-3566

Hours: 24 hours daily
Casino Size: 4,000 Square Feet
Other Games: Blackjack, Poker
Special Features: Deadwood Poker Hall of Fame. Various drawings for free cash giveaways.

Days Inn 76 Motel
68 Main Street
(605) 578-3476

Reservation Number: 800-526-8277
Rooms: 38   Price Range: $40-$75
Restaurants: 1

Deadwood Dick's Saloon/Nickel Dick's
55 Sherman Street
(605) 578-3224

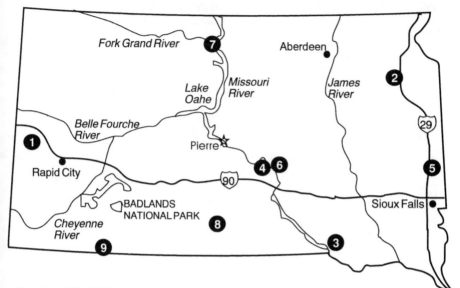

Deadwood Gulch Resort
Highway 85 South
(605) 578-1294

Reservation Number: 800-695-1876
Rooms: 95   Price Range: $50-$95
Suites: 2   Price Range: $100-$135
Restaurants: 2
Hours: 24 hours daily
Casino Size: 7,000 Square Feet
Other Games: Blackjack
Fun Book: Given to guests at check-in
Special Features: Convenience store and gas station. Fun park with go-carts, bumper boats, miniature golf, batting cages, kiddie play land and arcade. Outdoor swimming pool.

Deadwood Gulch Saloon
560 Main Street
(605) 578-1207

Depot/Motherlode
155 Sherman Street
(605) 578-2699

Toll-Free Number: (800) 31-DEPOT
Restaurants: 1
Buffets: Sun Brunch-$7.95
Other Games: Blackjack
Fun Book: Call or write to receive
Special Features: Live country entertainment. Dance floor. Fine dining restaurant specializing in steak and seafood. Motherlode Players' Club offers slot club points and monthly newsletter with special offers.

Eagles Club
409 Cliff Street
(605) 578-1064

Elk's Lodge
696 Main Street #508
(605) 578-1333

First Gold Hotel & Gaming
270 Main Street
(605) 578-9777

Reservation Number: 800-274-1876
Rooms: 50   Price Range: $29-$99
Suites: 3   Price Range: $89-$129
Restaurants: 2
Buffets: D-$4.95
Hours: 24 hours daily
Casino Size: 7,000 Square Feet
Other Games: Blackjack
Fun Book: Given to hotel and RV guests
Special Features: RV park located next door.

Four Aces
531 Main Street
(605) 578-2323

Restaurants: 1
Buffets: L-$4.95 D-$8.95
Casino Size: 12,000 Square Feet
Other Games: Blackjack, Poker
Fun Book: Ask at Club counter

Franklin Hotel
700 Main Street
(605) 578-2241

Reservation Number: 800-688-1876
Rooms: 65   Price Range: $39-$82
Suites: 10 Price Range: $79-$155
Restaurants: 1
Other Games: Blackjack, Poker
Fun Book: Given to hotel guests and
          when you join the slot club
Special Features: Historic 91-year-old hotel
with Irish pub that features entertainment on
weekends.

Gold Dust Gaming &
Entertainment Complex
688 Main Street
(605) 578-2100

Toll-Free Number: 800-456-0533
Restaurants: 1
Buffets: B-$3.99 L-$4.99 D-$7.99
Hours: 24 hours Daily
Casino Size: 22,000 Square Feet
Other Games: Blackjack, Poker
Fun Book: Write to Shelly in sales dep't.
           to get by mail
Special Features: Largest gaming complex in
Deadwood with three casinos (Legends/French
Quarter/Silver Dollar) and two lounges. Gold
Dust Players Club offers free parties, Com-
edy Club and instant winner drawings.

Gold Country Inn
801 Main Street
Deadwood, SD 57732
(605) 578-2393

Reservation Number: (800) 287-1251
Rooms: 53   Price Range: $35-$70
Restaurants: 1

Gold Street
653 Main Street
(605) 578-1705

Goldberg's
670 Main Street
(605) 578-1515

Hours: 24 hours daily
Other Games: Blackjack, Poker

Goldigger's Hotel &
Gaming Establishment
629 Main Street
(605) 578-3213

Reservation Number: 800-456-2023
Rooms: 6 Price Range: $89
Suites: 3 Price Range: $129
Restaurants: 1 (open 24 hours)
Hours: 24 hours daily
Other Games: Blackjack, Poker
Fun Book: Ask at gift counter
Special Features: Restaurant offers $2.99 steak
and eggs, barbecue and daily specials. Hotel
rooms include complimentary champagne
upon arrival, plus breakfast each morning.

Hickok's Saloon
685 Main Street
(605) 578-2222

Other Games: Blackjack

Iron Horse/Gold Coin/Gold Rush
P.O. Box 370
(605) 578-7701

Jack Pot Charlies/Green Door
616 Main Street
(605) 578-2779

Jesse James Gaming Saloon
669 Main Street
(605) 578-7725

Lady Luck
660 Main Street
(605) 578-1162

Lariat Motel
360 Main Street
(605) 578-1500

Rooms: 20 Price Range: $48-$69

Lillies
671 Main Street
(605) 578-3104

Lucky Wrangler/Mama Leon's
638 Main Street
(605) 578-3260

Midnight Star
677 Main Street
(605) 578-1555

Toll-Free Number: (800) 999-6482
Restaurants: 2
Hours: 24 hours daily
Other Games: Blackjack
Fun Book: Call (800) 999-6482 to
          receive by mail
Special Features: Kevin Costner is part owner and the walls are adorned with memorabilia from his movies. Bicycle drawn carriage rides for a nominal fee.

Mineral Palace Hotel & Gaming Complex
601 Main Street
(605) 578-2036

Reservation Number: (800) 84-PALACE
Rooms: 63 Price Range: $59-$195
Restaurants: 1
Hours: 24 hours daily
Other Games: Blackjack
Casino Marketing: (800) 84-PALACE
Special Features: Contains Cousin Jack's, Carrie Nation's and Deadwood Livery casinos. Non-smoking rooms available. Cappuccino and espresso bar.

Miss Kitty's Chinatown/Wilderness Edge
647 Main Street
(605) 578-1811

Other Games: Blackjack, Poker

Old Style Saloon #10
657 Main Street
(605) 578-3346

Toll-Free Number: (800) 952-9398
Restaurants: 1
Casino Size: 4,000 Square Feet
Other Games: Blackjack, Poker
Special Features: During summer there is a reenactment of the "Shooting of Wild Bill Hickok" four times daily. Wild Bill's chair and other Old West artifacts on display.

Oyster Bay
628 Main Street
(605) 578-2205

Restaurants: 1
Special Features: Historic restoration of 1895 brothel and spa. Features first-class oyster bar.

Painted Pony Gaming
692 Main Street
(605) 578-1012

Peacock Club
634 Main Street
(605) 578-2025

Shedd Jewelers
674 Main Street
(605) 578-2494

Silverado Gaming & Restaurant
709 Main Street
(605) 578-3670

Toll-Free Number: (800) 584-7005
Restaurants: 2
Buffets: L-$4.95 D-$8.95
Hours: 24 hours daily
Casino Size: 10,000 Square Feet
Other Games: Blackjack
Casino Marketing: (800) 584-7005
Fun Book: Call or write for information
Special Features: $5.95 complete prime rib dinner

Slots of Luck
668 Main Street
(605) 578-1979

Super 8 Lodge/Lucky 8 Gaming Hall
196 Cliff Street
(605) 578-2535

Reservation Number: (800) 800-8000
Rooms: 51 Price Range: $40-$130
Suites: 3 Price Range: $75-$130
Restaurants: 1
Hours: 24 hours daily
Fun Book: Given to guests at check-in
Special Features: Video arcade. Trolley service. Indoor heated pool and spa. Non-smoking rooms available. Free breakfast bar. Video arcade.

Thunder Cove Inn
Highway 85 South
(605) 578-3045

Toll-Free Number: (800) 209-7361
Rooms: 24 Price Range: $25-$85
Suites: 1 Price Range: $75-$125
Special Features: Free continental breakfast for inn guests. Scheduled shuttle service to downtown Deadwood.

Tin Lizzie/Casey's/Mustang
555 Main Street
(605) 578-1715

Toll-Free Number: (800) 643-4490
Restaurants: 1
Hours: 24 hours daily
Casino Size: 8,300 Square Feet
Other Games: Blackjack
Fun Book: Write to receive by mail
Special Features: 99¢ breakfast special. Free parking. Free coffee.

Trolley Stop
673 Main Street
(605) 578-1276

Twin City Cleaners
795 Main Street
(605) 578- 1260

Veteran's Of Foreign War
10 Pine Street
(605) 578-9914

Wild Bill Bar and Gambling Hall
608 Main Street
(605) 578-2177

Toll-Free Number: (800) 873-1876
Restaurants: 1
Casino Size: 4,000 Square Feet
Other Games: Blackjack
Fun Book: Write to receive by mail
Special Features: Also contains Miss P.J.'s Parlor casino. Restaurant specializes in steaks.

Wild West Winners Club
622 Main Street
(605) 578-1100

Restaurants: 2
Other Games: Blackjack, Poker

Indian Casinos

Dakota Sioux Casino
Route 1, Box 107
Watertown, South Dakota 57201
(605) 882-2051
Map Location: #2 (104 miles N. of Sioux Falls)

Toll-Free Number: (800) 658-4717
Restaurants: 1 (open 24 hours) Liquor: Yes
Hours: 24 hours daily
Other Games: Blackjack, Poker
Fun Book: Go to Guest Services desk

Fort Randall Casino
West Hwy. 46
Wagner, South Dakota 57380
(605) 487-7871
Map Location: #3 (100 miles S.W. of Sioux Falls)

Recorded Information: (800) 553-3003
Reservation Number: (800) 362-6333
Rooms: 57 Price Range: $47.25
Restaurants: 1 Liquor: Yes
Hours: 24 hours daily
Other Games: Blackjack, Poker, Bingo

Golden Buffalo Casino
P.O. Box 204
Lower Brule, South Dakota 57548
(605) 473-5577
Map Location: #4 (45 miles S.E. of Pierre)

Rooms: 38 Price Range: $50-$75
Restaurants: 1 Liquor: Yes
Buffets: D-$5.95 (Sun 11am-4pm)
Hours: 9am-2am/24 Hours (Fri/Sat)
Other Games: Blackjack, Poker

Grand River Casino
P.O. Box 639
Mobridge, South Dakota 57601
(605) 875-7104
Map Location: #7 (240 miles N.E. of Rapid City)

Toll-Free Number: (800) 475-3321
Restaurants: 1 Liquor: Yes
Hours: 8am-12am/24 hours (Fri/Sat)
Other Games: Blackjack, Poker

Lode Star Casino
P.O. Box 140
Fort Thompson, South Dakota 57339
(605) 245-6000
Map Location: #6 (150 miles N.W. of Sioux Falls)

Restaurants: 1 Liquor: Yes
Hours: 8am-2am/4am (Fri/Sat)
Other Games: Blackjack, Poker

Prairie Wind Casino
HC 49, Box 10
Pine Ridge, South Dakota 57770
(605) 535-6300
Map Location: #9 (85 miles S.E. of Rapid City)

Toll-Free Number: (800) 705-WIND
Restaurants: 1 Snack Bar Liquor: No
Hours: 24 hours Daily

Other Games: Blackjack, Poker
Special Features: Casino is located in Oglala
which is 15 miles N. of Pine Ridge.

Rosebud Casino
P.O. Box 21
Mission, South Dakota 57555
(605) 378-3800
Map Location: #8 (200 miles S.E. of Rapid
City)

Toll-Free Number: (800) 786-7673
Restaurants: 2 Liquor: Yes
Buffets: D-$6.95
Hours: 24 hours daily
Other Games: Blackjack, Poker, Bingo
Senior Discount: If 55, or older, ask for
Senior Club Cards

Royal River Casino & Bingo
Veterans Street, Box 326
Flandreau, South Dakota 57028
(605) 997-3746
Map Location: #5 (35 miles N. of Sioux Falls
on I-29)

Toll-Free Number: (800) 833-8666
Restaurants: 1 Liquor: Yes
Hours: 24 hours daily
Buffets: L-$3.95/$5.95 (Sun) D-$5.95
Casino Size: 15,000 Square Feet
Other Games: Blackjack, Poker,
Bingo (Wed-Sun)
Fun Book: Only given to groups

WASHINGTON

As of September 1996 there were 15 Indian casinos operating in Washington. Ten of the casinos are affiliated with tribes that have compacts with the state that allow them to only offer table games - no electronic gambling devices of any kind are allowed.

Of the remaining five casinos, two are affiliated with the Spokane Tribe and the other three are operated by the Colville Confederated Tribes. Both of these tribes have an ongoing dispute with the state and are operating without compacts. All five of their casinos offer slot machines as well as table games.

A state-wide referendum was scheduled for November 1996 to allow slot machines at the 10 Indian casinos with compacts. If passed, it would allow the machines to be introduced in two stages. In the first year each tribe would be allowed 295 slots per casino. After that first year each casino would be allowed to add 200 more slots, subject to approval by the state's gaming commission.

Unless otherwise noted, all casinos are open 24 hours and offer: blackjack, craps, roulette and pull tabs. Optional games offered include: baccarat (B), mini-baccarat (MB), poker (P), pai gow poker (PGP), Caribbean Stud Poker (CSP), keno (K) and bingo (BG). The minimum gambling age is 18 (21 if liquor

is served). Although most of the casinos have toll-free numbers be aware that some of those numbers will only work for calls made within Washington.

Coulee Dam Casino
515 Birch Street
Coulee Dam, Washington 99155
(509) 633-0766
Map Location: #11 (190 miles E. of Seattle)

Toll-Free Number: (800) 556-7492
Restaurants: 1 Snack Bar Liquor: No
Hours: 10am-1am/2am (Fri/Sat)
Other Games: Slots, Video Poker and Keno,
No Craps or Roulette.
Senior Discount: If 55, or older, ask to join
Senior Sunrise Club

Clearwater Casino
15347 Suquamish Way N.E.
Suquamish, Washington 98392
(360) 598-1835
Map Location: #14 (15 miles W. of Seattle
via Bainbridge Ferry)

Toll-Free Number: (800) 375-6073
Restaurants: 2 Liquor: Yes
Hours: 2pm-2am/4am (Fri/Sat)
Other Games: B, MB, P, PGP, K, BG

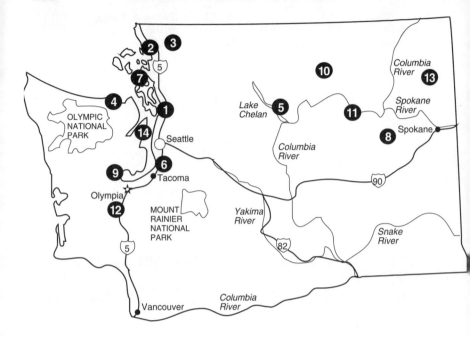

Double Eagle Casino
2539 Smith Road
Chewelah, Washington 99109
(509) 935-4406
Map Location: #13 (50 miles N. of Spokane)

Restaurants: 1 Deli Liquor: No
Hours: 9am-12am/24 Hours (Fri/Sat)
Other Games: Slots, Video Poker, P

Harrah's Skagit Valley Casino
590 Dark Lane
Bow, Washington 98232
(360) 724-7777
Map Location: #2 (75 miles N. of Seattle)

Toll-Free Number: (800) HARRAHS
Restaurants: 3 Liquor: Yes
Buffets: B-$12.99 (Sun) L-$6.99
        D-$9.99/$12.99 (Fri/Sat)
Hours: 11am-3am/5am (Fri/Sat)
Casino Size: 26,075 Square Feet
Other Games: B, MB, P, PGP, BG

Little Creek Casino
West 91 Highway 108
Shelton, Washington 98584
(360) 427-7711
Map Location: #9 (23 miles N. of Olympia)

Toll-Free Number: (800) 667-7711
Restaurants: 2 Liquor: Yes
Hours: 10am-6am Daily
Casino Size: 36,000 Square Feet
Other Games: MB, P, PGP, CSP, K, BG
Fun Book: Look for ads in newspaper

Lucky Eagle Casino
12888 188th Road S.W.
Rochester, Washington 98579
(360) 273-2000
Map Location: #12 (10 miles S. of Olympia)

Restaurants: 1 Liquor: Yes
Hours: 12pm-4am/6am (Fri/Sat)
Casino Size: 50,000 Square Feet
Other Games: MB, P, PGP, K, BG

Lummi Casino
2559 Lummi View Drive
Bellingham, Washington 98226
(360) 758-7559
Map Location: #2 (90 miles N. of Seattle)

Toll-Free Number: (800) 776-1337
Restaurants: 1 Liquor: No
Buffets: L-$8.00 D-$8.00
Casino Size: 10,000 Square Feet
Other Games: B, P, PGP, K,
          BG, Simulcasting

Mill Bay Casino
455 E. Wapato Lake Road
Manson, Washington 98831
(509) 687-2102
Map Location: #5 (200 miles N.E. of Seattle on the N. shore of Lake Chelan)

Toll-Free Number: (800) 648-2946
Restaurants: 1 Liquor: No
Buffets: B-$1.99 L-$4.95 D-$7.77
Other Games: Slots, Video Poker, M, PGP
Senior Discount: If 55, or older, ask to join Senior Sunrise Club
Fun Book: Distributed by local motels and also given to groups

Muckleshoot Casino
2402 Auburn Way South
Auburn, Washington 98002
(206) 804-4444
Map Location: #6 (20 miles S. of Seattle)

Toll-Free Number (800) 804-4944
Restaurants: 2 Liquor: Yes
Hours: 10am-6am Daily
Other Games: B, P, PGP, K

Nooksack River Casino
5048 Mt. Baker Highway
Deming, Washington 98244
(360) 592-5472
Map Location: #3 (14 miles E. of Bellingham)

Toll-Free Number: (800) 233-2573
Restaurants: 1 Liquor: Yes
Buffets: Sun Brunch-$6.95 L-$6.95 D-$7.95
Hours: 10am-6am Daily
Casino Size: 21,500 Square Feet
Other Games: MB, P, PGP, CSP, Red Dog, Big Six Wheel
Special Features: Live entertainment Wednesday through Sunday.

Okanogan Bingo and Casino
41 Appleway Road
Okanogan, Washington 98840
(509) 422-4646
Map Location: #10 (165 miles E. of Seattle)

Toll-Free Number: (800) 559-4643
Restaurants: 1 Snack Bar Liquor: No
Hours: 10am-1am/2am (Fri/Sat)
Other Games: Only Slots, Video Poker and Bingo (Thu-Tue)

Seven Cedars Casino
270756 Hwy. 101
Sequim, Washington 98382
(360) 683-7777
Map Location: #7 (70 miles N. of Seattle via ferry)

Toll-Free Number: (800) 4-LUCKY-7
Restaurants: 1 Liquor: Yes
Hours: 3pm-1am (Mon-Thu)
        12pm-1am (Sun)/4am (Fri/Sat)
Other Games: P, PGP, K, BG, Red Dog

Swinomish Casino and Bingo
837 Swinomish Casino Drive
Anacortes, Washington 98221
(360) 293-2691
Map Location: #7 (70 miles N. of Seattle, between I-5 and Anacortes on Hwy. 20)

Toll-Free Number: (800) 877-7529
Restaurants: 2 Liquor: Yes
Buffets: B-$7.95 (Sat/Sun) L-$6.95 D-$7.95
Hours: 11am-4am/6am (Fri/Sat)
Other Games: MB, P, PGP, CSP, BG, Sic Bo, Red Dog, Big Six Wheel, Simulcasting

Tulalip Casino
6410 33rd Avenue N.E.
Marysville, Washington 98271
(360) 651-1111
Map Location: #1 (30 miles N. of Seattle)

Toll-Free Number: (888) 272-1111
Restaurants: 2 Liquor: Yes
Hours: 10am-6am Daily
Other Games: B, P, PGP, K, BG

Two Rivers Casino
6828-B Highway 25 South
Davenport, Washington 99122
(509) 722-4000
Map Location: #8 (60 miles W. of Spokane)

Toll-Free Number: (800) 722-4031
Restaurants: 1 Snack Bar Liquor: No
Hours: 10am-2am/24 Hours (Fri/Sat)
Casino Size: 10,000 Square Feet
Other Games: Slots, Video Poker, MB, PGP, K
Fun Book: Only given to groups
Special Features: Shuttle bus service from major locations in Spokane ($20 charge, however, you are given back $10 in credit to use on any game) - call (800) 989-6766 for details. Full-service 35-space RV park. 100-slip marina.

WEST VIRGINIA

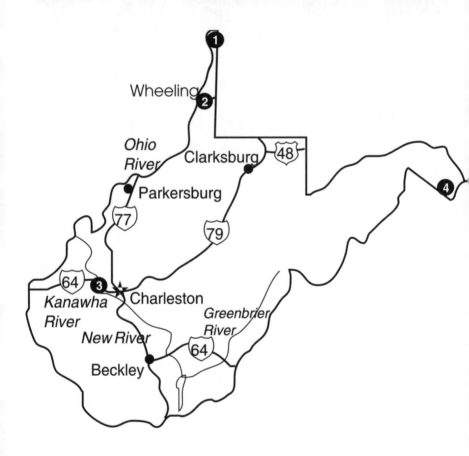

West Virginia has three pari-mutuel facilities that feature video lottery terminals. The VLT's are the same as regular video gaming devices but are called lottery terminals because they are regulated by the state's lottery commission which receives a share of each machine's revenue.

The maximum allowable bet on a machine is $2 and although the machines will accept cash they will not pay out in cash; instead, they print out a receipt which must be taken to a cashier. West Virginia law requires that VLT's return a minimum of 80% to a maximum of 95% over time. For the nine-week period from July 1, 1996 through August 31, 1996 the average return on all West Virginia VLT's was 91.54%

The state's fourth pari-mutuel facility, Charles Town Races (map location #4), did not have VLT's because it was not approved by voters in a county-wide referendum in November, 1994. A new referendum was scheduled for November 1996, however, and if it passed the track would also offer VLT's. To check on the status of the VLT's you can call the track at (304) 725-7001.

All VLT's games include: slots, blackjack; keno; and numerous versions of poker. The minimum gambling age is 18.

Mountaineer Park & Gaming Resort
State Route #2
Chester, West Virginia 26034
(304) 387-2400
Map Location: #1 (35 miles N. of Wheeling)

Toll-Free Number: (800) 804-0468
Restaurants: 4
Hours: 9am-3am (Mon-Sat) 1pm-12am (Sun)
Special Features: Live horse racing Thur-
Mon. Daily simulcasting of horse and dog
racing.

Tri-State Greyhound Racing
1 Greyhound Lane
Cross Lanes, West Virginia 25356
(304) 776-1000
Map Location: #2 (10 miles N.W. of Charleston)

Toll-Free Number: (800) 224-9683
Restaurants: 2
Hours: 11am-12:30am/2am (Fri/Sat)
         1pm-12:30am (Sun)
Special Features: Live dog racing Wed-Mon.
Daily simulcasting of horse and dog racing.

Wheeling Downs
1 S. Stone Street
Wheeling, West Virginia 26003
(304) 232-5050
Map Location: #3

Toll-Free Number: (800) 445-9475
Restaurants: 1
Hours: 11am-1am/2:30am (Fri/Sat)
         1pm-1am (Sun)
Special Features: Live dog racing Wed-Mon.
Daily simulcasting of horse and dog racing.

WISCONSIN

All 16 Wisconsin casinos are located on Indian reservations. Most of the casinos are
small with 8 to 12 blackjack tables and food
facilities that are closer to concession stands
rather than restaurants. The largest operation
is Oneida Bingo & Casino with 84 blackjack
tables and 2,500 reel slots and video machines.

The Indian tribes are not required to release
information on their slot machine percentage
paybacks, but according to the terms of the
compact between the state and the tribes each
machine is required to return a minimum of
80% and a maximum of 100% of the amount
wagered.

Unless otherwise noted, the games offered
are: slots, video poker and blackjack. The
minimum gambling age is 18 (21 if liquor is
served).

Bad River Bingo & Casino
P.O. Box 39
Odanah, Wisconsin 54861
(715) 682-7121
Map Location: #1 (half-way between Iron-
wood, MI and Ashland, WI; 45 miles east of
Duluth, MN on US 2)

Restaurants: 1   Liquor: Yes
Other Games: Video Keno, Bingo
Casino Marketing: (715) 682-7122

Grand Royale Casino
Highway 55
Mole Lake, Wisconsin 54520
(715) 478-5290
Map Location: #3 (100 miles N.W. of Green
Bay on Hwy. 55, 7 miles S. of Crandon)

Toll-Free Number: (800) 236-WINN
Restaurants: 1 Snack Bar Liquor: Yes
Hours: 10am-1am/3am (Fri/Sat)
Other Games: Only Slots and Video Poker
Casino Marketing: (800) 236-WINN
Special Features: 1/2 block from Regency
Resort Casino.

Ho Chunk Casino
S3214A Highway 12
Baraboo, Wisconsin 53913
(608) 356-6210
Map Location: #4 (40 miles N. of Madison.
On Hwy. 12 just S. of Delton)

Toll-Free Number: (800) 7HO-CHUNK
Restaurants: 2 (1 open 24 hours) Liquor: No
Buffets: B-$5.50 L-$6.50/$7.50 (Sun)
         D-$9.50/$12.75 (Wed)
Casino Size: 86,000 Square Feet
Hours: 24 Hours Daily
Other Games: Bingo, Video Keno
Special Features: Valet parking. Gift shop.
Discount smoke shop. Shuttle service from all
local area motels.

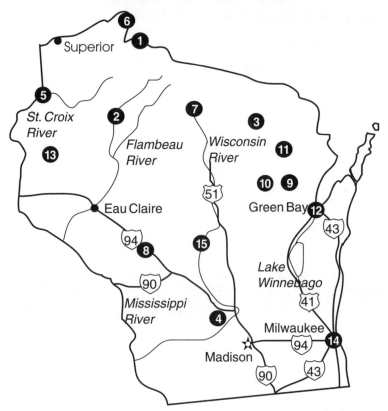

Hole In The Wall Casino
P.O. Box 98, Highways 35 & 77
Danbury, Wisconsin 54830
(715) 656-3444
Map Location: #5 (26 miles E. of Hinckley, MN)

Toll-Free Number: (800) BET-U-WIN
Rooms: 38 Price Range: $40-$50
Restaurants: 1 Snack Bar Liquor: Yes
Hours: 8am-2am/4am (Fri/Sat)
Other Games: Video Keno
Special Features: Save $10 on room rate by showing slot club card (which is available for free inside casino). 35-site RV park. Gift shop. Live music on weekends.

Isla Vista Casino
Highway 13 North
Bayfield, Wisconsin 54814
(715) 779-3712
Map Location: #6 (70 miles E. of Duluth, MN on Hwy. 13, 3 miles N. of Bayfield)

Toll-Free Number: (800) 226-8478
Restaurants: 1 Liquor: Yes
Hours: 10am-2am Daily
Other Games: Video Keno, Bingo (Thu/Sat/Sun)

Lac Courte Oreilles Casino
Route 5
Hayward, Wisconsin 54843
(715) 634-5643
Map Location: #2 (55 miles S.E. of Duluth, MN. From Hayward go 9 miles S.W. on county trunk E)

Toll-Free Number: (800) 422-2175
Restaurants: 1 Liquor: No
Buffets: B-$4.25/$7.99 (Sun) L-$6.95
          D-$7.99/$15.99 (Wed)
Casino Size: 35,000 Square Feet
Hours: 9am-4am Daily
Other Games: Bingo
Special Features: Free valet parking. Sports lounge.

Lake of the Torches Casino
567 Peace Pipe Road
Lac du Flambeau, Wisconsin 54538
(715) 588-7070
Map Location: #7 (160 miles N.W. of Green
Bay. Heading N. on Hwy. 57, go left on Hwy.
47, 12 miles to casino)

Toll-Free Number: (800) 25-TORCH
Restaurants: 1 Liquor: Yes
Buffets: B-$5.95 (Sat/Sun) L-$5.95 D-$8.95
Hours: 24 Hours Daily
Other Games: Video Keno, Bingo (Tue-Sun)

Majestic Pines Casino
Highway 54
Black River Falls, Wisconsin 54615
(715) 284-9098
Map Location: #8 (110 miles M.W. of Madison on Hwy. 54, 4 miles E. of I-94)

Toll-Free Number: (800) 657-4621
Restaurants: 2 Liquor: Yes
Hours: 9am-2:30am/24 hours (Fri/Sat)
Other Games: Bingo, Video Keno,
            Video Blackjack (No Tables)

Menominee Casino
P.O. Box 760, Highways 47 & 55
Keshena, Wisconsin 54135
(715) 799-3600
Map Location: #9 (40 miles N.W. of Green
Bay on Hwy. 47, 7 miles N. of Shawano)

Toll-Free Number: (800) 343-7778
Rooms: 100 Price Range: $49-$75
Suites: 8 Price Range: $85-$144
Restaurants: 1 Liquor: Yes
Buffets: B-$2.59/$3.99 (Sat/Sun)
          L-$6.95 D-$8.95/$11.50 (Sat)
Hours: 24 Hours Daily
Casino Size: 21,402 Square Feet
Other Games: Bingo, Video Keno
Fun Book: Only for bus groups and guests
of local motels.
Senior Discount: If 55, or older, 10%
            discount on room.
Special Features: Weekly blackjack and slot
tournaments. Lounge with entertainment. Gift
shop. Smoke shop.

Mohican North Star Casino
W12180A County Road A
Bowler, Wisconsin 54416
(715) 787-3110
Map Location: #10 (50 miles N.W. of Green
Bay)

Toll-Free Number: (800) 952-0195
Restaurants: 1 Snack Bar Liquor: Yes
Hours: 8am-2am/24 Hours (Thu-Sun)
Other Games: Video Keno, Bingo (Wed-Sun)
Special Features: Local area motels offer
casino packages.

Northern Lights Casino
P.O. Box 140, Highway 32
Carter, Wisconsin 54566
(715) 473-2021
Map Location: #11 (85 miles N. of Green Bay
on Hwy. 32)

Toll-Free Number: (800) 487-9522
Lodge Reservations: (800) 777-1640
Rooms: 70 Price Range: $59-$104
Suites: 29 Price Range: $64-$149
Restaurants: 2 Liquor: Yes
Casino Size: 12,000 Square Feet
Hours: 9am-1am/4am (Fri/Sat)
Other Games: Bingo
Special Features: Indian Springs Lodge is
located across the parking lot from the casino
and offers hotel/casino packages. 10% discount on room rate for AAA and AARP
Members.

Oneida Bingo & Casino
2100 Airport Drive
Green Bay, Wisconsin 54313
(414) 494-4500
Map Location: #12 (across from Austin
Straubel Airport, take Interstate 43 to Highway 172)

Toll-Free Number: (800) 238-4263
Reservation Number: (800) 333-3333
Rooms: 301 Price Range: $79-$114
Suites: 29 Price Range: $179-$229
Restaurants: 3 Liquor: No
Buffets: Sun Brunch-$9.95 L-$6.95 D-$7.95
Hours: 24 Hours Daily (Slots)
Hours: 10am-4am (Tables)
Other Games: Bingo, Video Keno
Casino Marketing: (800) 238-4263
Fun Book: Only offered to bus groups
Special Features: Complex features two casinos, one of which is connected to the Radisson
Inn where the rooms are located. Shuttle bus
service available from airport and local hotels/motels. Gift shop. Discount tobacco.
Handicap accessible.

Potawatomi Bingo Casino
1721 W. Canal Street
Milwaukee, Wisconsin 53233
(414) 645-6888
Map Location: #14

Toll-Free Number: (800) 755-6171
Restaurants: 1 Snack Bar Liquor: No
Hours: 8am-3am Daily
Games Offered: No Blackjack, Bingo

Rainbow Casino
494 County Road G
Nekoosa, Wisconsin 54457
(715) 886-4560
Map Location: #15 (50 miles S. of Wausau)

Toll-Free Number: (800) 782-4560
Restaurants: 2 Liquor: Yes
Hours: 10am-2am/24 hours (Fri/Sat)
Other Games: Video Keno, Bingo

Regency Resort Casino
Highway 55
Mole Lake, Wisconsin 54520
(715) 478-5290
Map Location: #3 (100 miles N.W. of Green Bay on Hwy. 55, 7 miles S. of Crandon)

Toll-Free Number: (800) 236-WINN
Restaurants: 1 Liquor: Yes

Hours: 10am-3am Daily
Other Games: Bingo (Fri-Tue)
Casino Marketing: (800) 236-WINN
Special Features: 1/2 block from Grand Royale Casino

St. Croix Casino & Hotel
777 US Highway 8
Turtle Lake, Wisconsin 54889
(715) 986-4777
Map Location: #13 (105 miles S. of Duluth, MN on Hwy. 8)

Toll-Free Number: (800) U-GO-U-WIN
Reservation Number: (800) STAY-W-US
Rooms: 158 Price Range: $40-$59
Restaurants: 3 (1 open 24 hours) Liquor: Yes
Buffets: B-$2.99 L-$6.75 D-$8.75
Casino Size: 95,000 Square Feet
Hours: 24 Hours Daily
Other Games: Video Keno
Special Features: 20% discount on hotel rates if you have a player's card (which is available for free inside the casino). Free valet parking. Banquet and meeting facilities.

Casino Index

Casino Vacations

Two Free Production Show Tickets
A $40 Value

To receive your two **FREE** show tickets, call 1-800-932-0734, Monday-Friday, 10am-6pm and ask for VACATIONS. Offer valid Monday through Thursday through December 27, 1997. See reverse for full details.

CASINO COUPON

Casino Vacations

Buy One Buffet Get One Free!

The Trump Taj Mahal invites you to try our world famous Sultan's Feast Buffet. And now, when you purchase one buffet and present this coupon you'll receive a second buffet dinner FREE!

Coupon redeemable Sunday through Friday
See reverse side for full details

CASINO COUPON

Casino Vacations

Two Free Show Tickets
A $40 Value

Harrah's Atlantic City invites you and a guest to enjoy one of our fabulous shows! Just present your Harrah's Gold Card and this coupon at the Box Office 2 hours prior to showtime. To instantly become a Gold Card customer, simply present a valid ID at the Gold Card Center during your next visit. It's your key to A Great Time, Every Time.SM

FOR SHOW SCHEDULE AND RESERVATIONS
1-800-2-HARRAH (1-800-242-7724)

Coupon redeemable Sunday through Friday • See reverse for details

CV1

CASINO COUPON

North Carolina Ave. and the Boardwalk Atlantic City, NJ 08401 (609) 344-6000

Present this certificate and Star Card at the Lobby Box Office after 1pm to receive your two FREE show tickets. (To receive your Star Card, visit the Celebrity Marketing Center located on the casino floor). Offer not valid with any other promotion. Program subject to change or cancellation without notice. Tickets not transferable. Show schedule subject to change. Must be 21 years of age or older. Tickets subject to availability. Gambling Problem? Call 1-800-GAMBLER.

Terms & Conditions

• Subject to availability
• Offer valid through 12/30/97
• One coupon per person
• No facsimiles accepted
• Not valid with any other offer
• Program subject to change or cancellation without notice
• All information must be completed prior to redemption
• Photo identification required

Boardwalk at Virginia Avenue
Atlantic City, NJ 08401
(609) 449-1000
http://www.trumptaj.com

Name

Address

City

State   Zip

Date of Birth

Terms & Conditions:

• Subject to availability
• Reservations must be made in advance
• Offer valid through 12/29/97; some days may be unavailable
• Must be 21; one coupon per person
• Offer not valid with any other promotion
• Program subject to change or cancellation without notice
• All information must be completed prior to redemption
• Not valid for some shows
• No shows Mondays

Gambling Problem?
Call 1-800-GAMBLER

Name

Address

City

State   Zip

Gold Card #

                                    CV1

CASINO AND RESORT

FREE buffet breakfast, lunch or dinner when you buy one at the Beachfront Buffet! See back for complete details.

CASINO COUPON

Ca**S**ino Vacations

Sands.
Hotel & Casino · Atlantic City

Paradise Cafe

Buy One Dinner Entree, Get One FREE!

Simply present this coupon with your AMBASSADOR Card prior to ordering at the Paradise Cafe on the fourth floor. Reservations are not required, however, seating is subject to availability. Offer good 7 days a week, 5pm to 2am. Holiday weekends are excluded. Offer expires 12/30/97.

4505-CVG7

CASINO COUPON

Ca**S**ino Vacations

Sands.
Hotel & Casino · Atlantic City

Buy One Dinner Buffet and Receive One at 1/2 Price

Simply present this coupon with your AMBASSADOR Card to the hostess upon arrival at Rossi's Gourmet Italian Dinner Buffet on the third floor. Reservations are recommended: 609-441-4400. Offer good Sunday through Friday from 6pm to 10pm. Holiday weekends are excluded. Offer expires 12/30/97.

4528-CVG7

CASINO COUPON

Casino Vacations

Free Cruise For Two
aboard
"Florida's Best Value Casino Ships"

Use this coupon for a FREE cruise aboard
SunCruz - Hollywood, Key Largo or Port Richey and
receive a $5 matchplay. **Offer Expires 12/30/97.**
See other side for full details.

Ship's registry U.S.

CASINO COUPON

Casino Vacations

Free* Cruise

Good on all cruises except Friday and Saturday night. Valid at all
Empress locations: Clearwater, Treasure Island, St. Petersburg
and Sarasota. Reservations: 813/895-DEAL (3325). or 1-800-
486-8600. Offer Expires 11/30/97. See other side for full details.

CASINO COUPON

Casino Vacations

Two-For-One Cruise

Locations in Miami Beach*, Ft. Myers Beach* and Madeira Beach**
Experience Florida's best Dining, Dancing and Casino value!
See reverse for terms and conditions. **Call 1-800-688-PLAY**
Offer Expires 12/30/97. Ship's registry * Panama, ** United States

CASINO COUPON

"Florida's Best Value Casino Ships"
Hollywood • Key Largo • Port Richey
1-800-474-DICE

Offer valid for two persons on SunCruz Hollywood, Key Largo or Port Richey. Space subject to availability. Reservations required. Match Play valid for any table game, even money bet only, cannot be redeemed for cash. For information call 1-800-474-DICE.

Sailing From
• Kingfish Wharf, John's Pass, Treasure Island
• Clearwater Bay Marina, Downtown Clearwater
• Port Manatee, Sarasota
• Port of St. Petersburg, Downtown St. Petersburg

For Reservations or Information call 813-895-DEAL or 1-800-486-8600

*$10 cruise line service fee is applicable. Limit one per person, per coupon. Offer not good with other discounts or offers. Not valid holidays and selected cruises. Not valid New Year's Eve. Restrictions apply. Offer expires 11/30/97.

Name

Address

City, St, Zip

1-Advance reservations required. 2-This coupon is not combinable with any other SeaKruz offer 3-Applies to full fare purchase only plus taxes and surcharges. 4-Coupon must be presented at ticket booth on day of sailing. 5-Only one (1) coupon per person. 6-Taxes and surcharges not included in this offer. 7-Certain restrictions apply. Offer subject to change without notice. 8- Coupon expires on date indicated. Service charges will be applicable on extension requests. 9-This coupon is not transferable

VIKING PRINCESS COASTAL CRUISES

Funshine Cruises
Monday, Wednesday & Friday
Departs 10am • Returns 4pm

Moonlight Cruises
Monday & Wednesday
Departs 7pm • Returns Midnight

Friday Party Cruise
Departs 7pm • Returns 1am

Sunday Brunch Cruise
Departs 11am • Returns 5pm

Port, gov't & service fees additional. Certain restrictions apply. Not valid with other discounts/promotions, hotel packages or on holidays. Advance reservations/payment required. Ship's resgistry Panama.

C-400

Name

Address

City, St, Zip

1-Advance reservations required. 2-This coupon is not combinable with any other Vegas Express offer. 3-Applies to full fare purchase only plus taxes. 4-Coupon must be presented at ticket booth on day of sailing. 5-Only one (1) coupon per person. 6-Not valid on special events and holidays. 7-Certain restrictions apply. Offer subject to change without notice. 8-Coupon expires on date indicated. 9-This coupon is not transferable

---

Coupon valid Sundays through Fridays only. Limit one coupon per person, per cruise. Offer not valid with any other discount or coupon. Not valid on holidays or selected cruises. Coupon expires 11/30/97.

Emerald Princess
D O W N T O W N   B R U N S W I C K

Golden Isles Cruise Lines, Inc.
1 St. Andrews Court, Brunswick, GA 31520
(BRUNSWICK, GEORGIA IS LOCATED MIDWAY BETWEEN SAVANNAH, GA AND JACKSONVILLE, FL.)
SHIP'S REGISTRY: PANAMA

For cruise schedules and reservations:
(800) 842-0115

Casino Vacations

At The Nassau Marriott Resort

$10 Match Play Certificate

Redeem this certificate at the box office in the Crystal Palace Casino at the Nassau Marriott Resort in Nassau, Bahamas for $10 in match play coupons. See other side for full details.

CASINO COUPON

Casino Vacations

BUY 1 GET 1 FREE

$49* SEE BACK FOR DETAILS & SCHEDULE

Jet Charter From Ft. Lauderdale To

THE ONLY BEACHFRONT CASINO IN GRAND

INCLUDES: Roundtrip Jet Air, **BAHAMA!** Transfers, $10 Food & Beverage Coupon, $20 Match Play or Buy In $20 Coins Receive $22

Call Today! 1-800-772-1226 Ext. - 241

CASINO COUPON

Casino Vacations

PARADISE ISLAND, BAHAMAS

2-For-1 Admission To *Sunsation! At Atlantis* Musical Revue

The Atlantis Showroom proudly presents *Sunsation! At Atlantis* a sizzling contemporary island musical revue. Present this coupon at the restaurant reservations desk, located adjacent to the Atlantis Showroom to receive 2-for-1 admission to *Sunsation! At Atlantis* cocktail show. See reverse for full details.

CASINO COUPON

Casino Vacations

PRESIDENT

CASINO AT THE BROADWATER
Biloxi, Mississippi

2-FOR-1 BUFFET

Enjoy one complimentary buffet with the purchase of one buffet at the regular price. Present this coupon at the Captain's Club Booth. One coupon per person, per day. Cannot be combined with any other offer. Gratuity not included. Offer expires 12/30/97

CASINO COUPON

Casino Vacations

$5 Diamond Dollars

$5 Match Play On Any Table Game

Bet this coupon with a minimum $5 bet and win an extra $5. Even money bets only. Limit one per person. Palace Casino reserves the right to cancel or change without notice. Not valid with any other offer. NO CASH VALUE. Expires 12/30/97.

CASINO COUPON

Casino Vacations

Buffet

Free Meal!

With the purchase of one meal of equal or greater value.

151 Beach Blvd. (Hwy. 90 E)
at Point Cadet, Biloxi, MS
1-800-THE ISLE
A Casino America Property

CASINO COUPON

Casino Vacations

GRAND CASINO
GULFPORT & BILOXI
MISSISSIPPI

1/2 Off
Two Show Tickets!

Get 1/2 off the regular price of up to two show tickets to the current Las Vegas-style show at Grand Casino Gulfport or Grand Casino Biloxi

For show information, call:
1-800-WIN-7777 (Grand Casino Gulfport)
1-800-WIN-2-WIN (Grand Casino Biloxi)

CASINO COUPON

Casino Vacations

The Veranda Buffet

Casino Magic!
Bay St. Louis

Buy One Meal and Get One FREE
at the Veranda Buffet!

Offer expires 12/24/97.   Coupon #78

CASINO COUPON

Casino Vacations

BAYOU CADDY'S
JUBILEE CASINO
GREENVILLE, MS

Free Fun Book
A $40 Value!

Includes: 2-for-1 lunch buffet • $1 discount on dinner buffet
Free cocktail • Free $5,000 slot pull • $5 match play coupons for craps, roulette and blackjack • $22 for $20 poker buy-in • $25 in coin for $20 • Free sports cap with slot club membership offer

CASINO COUPON

Casino Vacations

Room Discount and 2 FREE Buffets

This coupon, along with your Harrah's Gold Card, is valid for 10% off the current hotel rate at Harrah's Tunica Mardi Gras Casino & Hotel **and** two free buffets at Magnolia Gardens Restaurant or the Fresh Market Square Buffet.

TUNICA CASINOS & HOTEL

Call 1-800-HARRAHS for reservations and mention promotional offer ACGTUN.

CASINO COUPON

Casino Vacations

SAM'S TOWN
HOTEL & GAMBLING HALL

Casino Strip • Just South of Memphis

Free Fun Book

Includes: Free hot dog • 1,000 Free bonus points • Free buffet $7 for $5 and $25 for $10 on table games • Free gaming lessons $2 off Western Emporium purchase of $10 or more • $3 off any entree with purchase of another • Keno special (6 for price of 5)

CASINO COUPON

Casino Vacations

SHERATON CASINO
at casino center

Just 12 miles South of Memphis, TN off Hwy. 61

Buy One Get One Free!

Purchase one buffet meal and receive the second free. Offer valid 7 days a week. *See reverse for details.*

CASINO COUPON

Casino Vacations

Free Fun Book

Present this voucher at the Banana Cabana Gift Shop and receive a Red Hot Deals Coupon Book, One coupon per person, per day. Must be 21 years of age. Must present your Island Gold Card and this voucher to redeem. Offer subject to change or cancel without notice. Offer expires 12/30/97.

CASINO COUPON

Casino Vacations

VICKSBURG CASINO & HOTEL

Double Your Points!

Use Your Gold Card and Double Your Points! Redeemable at the Gold Card Center during normal operating hours.

Name

Signature

Gold Card #

CV-1

CASINO COUPON

Casino Vacations

Free! Stardeals Coupon Book
$15 in Valuable Offers!

REDEEM VOUCHER AT THE PLAYERS CLUB BOOTH

One coupon book per person, per day. Reproductions of voucher are not accepted. Must be 21 years of age or older to participate. Must be a Player's Club Member. Offer not valid in conjunction with any other offer. Management reserves the right to change or alter this promotion without notice. Offer expires 12/30/96

CASINO COUPON

3990 Washington Street • Vicksburg, MS • 39180

(601) 636-5700 • (800) WIN-ISLE

VICKSBURG
CASINO & HOTEL

1310 Mulberry Street
Vicksburg, MS 39180
(601) 636-3423
(800) - HARRAHS

Must be 21 • Must be redeemed in person • Subject to availability • One coupon per guest, per day • May be modified or discontinued at Harrah's discretion • No cash value • Offer not valid without coupon • Harrah's is not responsible for stolen or lost coupons • Cannot be used in conjunction with any other point offer • Alteration or unauthorized use voids this voucher and may lead to criminal prosecution • Employees of Harrah's are not eligible • Offer expires 12/29/97

Name

Address

City   State   Zip

Phone #   Your Birthday

Spouse's Name   Spouse's Birthday

Anniversary Date   Shirt Size

Ameristar Casino • I-20, Exit 1-A, Vicksburg, MS • 1-800-700-7770

Casino Vacations

 Free Buffet!

This coupon entitles the bearer to one FREE Breakfast, Lunch or Dinner in the Aladdin's Marketplace Buffet when accompanied by a paying guest. Tax and gratuity not included. See other side for full details.

CASINO COUPON

Casino Vacations

Two-For-One Show Tickets

Las Vegas' original comedy showcase. Two shows nightly at 8:00 and 10:00. Extra 11:45 show on Friday and Saturday. See other side for full details.

CASINO COUPON

Casino Vacations

RIVIERA
Hotel & Casino
The Entertainment Center
of Las Vegas

The Alternative for Grown-Ups

Crazy Girls

Two-For-One Show Tickets

Las Vegas' sexiest topless revue. Two shows nightly (except Monday) at 8:30 and 10:30. Extra midnight show on Saturday. See other side for full details.

CASINO COUPON

3667 Las Vegas Blvd. S.
Las Vegas, NV 89109
(702) 736-0111
(800) 634-3424

This offer is not valid with any other discount coupon. Anyone under 21 years of age must be accompanied by an adult. Not valid Saturdays, Sundays or Holidays. Management reserves all rights. Expires December 27, 1997.

The Alternative for Grown-Ups

2901 Las Vegas Blvd. S. • Las Vegas, NV •

(702) 734-5110

Coupon must be presented to Riviera box office. Must be 21. Not valid Saturdays or Saturdays and Sundays of a holiday weekend or with any other offer. One coupon per person. Offer may be cancelled at any time without notice. No cash value. Offer expires 12/30/97.

RIVIERA SM
Hotel & Casino
The Entertainment Center
of Las Vegas

The Alternative for Grown-Ups

2901 Las Vegas Blvd. S. • Las Vegas, NV •

(702) 734-5110

Coupon must be presented to Riviera box office. Must be 21. Not valid Saturdays or Saturdays and Sundays of a holiday weekend or with any other offer. One coupon per person. Offer may be cancelled at any time without notice. No cash value. Offer expires 12/30/97.

Casino Vacations

FREE Backstage Tour for 2 of the Folies Bergere

Get a glimpse into the glamorous world of showgirls and see what happens behind-the-scenes at Las Vegas' longest running production show. See back for complete details.

CASINO COUPON

Casino Vacations

 CACTUS JACK'S # Two Free Bus Tours!

Cactus Jacks Wild West Tour Co. cordially invites you to enjoy two FREE one day bus tours to Laughlin, Nevada. Includes FREE pick-up and return from your Las Vegas hotel, FREE buffet lunch and FREE Fun Book from your host hotel on the Colorado River. See reverse for full details.

CASINO COUPON

Casino Vacations

HÔTEL SAN RÉMO

LAS VEGAS · CASINO AND RESORT

$10 Room Discount

Save $10 on our prevailing daily room rate when you use this coupon. See reverse for full details.

CASINO COUPON

An Aztar Corporation Casino
3801 Las Vegas Blvd. South
Las Vegas, NV 89109
(702) 739-2222

<u>**TOUR TIMES**</u>
Sunday through Thursday
12:30 pm • 1:30 pm • 2:30 pm

Redeem this coupon at Tropicana Show Reservations (across from the Tiffany Showroom) to receive up to two free admissions. Tour dates and times subject to change. Management reserves all rights. Offer expires December 12, 1997.

Reservations required. Call (702) 731-9400 Based on availability and not valid in combination with any other discount or special offer. Offer expires 12/30/97.

Cactus Jack's
Wild West Tour Co.

Daily Departures
24-Hour Reservations
CALL NOW!
(702) 731-9400

115 E. Tropicana Avenue
Las Vegas, Nevada 89109
(702) 739-9000
(800) 522-7366

Call 1-800-522-7366 and ask for the American Casino Guide special to receive an automatic $10 off our prevailing daily room rate. Based on availability. Single or double occupancy. Not available during holidays or convention periods. Maximum stay 7 nights.

Advance reservations required and coupon must be presented on arrival. Offer expires 12/30/97.

Casino Vacations

Peppermill
Hotel Casino

Free Fun Book

Includes complimentary cocktail, match play for Keno and Blackjack, discounts on playing cards, souvenir gift and other offers.   Bring this coupon to our promotion booth.   See reverse side for full details.

CASINO COUPON

Casino Vacations

SUNDOWNER
HOTEL CASINO • Downtown Reno

Free Action Card

Includes: $4 in FREE credit play • $1 food credit • 50-cent keno discount • Two 2-for-1 drinks • 3 Gift Shop discounts
See back for full details

CASINO COUPON

Casino Vacations

Don Laughlin's
RIVERSIDE RESORT
HOTEL & CASINO
Laughlin, Nevada

For Reservations or
Information Call
1-800-227-3849

One Free Breakfast Buffet

Redeem this coupon
at the King of Clubs
Slot Club Booth

Offer Expires 12/20/97

CASINO COUPON

Casino Vacations

Primadonna®
C A S I N O   R E S O R T S

Two-For-One Desperado Ride

FREE Ride on the Desperado, the world's tallest and fastest roller coaster, with the purchase of one ride at regular price. Must present coupon for validation. Offer Expires 12/24/97

CASINO COUPON

Casino Vacations

Free Boarding
For Up To 4 People

Complimentary boarding pass for one, or up to four people with coupon. Call 1-800-888-2WIN or 816-279-7577. See other side for full details.

CASINO COUPON

Casino Vacations

PRESIDENT CASINO ON THE
ADMIRAL
Dockside At The Arch
Saint Louis, Missouri

Buy One Buffet
Get One Free!

President Casino on the Admiral invites you and a guest to try our sumptuous President's Buffet. Purchase one buffet at regular price, present this coupon and receive a second buffet FREE!

Coupon Redeemable Sunday Through Thursday Only. Good For Lunch, Dinner Or Sunday Brunch. Offer Expires December 30, 1997.

CASINO COUPON